ATOMIC BULLETS IN ACTION

Rockets powered with carbon dioxide being fired at a balloon representing an atom of uranium. The rockets simulate a beam of neutrons, and upon striking the balloon release smaller balloons representative of atomic fragments.

MARVELS OF

MODERN
SCIENCE

THE STORY OF THE DISCOVERIES OF MODERN
SCIENCE AND HOW THEY ARE APPLIED TO SHAPE
OUR LIVES AND DIRECT OUR FUTURES

ODHAMS PRESS LTD   LONG ACRE · LONDON

CONTENTS

PRIME FOCUS

200 in.
MIRROR

TUBE HOUSING CASSEGRAIN
AND COUDE MIRRORS

ADJUSTING THE GIANT 200-IN. TELESCOPE

The technical assistant in the mouth of the tube is adjusting the prime focus of the 200-in. telescope at Mount Palomar. This giant telescope will enable astronomers to study stars and nebulae a thousand million light-years away from our solar system. One important branch of research will be concerned with stellar energy, which is bound up with our knowledge of atomic energy.

6

CHAPTER 1 The universe about us

IF we watch the stars carefully on a clear night we will see that they gradually change their positions in the sky. Some stars are setting in the west, while others are rising in the east. But not all the stars rise and set; in the north there is a bright star, known as the Pole Star, whose apparent position remains fixed, or nearly so, while other stars in its vicinity, such as the well-known group called the Great Bear, circle round it. As the stars move across the sky their positions relative to one another do not change; they move just as though they are fixed to the vault of heaven, with the whole vault turning slowly round. The Pole Star remains fixed in position because it is on, or nearly on, the axis about which the vault turns. If we repeat our observations from night to night we shall find that the pattern of the stars and planets in the sky changes gradually in the course of the year.

The ancients were familiar with the fact that the stars remained fixed relatively to one another, and it was for this reason that they called them the fixed stars. But they knew also that there were a few celestial bodies whose positions relative to the fixed stars were continually changing. They called these bodies the wandering stars, or planets. The moon is the most conspicuous example. If we watch the moon on a clear night we will see, in the course of an hour or two, that her position among the stars is changing. She has a progressive movement eastwards among the stars, and the change in her position from night to night is considerable.

The moon to the ancients was one of the wanderers, a planet; so also was the sun. But there were other planets which appeared like bright stars, though careful watching could distinguish them from the stars, because they do not twinkle as the stars do. The movement of these star-like planets among the stars can be easily detected if sketches of their positions relative to neighbouring stars are made from night to night. Seven wandering stars or planets were known to the ancients, which they named Sun, Moon, Mercury, Venus, Mars, Jupiter, and Saturn.

Two thousand years ago the ancient Greek astronomers believed that the earth was fixed immovably at the centre of the universe. Each of the planets was attached to a crystal sphere, the order of increasing distance from the earth

TRACK FOR CRANE

PRIME FOCUS

TELESCOPE CAGE

PRIME FOCUS PLATFORM

ENTRANCE TO TUBE

CASSEGRAIN & COUDÉ MIRRORS

GHOSTED VIEW OF TELESCOPE SHOWING POSITION FOR ENTERING TUBE

PASSENGER LIFT

POLAR AXIS

200 in. MIRROR

ASCENSION DRIVE

COMPUTOR

CASSEGRAIN FOCUS

COUDÉ FOCUS

ELECTRICAL CONTROLS

SOUTH PIER

OFFICES

AIR CONDITIONING INLET DUCTS

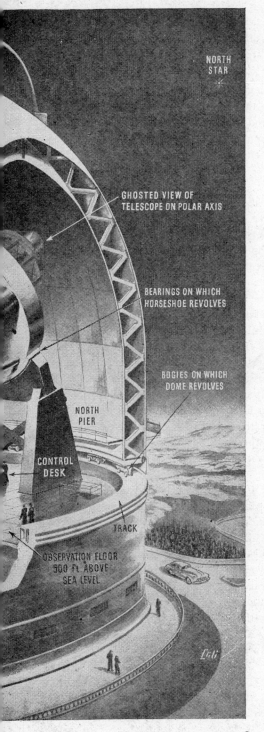

NORTH STAR

GHOSTED VIEW OF TELESCOPE ON POLAR AXIS

BEARINGS ON WHICH HORSESHOE REVOLVES

BOGIES ON WHICH DOME REVOLVES

NORTH PIER

CONTROL DESK

TRACK

OBSERVATION FLOOR 500 ft ABOVE SEA LEVEL

MT. PALOMAR OBSERVATORY

The 200-in. telescope housed in this observatory, and only very recently completed, will deal initially with confirming, if possible, certain theories. For example, it will determine whether or not there are canals on Mars, the relative abundance of chemical elements in the stars, and whether or not the universe is expanding as one theory maintains.

being the Moon, Mercury, Venus, the Sun, Mars, Jupiter and Saturn. The stars were fixed to an outer sphere, just beyond the sphere of Saturn, which turned round on its axis in the course of about a day, giving rise to the diurnal movement of the stars as a whole. The starry sphere caused the sphere of Saturn to rotate and this, in its turn, caused the sphere of Jupiter to rotate, and so on. But friction between successive spheres caused each one to turn rather more slowly than the one beyond it, so giving rise to the apparent movements of the planets relative to the stars.

The rotation of the sphere carrying the sun caused the alternation of daytime and nighttime; the changing face of the sky through the year was a consequence of the rotation of this sphere being slower than that of the starry sphere. The year was the period required for the eastward motion of the sun relative to the stars, resulting from this difference in rates of rotation, to carry it right round the heavens.

This, in broad outline, is the system of the universe that was universally accepted by scholars and divines until the middle of the sixteenth century. A complete revolution in thought was then brought about by the Polish astronomer, Copernicus, who said that instead of the sun moving round the earth, the earth moved round the sun. He placed the sun at the centre of the universe, with Mercury, Venus, Earth, Mars, Jupiter, and Saturn, in that order of distance, moving round it. The moon, on the other hand, revolved round the earth, and was carried along by it in its annual motion round the sun. He asserted also that the earth rotated about its axis in the course of a day, and that the fixed stars were at rest, their apparent daily motion being due to the rotation of the earth.

COPERNICUS ON THE STRUCTURE OF THE HEAVENS

Although the Copernican theory was proposed on the grounds of simplicity, it was slow in gaining general acceptance. There were objections on theological grounds to dethroning the earth, the home of man, of man made in the image of God, from its proved position as the centre of the universe. There were objections, also, on physical grounds.

A different meaning then had to be given to the term planet. The bodies which revolved round the sun as a parent body were to be regarded as planets. The sun, therefore, ceased to be considered as a planet, while the earth, in its turn, became a planet. The moon, as a satellite of the earth, also could no longer be called a planet. Further, since the fixed stars were no longer attached to a rotating sphere, it was no longer necessary to suppose that they were all at the same distance. The idea that the stars extended outwards in all directions, the fainter stars being on the whole more distant than the brighter stars, gradually gained general acceptance. If, however, the stars were not all at the same distance, no precise meaning could be given to the centre of the universe; the sun was in its turn displaced from the central position in which Copernicus had placed it.

One objection had been raised against the Copernican theory, however, which could not easily be disputed. If the earth revolved round the sun, as Copernicus supposed, and the stars were not far beyond the orbit of Saturn, then the motion of the earth should be made evident by annual changes in the relative positions of the stars. Two neighbouring stars would appear to be farther apart when the earth was nearest to them than when it was at its greatest distance from them. The fixed stars would not appear to be fixed. Such changes in the relative positions of the stars could not be detected and the failure could only be explained by supposing that the distances of the stars were extremely great. This was open to the objection that it was merely an hypothesis to suit the occasion, and what was needed was either the actual measurement of the distance of a star or some supporting argument.

Such an argument was provided by Sir Isaac Newton. He argued that, as the stars do not move in orbits round the sun like the planets, they must be so far away that they are not affected by the gravitational pull of the sun. They must be, at the very least, many hundreds of times as far away as Saturn. The

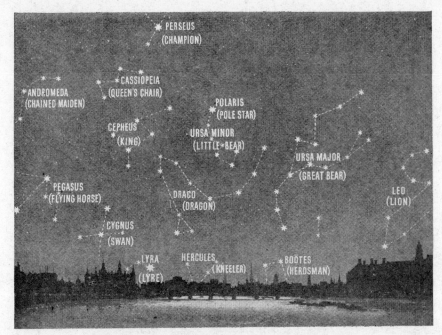

PRINCIPAL CONSTELLATIONS OF THE NIGHT SKY

Pictorial view of the night sky as seen from Westminster, London, on 1 January, at 10 p.m. At the top is a view looking north; at the bottom, looking south. In brackets are the colloquial names of the constellations.

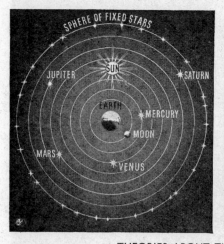 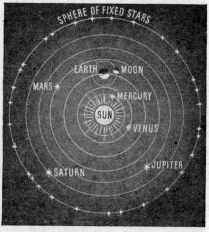

THEORIES ABOUT THE SOLAR SYSTEM
The Ptolemaic theory is illustrated on the left, and on the right the Copernican that superseded it in the middle of the sixteenth century.

stars must, therefore, be self-luminous bodies like the sun, or we should not be able to see them. He suggested that they are probably comparable with the sun in brightness or, in other words, that the sun is merely one of the many stars. He estimated that the sun would have to be moved to about 100,000 times its distance if it were to appear like Sirius, the brightest star. If, then, Sirius is comparable with the sun in actual brightness, it must be at a distance of about 10 million million miles.

This is actually an underestimate of the distance of Sirius, though the order of magnitude is correct. With distances so great as this, the changes in the relative positions of the stars caused by the orbital motion of the earth were far too small to be capable of detection in Newton's time. It was not, in fact, until well into the nineteenth century that the direct measurement of any stellar distance was successfully accomplished.

The planets in the solar systems move round the sun in accordance with laws which were discovered by Johannes Kepler early in the seventeenth century. The ancient Greeks tried to represent the movements of the planets by a combination of circular motions, because they considered the circle to be the perfect curve. Kepler proved empirically that the paths of the planets were not circular but slightly elliptical, and that there was a definite relationship between the distance of each planet from the sun and the time which it takes to complete a revolution in its orbit.

It was one of the great achievements of Sir Isaac Newton to prove that Kepler's laws were the necessary consequence of the principle of universal gravitation which he had formulated. According to this principle, every piece of matter attracts every other piece of matter. It is the gravitational pull of the earth on a stone which causes it to return to the ground when it is thrown upwards; it is the gravitational pull of the earth on the moon which holds it in its orbit; it is the gravitational pull of the sun and moon on the oceans which causes the tides and the changes in the heights of the tides from spring to neap according to whether the sun and moon are pulling together or in opposition.

For more than a century after Newton, the efforts of astronomers were largely directed to working out the consequences of the principle of gravitation in its smallest details. To Halley, the contemporary of Newton, was due the proof that comets also moved under the control of the sun's gravitational attraction.

Comets, those strange apparitions with the flowing tails which appear un-heralded in the sky for a brief space of time, had always been regarded as ill omens, as harbingers of some disaster. Halley found that the paths of the bright comets which had appeared in the years 1531, 1607 and 1682 were almost identical. He concluded that they were not three different comets, but separate appearances of the same comet, which moved in a very elongated orbit, and was only visible when it was near the sun. He predicted that the comet would return about the end of the year 1758. The comet was discovered on Christmas Eve, 1758, some sixteen years after Halley's death, providing a remarkable indication of Newton's law of universal gravitation.

Because gravitation is a universal force, every planet must continually attract every other planet. The mutual attraction between any two planets changes, of course, as the distance between the planets changes. To work out exactly the movements of a planet under the gravitational attraction of the sun and the combined gravitational attractions of all the other planets is a complicated

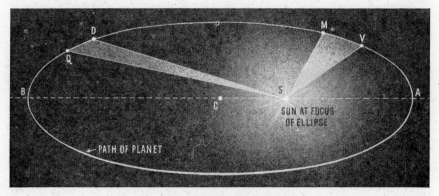

LAW OF PLANETARY MOTION
The second of Kepler's laws of planetary motion states that a planet moves not uniformly, but in such a way that a line drawn from it to the sun sweeps out equal areas of the ellipse in equal times, that is, the area VSM is equal to the area DSQ; VM and QD being distances along the planet's path.

problem to which the attention of the greatest geometers and mathematicians of the seventeenth century was devoted. A still more remarkable confirmation of Newton's law was to be provided by the discovery of an unknown planet.

Of the planets now known to us (apart from the earth), Mercury, Venus, Mars, Jupiter, and Saturn have been known from time immemorial. The first true discovery of a planet was made by William Herschel on 13 March, 1781. In the course of a careful survey of the heavens, Herschel noticed that a certain object to which his telescope was pointed had a different appearance from a star. It showed a small disk, unlike the point image of a star. Further observations proved that the object was a planet, hitherto unknown, moving in an orbit beyond the orbit of Saturn. The name of Uranus was given to this planet.

In the course of the succeeding years it was found that Uranus gradually deviated from its computed path, when the effect of the gravitational pulls of all the known planets was taken into account. It was suspected that these deviations were due to the gravitational pull of an unknown planet. Two astronomers, Adams in England and Leverrier in France, set out independently on a mathematical investigation to discover the position and path of this unknown planet. The positions they assigned were almost identical and on 23 September, 1846, the planet was discovered by Galle in Berlin, very close to the calculated position. Also it was found a week later by Professor Challis of Cambridge. The new planet, which moves in an orbit beyond that of Uranus, was named Neptune.

PLANETARY MOTION AND THE THEORY OF RELATIVITY

One further planet, Pluto, was discovered (in January, 1930) as the result of a search for a planet believed to be responsible for some small residual discordances between the observed and calculated positions of Uranus.

Although Newton had postulated the universal law of gravitation in order to account for the motions of the moon and planets, the tides, and other phenomena, he did not attempt to explain the nature of gravitation. The Newtonian views were universally accepted until the present century. A radically different point of view was put forward in 1915 by Prof. Albert Einstein in his generalized relativity theory.

Briefly, this theory requires that in the neighbourhood of matter the properties of space are changed: space may be said to become distorted or curved. Whereas in empty space a freely moving body would move in a straight line, in space distorted by the presence of matter its path becomes curved. Gravitation becomes a property of space.

According to the Newtonian view, a planet describes an ellipse about the sun because it is attracted by the gravitational field of the sun, but according to the Einstein view it merely moves along the path of a freely moving body in the space distorted by the presence of matter in the sun. The two theories give a slightly different representation of the motion. According to Newton's laws, the orbit (assuming no other planets to be present) is a closed ellipse, the

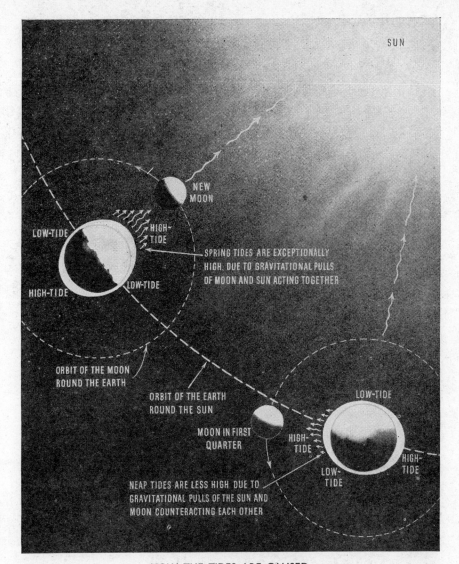

SUN

NEW MOON

LOW-TIDE

HIGH-TIDE

HIGH-TIDE

LOW-TIDE

SPRING TIDES ARE EXCEPTIONALLY HIGH, DUE TO GRAVITATIONAL PULLS OF MOON AND SUN ACTING TOGETHER

ORBIT OF THE MOON ROUND THE EARTH

ORBIT OF THE EARTH ROUND THE SUN

MOON IN FIRST QUARTER

HIGH-TIDE

LOW-TIDE

LOW-TIDE

HIGH-TIDE

NEAP TIDES ARE LESS HIGH DUE TO GRAVITATIONAL PULLS OF THE SUN AND MOON COUNTERACTING EACH OTHER

HOW THE TIDES ARE CAUSED

On the left the moon and sun are in direct line; their combined attraction causes the so-called spring tides, when the water level is very high or very low. A similar effect is caused at full moon, when the moon is on the opposite side of the earth, although the tides are not quite so high. The spring tides are highest at the spring and autumn equinoxes. Conversely, there is much less variation in the level between high and low-tides in the case of "neap" tides, at the first and last quarters of the moon, when the gravitational pull of the sun to some extent counteracts that of the moon (bottom right). One interesting theory suggests that tidal action is acting as a brake on the rotating earth, and increasing the length of the day until, in time, it will be as long as the lunar month.

The moon just passing from its full phase. This view appears inverted as compared with its appearance when seen by the naked eye. Inset is shown the edge of the dried-up Imbrium sea, and the Lunar Apennine mountains.

planet continuing to move along the same path. But according to the theory of relativity the orbit is not exactly closed, so that the path is always changing. The motion can be represented by supposing that the planet moves in an ellipse which is slowly rotating. That the planets had in fact a motion of this sort had been known for many years before the theory of relativity had been formulated; many attempts had been made without success to account for this rotation of the orbit on Newtonian principles. The theory of relativity has accounted exactly for the discordance.

The solar system shows a number of regularities which cannot be the effect of chance. The planets all move round the sun in the same direction and move very nearly in the same plane. Most of the planets have satellites. Mercury and Venus have none, Earth has one, Mars has two, Jupiter has eleven, Saturn has nine, Uranus has four, and Neptune has one. It is not known whether Pluto has any satellites. With slight exceptions, these satellites move round their primaries in the same direction as that in which the planets move round the sun. The sun and planets are all rotating in the same direction as the planetary motions, and their axes of rotation are for the most part nearly perpendicular to their orbital planes. The solar systems cannot, therefore, have been formed by the chance aggregation of the sun, planets and satellites. Some definite cause must have produced it.

ORIGIN OF THE SOLAR SYSTEM

Many theories of the origin of the solar system have been proposed; none of them is without difficulty and none has gained general acceptance. One theory supposes that in the remote distant past another star happened to pass close to the sun; in doing so, its gravitational attraction was so great that a jet of matter was drawn out from the sun, which condensed and formed the planets and their satellites, illustrated on page 48, Chapter 2.

There is a great difference between the physical conditions prevailing on the various planets. In the first place, the planets have no heat of their own. They receive heat from the sun and there is an exact balance between the heat which they receive and the heat which they radiate into space. The farther a planet is from the sun the less the heat it receives, and the lower, therefore, is its temperature. Mercury, the nearest planet to the sun, has a temperature of about 700 deg. F., whereas all the planets beyond Mars are intensely cold. Jupiter, which is the least cold of the five exterior planets, has a temperature of about —220 deg. F. (250 deg. of frost). Venus is hotter than boiling water. Only the earth and Mars have temperatures which are in the range within which it seems possible for life to exist.

The planets also differ very much in size and in weight. Jupiter, Saturn, Uranus, and Neptune are called the major planets, because they far surpass all the remainder in size. Jupiter is the largest and the most massive; it is so large that it could contain 13,000 bodies of the size of our earth. Venus is slightly

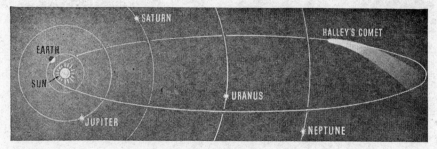

THE PATH OF HALLEY'S COMET

Comets follow elongated paths, passing very close to the sun and flying far out into space. If they break up on passing close to a planet, they form meteorites.

smaller than the earth, while Mercury is not much larger than the moon, which has a diameter of only 2,000 miles as compared with the earth's 8,000 miles. Mars is intermediate in size between the earth and Mercury.

The fact that the planets differ so much in size and weight has an interesting consequence. Most people have never bothered to wonder how it is that the earth is surrounded by an atmosphere—the air that we breathe. The natural tendency of any gaseous matter is to spread outwards in all directions. Why then does the earth's atmosphere not dissipate itself away into space? The reason is that it is held bound by the gravitational pull of the earth.

There is, indeed, a slow leakage into outer space at the upper limit of the atmosphere, and this leakage is much more rapid for the lighter constituents of the atmosphere than it is for the heavier. Now, the two lightest gases are hydrogen and helium and they are the two elements which are cosmically most abundant. The sun and the stars, for instance, contain far more hydrogen than

This picture of the Comet 1947-N was taken on 11 December, 1947, at Montevideo. The comet's tail, which may be many millions of miles in length, always points away from the sun, and is, therefore, roughly at right angles to the direction of flight of the comet instead of streaming behind it.

any other element and, after hydrogen, helium is the next principal constituent. The earth's atmosphere contains very little hydrogen or helium, as these light gases have almost entirely leaked away into space. The heavier gases, like oxygen and nitrogen, have a much slower leakage and, consequently, our atmosphere contains large quantities of them.

This provides a clue to the explanation of many of the differences between the planets and their satellites. The moon, for instance, is so small that its gravitational pull has been quite insufficient to retain any atmosphere at all. It can be calculated that the whole of the moon's original atmosphere must have leaked away into outer space within a few thousand years.

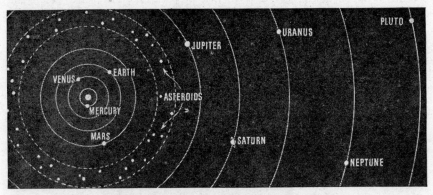

PLANETS COMPOSING THE SOLAR SYSTEM

Arrangement of the planets round the sun. Compare this with the early ideas of the construction of the solar system described and illustrated above. Because of space limitations the orbits are not to scale.

In the four major planets, Jupiter, Saturn, Uranus, and Neptune, we meet the other extreme. The gravitational pull of these massive planets is so great that they have lost practically none of their initial atmospheres.

The evolution of such an atmosphere can be traced out and it can be shown that, as the planets cooled from their initial hot states, a series of chemical changes took place, producing large quantities of water vapour, of the poisonous gas, methane or marsh gas, and of pungent ammonia gas. These planets are now so cold that all the water vapour has been deposited on the surface as a thick ice coating, while the atmospheres now contain large quantities of hydrogen and helium, together with marsh gas and ammonia. There is no free oxygen, because it was all used up by combining with some of the hydrogen to form water vapour, hence life cannot possibly exist on such planets.

The two planets, Venus and Mars, are, like our own earth, sufficiently massive to have retained some atmosphere, but not massive enough to have prevented hydrogen and helium from leaking out of their atmospheres into space. Venus is so nearly equal to the earth in size and weight that we might expect to find that it is a world not very unlike the earth. This proves not to be the case, however. Venus is a warm arid world, entirely devoid of any moisture. Its atmosphere contains no oxygen; in its place we find carbon dioxide. The atmosphere of our earth once contained a great deal of carbon dioxide also, but the action of vegetation has changed this. Plant cells absorb carbon dioxide, use the carbon for building more plant cells, and give oxygen back to the atmosphere. By this action of vegetation our own atmosphere has been changed. The lack of oxygen on Venus must point to an absence of vegetation, probably to be attributed to the lack of water. The circulation of the atmosphere of Venus is much more vigorous than that of our atmosphere, and causes dust from the desert surface to be carried high into the atmosphere. Because of this dust haze it is impossible for us ever to see the surface of Venus.

Mars is considerably smaller than the earth and has a much thinner atmosphere. There are caps of snow or ice in the polar regions, which melt and disappear in the summer months. Clouds are often visible over considerable areas. Changes of colour and of detail are plainly visible and are almost certainly due to the seasonal growth and dying away of some form of vegetation. The temperature is moderate in the daytime and falls rapidly towards sunset, and there is intense cold at night. It is not possible to say at this stage whether any forms of animal life exist on Mars.

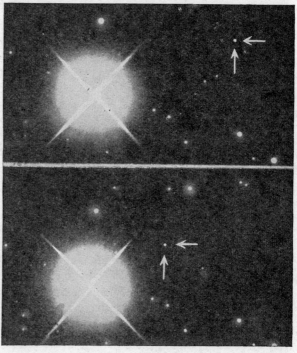

Pluto was discovered in 1930 as the result of photographic exposures. It has the distinction of travelling on the outermost orbit in space, being nearly 3,700 million miles away from the sun. The change in the position of the planet, indicated by arrows, is clearly seen on the photograph. Its orbit is the most eccentric of all the nine major planets.

SATURN AND ITS RINGS

The rings seen above are composed of small bodies rotating in their own orbits.
The inner and less dense ring is known as the Crepe Ring.

The sun is the parent of the earth and the other planets, and could contain about 1,300,000 bodies the size of our earth. It is a mere coincidence that the moon, which is much smaller than the earth, and the sun appear to be of the same size. The distance of the moon is about 240,000 miles, but the distance of the sun is 93 million miles. The sun is intensely bright and hot, and life on the earth is made possible by the continuous stream of light and heat which it receives from it. The surface of the sun is about five thousand times brighter per square foot than molten steel, and every square inch is continually radiating energy at the rate of a 62-horse-power engine. The earth receives only one part in

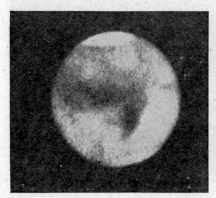

MARS AND JUPITER

To the left is a view of Mars, showing the polar cap. The view to the right
is Jupiter, showing the characteristic cloud belts parallel with its equator.

21

SUPPORT OF PHOTOHELIOGRAPH
WITH SLOW-MOTION FOR
ACCURATE ADJUSTMENT

VISUAL
TELESCOPE

CAMERA TO GIVE
ENLARGED IMAGE OF SUN
ON PHOTOGRAPHIC PLATE

SETTING CIRCLE
FOR SETTING POSITION
OF TELESCOPE

VIEWING EYEPIECE

SETTING A PHOTOHELIOGRAPH

This telescopic instrument is used by the astronomers for photographically recording such solar phenomena as sunspots, corona and prominences. The giant sunspot illustrated on page 26 was photographed on this type of instrument.

2,200 millions of this energy, yet this small fraction amounts to nearly five million horse-power per square mile of the earth's surface.

Because of the high temperature the sun is in a gaseous state. All chemical compounds are split up and dissociated when the temperature is raised sufficiently. No chemical compounds can exist in the sun except in its coolest outermost layers, where a few very simple compounds can be detected. Thus the iron, carbon, silicon contained in the sun exist entirely in the form of vapour.

By spectroscopically analysing the light which the sun sends out we can find what elements are present in the sun, with the result that the sun proves to be composed of elements similar to those found on the earth. The chief difference in the composition of the sun and the earth is that the sun contains a far greater amount of the two lightest elements, hydrogen and helium, so much so that the sun can be said to consist predominantly of hydrogen.

THE SUN'S INTERNAL TEMPERATURES

Although it is impossible to see into the sun for more than a very small distance, we can calculate the temperature deep down inside the sun by the application of simple physical principles. It is found that the temperature at the sun's centre is extremely high, about 20 million deg. C. We do not know of any hotter place. Many people think that the sun is a huge ball of burning material, but burning, or combustion, is a chemical process involving the combination of carbon with oxygen to form carbon dioxide, with the release of heat. As we have seen, chemical compounds such as carbon dioxide cannot exist in the sun. The process of combustion would in any case maintain the sun's radiation only for a very short time.

What we have to explain is how the sun has been able to pour out its stream of energy for some 4,000 million years, for this is the estimated age of the earth's crust, derived from the study and analysis of its radioactive materials (Chapter 2, page 79). The only source of energy which is at all adequate for the purpose is atomic energy and it is now certain that the sun maintains its great output of energy by drawing upon some of the energy that is locked up within the atom (see Chapter 7). The sun is able to utilize this energy because of the extremely high temperature in its interior. But the sun obtains its atomic energy in a different way from the atomic bomb. The energy released in the explosion of an atomic bomb is derived from the fission of heavy atoms of uranium or plutonium into lighter atoms. The sun, on the other hand, derives its energy from the building up of atoms of helium out of atoms of hydrogen, not directly, but through a complicated cycle of atomic transformations.

According to modern physical ideas, mass and energy are synonymous. When four atoms of hydrogen combine to form one atom of helium there is a slight loss of weight, which is balanced by the energy released. The sun is actually losing weight at the rate of four million tons every second, but this is a small fraction compared with the great mass of the sun.

SOLAR PROMINENCES

These great fountains formed of luminous gas, hundreds of thousands of miles long and up to half a million miles high, are called solar prominences. Some erupt explosively from the sun's surface ; others form tall, stationary feathery columns ; while some stream downwards on a curved path into the sun.

When we look at the sun through heavily smoked glass, or by projecting its image, formed in a telescope, on to a screen, dark spots are often to be seen on its surface. These spots are called sunspots, and their discovery by Galileo in 1609 was one of the first fruits of the application of the then newly discovered telescope to astronomy. The spots appear rather suddenly and at irregular times. They are shortlived, some lasting for only a day or two, others for a few weeks; occasionally one may last for a few months. But there is a certain regularity in the frequency with which they appear. Starting from a time when spots are rarely to be seen, called sunspot minimum, the spots become progressively more frequent for some four or five years, until the sunspot maximum is attained; thereafter their frequency diminishes progressively until the next minimum is reached. The whole cycle lasts for about eleven years, but it is not strictly regular. Both the length of the cycle and the frequency of appearance of spots at the maximum vary appreciably from cycle to cycle.

The darkness of a sunspot is a contrast effect. The temperature of a spot is considerably lower than that of the adjacent portions of the sun; the spot, though intensely hot and very bright, is much less bright than the normal solar surface and, therefore, appears dark against it. A spot is a hollow vortex in the sun's surface. A good analogy is provided by the hollow vortex formed when water is running out of a bath, if we imagine the flow to be reversed and the water to be streaming up into the bath through the outlet. Material from deeper down in the sun streams spirally outwards and then, cooled by expansion, falls back towards the surface.

Spots can be on the grand scale. A large spot may cover an area of two to three thousand million square miles. The largest spot which has occurred since 1873, when the Greenwich Observatory records commenced, appeared in April, 1947, and covered an area about one hundred and thirty times the cross-section of the earth, or about 6,500 million square miles.

Various terrestrial effects are associated with sunspots. Magnetic storms, when telegraph and telephone circuits can be badly upset and radio trans-missions interfered with, and displays of the aurora, both wax and wane in frequency with the sunspots. Sudden radio fade-outs frequently occur when a large spot appears, synchronizing with the outbreak of intensely bright eruptions which are liable to occur in the vicinity of the spot. The primary cause of the terrestrial effects is a stream of electrically charged particles shot out from the sun with the very great speed of about a thousand miles a second. The way in which such a stream of particles, on entering the earth's atmosphere, produces the observed effects is too complicated to describe here. The study of the various associated phenomena is of importance, however, for predicting the best frequen-cies to use for long-distance radio transmissions (which vary with the season of the year and through the solar cycle), and for predicting when the transmissions will become difficult.

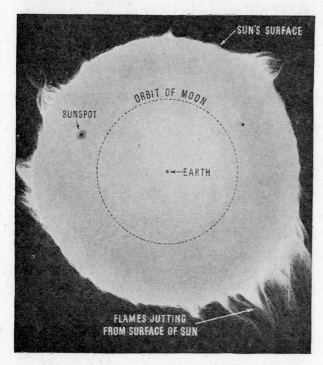

This drawing shows the size of the earth in relation to the sun and orbit of the moon and serves as a basis for comparing the surface areas covered by sunspots and the heights to which solar prominences extend.

Great flames of incandescent gas, often extending to heights of many tens of thousands of miles, can often be seen (when suitable means are employed) standing out from the surface of the sun. They may persist for weeks or months without very much change, and then suddenly be thrown into a state of eruption, when the gases seem to be blown violently away from the sun. This sometimes happens with such violence that the material is able to escape from the sun's immense gravitational pull and is shot off into space.

The sun is surrounded by a faint tenuous appendage, which is too faint to be visible by the eye except on the infrequent occasions when the moon passes directly between the earth and the sun. It is just possible for the moon to cover the sun completely as seen from a narrow belt on the earth's surface, entirely cutting off its light and producing a total eclipse of the sun. As the last thin crescent of sunlight is cut off the corona appears to open out like a flower, extending long streamers out to a distance of a couple of million of miles from the sun. The shape of the corona changes through the sunspot cycle; when sunspots are few the streamers are mainly in the equatorial regions, but when sunspots are many they extend all round the sun.

When we look at the sky on a clear moonless night we can see with the naked eye only a few thousand stars. With every increase in telescopic power more stars become visible. The reason is that the stars differ considerably in brightness. The light received directly by the eye from a faint star is not enough to produce the sensations of vision, but the larger amount of light collected by the telescope will do so if the aperture of the telescope is sufficiently large. What we are here

Sunspots are not permanent features, but disappear after several days or weeks; their greatest frequency occurs in eleven-year cycles, a few small spots appearing near the poles of the sun, more and more spots occurring nearer and nearer the equator, until after 5½ years the maximum frequency occurs.

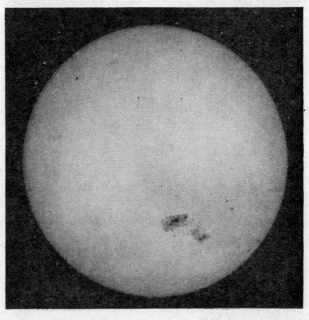

THE SOLAR CORONA PHOTOGRAPHED DURING AN ECLIPSE
This glowing, tenuous corona is visible only when the incandescent mass of the sun is hidden by the moon during a total eclipse; prominences can also be seen.

concerned with is the apparent brightness of the light emitted by the stars.

The ancient Greeks believed that the stars were all fixed to a crystal globe and were, therefore, all at the same distance. If this were so, the apparent brightness would also be a measure of the intrinsic brightness. We know now, however, that the distances of the stars from the earth differ very greatly. If all the stars were of the same intrinsic brightness, their apparent brightness would provide a measure of their relative distances. But, since the stars differ considerably in intrinsic brightness, it is not possible to draw any conclusions from their apparent brightness about either their intrinsic brightness or their distances.

The principle of the method used for measuring the distances of the stars is simple. As the earth moves in its orbit round the sun a relatively near star will appear to swing slightly backwards and forwards relatively to more distant adjacent stars. But the displacements of even the nearest stars are so small that their measurement must be made with very high accuracy; this calls for many refinements of technique. Success was only attained after many failures.

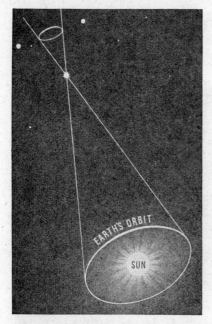

By carefully observing the change in the position of a star in relation to other stars, due to the movement of the earth round the sun, the distance of a star from the earth can be calculated. The apparent movement of the star is called parallax, and derives from the Greek word meaning shift.

The nearest known star, apart from the sun, is at a distance of about 25 million million miles. In order more easily to grasp such great distances it is convenient to express them in terms of the light-year, the distance which light travels in the course of a year. As the speed of light is 186,000 miles a second, the light-year is about 6 million million miles. We can, therefore, say that the distance of the nearest star is about four light-years. Expressed also in units of light-time we can say that the distance of the sun is about eight light-minutes, and the distance of the moon is about one and a quarter light-seconds. As radio waves have the same speed as light it follows that a radar reflection from the moon would be received two and a half seconds after the radar signal was sent.

Looked at in a different way, a physical interpretation can be given to the light-time. If the sun were to be suddenly blotted out, we should continue to see it for eight minutes after it had ceased to exist, by means of the light from it which would still be travelling through space towards us. Similarly, if the nearest star were to be suddenly annihilated, it would not be until four years later that we would be aware of the fact.

When the distances of the stars have been measured, we are able to allow for their differing distances and to use the measures of their apparent brightness to provide information about their intrinsic brightness or candle-power. We then find that the stars shine with very unequal light; some emit less than a 300,000th part of the light of the sun, and some more than 300,000 times as much.

The stars differ appreciably from one another in colour. Some are steely blue, some are white, some are yellow, and some are ruddy or red in colour. The sun itself is a yellow star. The colours of the stars are not so obvious to the eye as the colour of the sun, but are easily apparent if the stars are observed intently on a clear night. These differences of colour are due to differences of temperature. Just as molten steel in cooling passes through the succession of colours, white, yellow, bright red, dull red, so the sequence of colours of the stars—from blue to red—corresponds to progressively lower surface temperatures. As the surface brightness of a star depends only on the temperature of the star, the colour gives us information about the brightness per unit area of surface. The candle-power of the star, on the other hand, is the total surface brightness of the hemisphere of the star which we see. Combining these data we derive the total area of the surface of the star, or, in other words, we determine its actual size.

The range in size of the stars is surprisingly great. There are some stars which are so large that if the sun were placed at the centre of one of them the whole of the orbit of the planet Mars would easily lie within the star: they could contain about 75 million bodies of the size of the sun. There are others which are so small that they are comparable in size with the planet Neptune; yet though of planetary dimensions, they are stars and not planets, for they are hot, self-luminous bodies. The very large stars are known as giants, which are composed of diffuse matter, and the very small stars as dwarfs, which are extremely dense.

It is a more difficult matter to obtain information about the mass or weight of the stars. It is impossible to obtain any direct information about the weight of a single star. It is only through the gravitational pull of one star on another that we can learn about their weight. Fortunately, there are many stars which, though they appear as normal stars to the naked eye, are actually twin systems, consisting of two stars revolving about each other under their mutual gravitation. Many of these stars are seen to consist of two stars when they are viewed through a powerful telescope, but there are many others which still appear single in the most powerful telescopes and whose twin nature is only discovered by some other method, such as the alternate eclipsing of one by the other as they revolve.

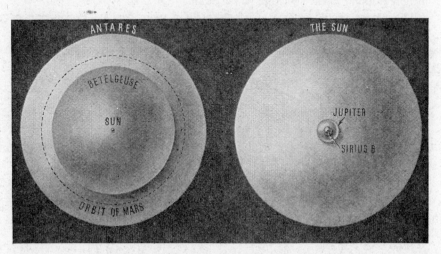

THE RELATIVE SIZES OF THE PLANETS AND STARS

This diagrammatic illustration shows the relative sizes of the stars, sun and planets. On the left are shown Antares and Betelgeuse, both much greater than the sun ; on the right the sun dwarfs the planet Jupiter and the star Sirius B.

The study of these twin systems has enabled many stars to be weighed by measuring the gravitational pull of one on the other. An interesting result has followed. When the masses of the stars are compared with their candle-powers it is found that the most massive stars are also the most luminous, and that the least massive stars are the least luminous. The correlation between the mass of a star and its candle-power proves to be so close that when one of these quantities has been determined we can infer the other. We are thus provided with a means of assigning a mass to any single star, provided that its candle-power has previously been derived. But it was, of course, the information obtained from the twin stars that has made this possible.

MASS AND LUMINOSITY

The range in mass of the stars proves to be small compared with their range in size or in luminosity. There are not many stars which weigh more than fifty times the sun, and not many which weigh less than one-tenth of the sun. The relatively small range in mass, taken in conjunction with the great range in size, means that there is a very wide range in the density of the matter of which the stars are composed. There are, on the one hand, giant stars which are so tenuous that the weight of sufficient of their material to fill an average-sized room would be only about one ounce; the density of the material is comparable with that of air in an ordinary vacuum. On the other hand, the material of which some of the dwarf stars are composed is many thousands of times denser than platinum, so that a matchbox full would weigh about a ton. The explanation of this phenomenon is found in the structure of the atom.

The reader should refer to Chapter 7 for a more detailed explanation of atomic structure. For our immediate purpose, however, it is only necessary to understand that an atom consists of a central nucleus surrounded by a number of smaller particles, the electrons. If we think of the electrons as circling within a sphere of a certain size, the interior of the sphere is practically empty space, because the total volume of the nucleus and of the electrons is only a minute fraction of the total volume of the atom. The sphere can be considered as an invisible boundary. In a solid body these spheres are packed closely together and it is not possible to obtain a much greater density by compressing them; the invisible boundaries of the atoms cannot be made to overlap. When the temperature of a substance is raised sufficiently some of the outer electrons are driven off; the atoms are then said to be ionized. If the temperature is progressively increased, more and more electrons are driven off.

At the extremely high temperatures of several million degrees in the interior of the stars the atoms are completely ionized, or, in other words, all the electrons are driven off, so that there is a hurly-burly of nuclei and electrons, flying about at extremely high speeds, continually colliding with one another and rebounding. The invisible walls of the atoms have been entirely shattered: they have ceased to exist. Under such circumstances it is easy to understand how the gas can be compressed to densities which are very much greater than are possible in a solid, while still allowing plenty of freedom of movement to the atomic nuclei and to the electrons.

Though there is, as we have seen, very great diversity in the physical conditions within the stars, there is considerable uniformity in chemical composition. We have no evidence of an element being present in any star which is not already known on the earth.

It is true that from time to time it has been suspected that there was an unknown element in some celestial body, but it has always turned out to be a known element in an unfamiliar guise. There is a limited way in which different elements can be built up and there are no gaps in the building scheme to be filled by unknown elements. So it is really in accordance with what we should expect that the stars prove to be built up of the same familiar elements as the earth. What is surprising, however, is the general uniformity of composition; the relative abundance of different metals, for instance, is closely the same in the stars, the sun and the earth.

The output of heat from the sun is remarkably uniform, which is fortunate for mankind, because if the sun brightened up a little, increasing its output of heat, life on the earth would soon become impossible, as the earth would be too hot; similarly, a moderate decrease in the output of heat would be sufficient to cause a great freeze-up which would extinguish all life. Geologists tell us that there have been warmer periods and ice ages in the past history of the earth, which have probably been caused by small slow variations in the sun's heat. Many of the stars behave quite differently from the sun and vary considerably in brightness.

NATURE OF PULSATING STARS

In some stars these changes occur in an irregular and unpredictable manner; in others they occur with absolute regularity and can be predicted for long ahead. The cause of the light-changes in many stars is unknown: it is possible that the atomic processes which provide the energy which a star radiates are not under strict control in all stars. There is, however, one group of stars of special interest because the phenomena are fairly well understood, and the stars are particularly useful to astronomers.

This group of special interest consists of the pulsating stars. Such stars undergo a regular pulsation, expanding and contracting alternately. The brightness of the star varies in a characteristic manner, the increase in brightness being more rapid than the subsequent fall. The period of the pulsation or light-variation may be as short as a few hours or as long as a few weeks.

What makes these stars so important is that there is a relationship between the candle-power of the star and the period of the pulsation; the brighter the star, the slower the pulsation. In a general way, such a relationship might be expected, for the brighter the star the more massive it is, and we might expect that the pulsations would be slower for the more massive stars.

THE MILKY WAY

The brightest portion of the Milky Way, in the constellation of Sagittarius, the Archer, showing the myriad stars clustered together.

The significance of the relationship is that it enables the pulsating stars to be used as standard beacons in space, for it is a fairly simple matter to determine the period of the variation in brightness, and this then gives us the candle-power of the star. The pulsating stars happen to be stars of high intrinsic brightness which are visible at very great distances. They, therefore, serve to extend our measurement of stellar distances far beyond the range at which direct measures cease to be practicable. Some examples are given in the following table:

Period of light variation in days	1	$2\frac{1}{2}$	5	10	20	40
Number of times brighter than sun	160	330	640	1,600	4,400	12,000

On a clear dark night we can see, in addition to individual stars, a broad belt of hazy light stretching right across the sky; it is known as the Milky Way, from its milky appearance. It encircles the whole heavens, extending across the southern sky as well as across the northern sky. When looked at in a telescope the Milky Way is seen to consist of a great number of faint stars.

The individual stars are too faint to be seen with the naked eye, but the integrated effect of the faint light from many stars is sufficient to produce a visual impression. If the stars in our stellar universe are distributed approximately uniformly, the appearance of the Milky Way can be explained by supposing that our stellar universe is a much flattened system, rather like a disk or a millstone, with great breadth but small depth. The distribution of stars in the Milky Way regions is far from uniform, with many localized aggregations of stars or star clouds. The brightest portion of the Milky Way is in the southern constellation of Sagittarius, the Archer.

The Milky Way is not composed entirely of stars, however. Observation, either visually or preferably by photography, reveals here and there diffuse irregular bright patches, shining with a characteristic greenish light. These are called nebular patches, from the Latin word for clouds. The nebulæ have been found to be composed of matter in the gaseous state, which is not self-

OBSCURING NEBULAR CLOUDS

In this reproduced photograph of a section of the Milky Way, some of the stars are obscured by clouds of dust and debris which form curtains on the night sky. The dark patches were thought to be vacant lanes through the stars.

luminous, but is rendered luminous by the stars embedded in them, in much the same way as a motor-car headlamp on a foggy night illuminates the fog and produces a large bright patch of light.

Another striking feature of the Milky Way is the frequent occurrence in densely populated star regions of blank patches, devoid or almost devoid of stars. These were once thought to be vacant lanes through the stars. But there are so many of them that it is impossible to suppose that there could be so many vacant lanes extending to a great distance and pointing directly towards us. The only alternative explanation is that the blank patches are due to obscuration of the stars by dark clouds. This explanation is now known to be correct and the blank patches are, therefore, called dark nebulæ. These dark nebulæ or obscuring clouds are composed of solid particles; we can think of them as clouds of dust.

DISTRIBUTION OF MATTER IN INTERSTELLAR SPACE

The bright nebulosity and the dark clouds are often found to be closely associated with one another. We must, therefore, think of interstellar space as not being entirely empty. It contains a great deal of matter in the form partly of separate atoms and molecules (diffuse gaseous matter), and partly of small solid particles. This matter, like the stars themselves, is strongly concentrated towards the Milky Way, and is of extremely low density.

The most perfect vacuum which we can produce with the aid of modern vacuum pumps is quite dense in comparison. Where the solid particles are more closely aggregated, the stars lying beyond are completely hidden from sight, but in other regions, where the particles are fewer, the distant stars are both dimmed and reddened, just as the sun is when seen through a smoke haze.

This dimming or even complete obscuration of distant stars is very troublesome to the astronomer in his endeavours to find out the dimensions of our stellar universe and the position of the sun in it. If we find ourselves in a forest in a fog we see trees in all directions as far as the limiting distance of vision: we might conclude from what we see that we are in the middle of the forest. In the absence of the fog, however, we might be able to see the limits of the forest in some directions and not in others, and might find that we are not very far from one edge of the forest.

The early attempts to investigate the structure of the universe, before the importance of the dimming or obscuration of distant stars had been realized, did in fact place the sun in the centre. The best chance of obtaining reliable information is by the study of remote objects which are at some distance from the Milky Way. Because the cosmic dust is so strongly concentrated in the Milky Way, we must look out of the Milky Way in order to reduce the effects of the dimming which it causes. There happens, fortunately, to be a class of objects which is ideal for the purpose. These objects are known as globular star clusters; each cluster consists of a globular aggregation of some thousands of stars, the star density decreasing from the centre of the cluster outwards.

THE NEBULOSITY IN THE CONSTELLATION OF CYGNUS

The great tenuous mass of glowing gas, interspersed with stars, which is flung across interstellar space in the constellation of Cygnus, the Swan, is very appropriately named the Bridal Veil Nebula. This beautiful gaseous nebula is located within the confines of our own Milky Way.

CELESTIAL CATHERINE-WHEEL

Here the spiral nebula in the constellation of Ursa Major, the Great Bear, is seen broadside-on, and shows clearly the whirling motion of the nebula.

These clusters are mostly at considerable distances, many thousands of light-years. Though the distances are great, they can be well determined, because pulsating stars are found in each cluster. Their distribution in the sky shows two significant features: there are none at all in the Milky Way itself and they are mostly in one hemisphere of the sky. Their absence from the Milky Way is merely an obscuration effect; their comparative absence from half the sky shows that the sun is far out from the centre of our stellar universe.

The globular clusters are distributed more or less at random throughout a spherical space which is co-extensive with our stellar universe. The centre of this sphere is at a distance of about 30,000 light-years from the sun, and lies in the direction of the constellation of Sagittarius, where we see the brightest and densest regions of the Milky Way. The diameter of the region occupied by the globular clusters is about 100,000 light-years.

These results have received confirmation in an unexpected way. A detailed study of the motions of the stars shows that they do not move entirely at random.

The motions have the characteristics of the movements of the planets in the solar systems in which the inner planets move round the sun faster than the outer ones. It is found that the stars on one side of us in space are collectively moving faster than we are, and that those on the other side are moving slower. Superposed on these mass movements are the random motions of the individual stars, which are considerably smaller in magnitude. The study of the motions gives us information about the position of the centre round which the stars as a whole are moving; it is in the direction of Sagittarius, the same direction as that of the centre of the system of globular clusters.

Now, just as the planets would scatter into space if it were not for the controlling force of the sun's gravitational pull, so the individual stars would scatter into space if they were not prevented from doing so by the gravitational pull of the entire stellar system. By some fairly straightforward calculations, the total mass of the system can be worked out. The results are of much interest.

ORBITS OF THE SUN AND STARS

The distance of the sun from the centre of the system is, as we have already mentioned, about 30,000 light-years. The sun, together with the neighbouring stars, is moving in its immense orbit around the centre at the tremendous speed of about 170 miles a second, carrying the planets with it as it goes, but because of the smoothness of the motion and the absence of any abrupt changes in speed or direction we are not any more conscious of this motion than we are of the speed of eighteen miles a second with which the earth moves round the sun.

Relative to the neighbouring stars, the sun has its own proper motion of about thirteen miles a second, towards the constellation of Hercules. The distance to the centre is so great that despite the tremendous speed of 170 miles a second, it takes the sun about 225 million years to complete one revolution of its orbit. It may be mentioned that most of the stars that are near enough to the sun to be visible to the naked eye are moving at about the same speed.

The total mass of our stellar system, or galaxy, as it is often termed, whose gravitational pull provides the controlling force, proves to be of the order of 150,000 million suns like our own. As the largest telescope in the world shows only about 1,500 million stars, it is possible to see only about one in every hundred stars. The remainder are invisible to us, either because they are too distant and too faint or because they are hidden from view by the interstellar dust.

From careful estimates of the density of this interstellar dust it is concluded that the total amount of this matter is about equal to the total amount of matter in all the stars. The stars as they move through space gradually collect this dust by their gravitational pulls.

The stars occupy a very small volume of the total space in the galaxy. When we look at a long-exposure photograph of a region of the Milky Way, the stars are so numerous that we might think they are almost touching one another. To get the correct perspective we must recall that the nearest star to the sun is 25 million million miles away. If we take a hollow globe the size of our earth, 8,000 miles in diameter, and suppose six tennis balls to be flying about inside it, we have a pretty good representation of the density of stars in space, each tennis ball representing a star of the size of the sun, and the distances between the separate balls representing the distances between the stars.

Now suppose that we could travel through space with the speed of light and that we set out towards the centre of our galaxy. The density of the stars would gradually increase towards the centre, which we would reach in about 30,000 years. Continuing to travel onwards for another 50,000 years we would find the stars becoming fewer and fewer, and eventually we would have left all the stars behind us and would find ourselves in outer space. If we went on and on, should we ever find any more stars or should we merely find nothing but empty space?

If we continued our journey for about 750,000 years, in the right direction, we would begin to meet stars again and these would become gradually more numerous. A new galaxy, or stellar universe, would have been entered, which would be found to resemble in all its main features the universe which we had long ago left behind. This universe has been known for more than three hundred years. Marius, in 1612, looking at it with the then newly invented telescope, described it as "like a candle-light seen through horn." It is, indeed, visible to the naked eye as a faint blur, in the constellation of Andromeda, but only within recent years has it been possible to prove that it lies far beyond the bounds of our galaxy, and that it is, in fact, an island universe in space.

PULSATING STARS AND ISLAND UNIVERSES

Once again it is the pulsating stars which have provided the key. With our modern telescopes we can photograph this blur of light and record all its details, and we can recognize many of the features that characterize our galaxy—star clouds, bright nebulosity, obscuration by clouds of dust, and pulsating stars. These standard beacons make it possible to determine its distance as 750,000 light-years; then, knowing its distance, we can find its linear dimensions, which prove to be about the same as those of our own galaxy—roughly 100,000 light-years in diameter. We find, also, that it is slowly rotating, like our own galaxy, and that its mass is about 100,000 million times that of our own sun.

This island universe, which we see in the constellation of Andromeda, is but one—and the nearest to us—of many. We see them inclined at all angles to the line of sight. Some we see edgewise-on, showing the same flattened shape as our own galaxy, with a conspicuous belt of obscuring matter concentrated towards the central plane—the Milky Way of the other universe. Others are seen broadside-on, and we find that they have a characteristic spiral structure. From a central nucleus, where there seems to be a conspicuous concentration of matter, spiral arms emerge which contain aggregations of stars.

Some, like the one in Andromeda, are seen obliquely, but the spiral arms can still be traced. There is such a continuous gradation in the angle of view, from broadside-on to edgewise-on, that we can be quite certain that these various universes, which appear so different from one another in photographs, are essentially similar in their main structural details.

Our own galaxy is no doubt a system with a similar spiral structure, but as the sun lies practically on the plane of the Milky Way it is not possible for us to recognize this structure, particularly as our view is so much obscured by the dust clouds. If the sun were well outside the plane of the Milky Way we should be able to see the spiral formation of the arms.

Rotation is a common feature of these universes, and we can think of them as celestial catherine wheels, spinning round in space. The rotation is slow by our ordinary terrestrial time standards, but it is sufficient for gravitation to take control and to prevent a slow dissipation of the stars away into space. In the nearer of these universes pulsating stars can be detected, and so their distances and dimensions can be derived.

DISTANCES OF THE REMOTE NEBULÆ

In order to estimate the distances of these more remote systems we must make some assumption. We find that the actual dimensions of the island universes, whose distances we can determine by means of the pulsating stars, are much about the same, and so also are their intrinsic luminosities. It does not seem unreasonable to suppose that this is true also for the distant universes. We have seen that the assumption of equal luminosity for the individual stars is very far from the truth, but for the universes it holds as a first approximation. With these assumptions we can make estimates of the distance of any universe which we photograph. No very great accuracy can be claimed for distances derived in this way; they do, however, serve as a rough guide.

Now we come to a very curious result. It is found that these universes are all, seemingly, moving away from us, and that the farther away they are the more rapidly they are receding.

The change in the pitch of the whistle of a train as it passes us is familiar. When the train is approaching, the sound waves which reach us are crowded together by the motion of the train; the wavelength of the sound is shortened and the pitch of the note of the whistle is raised. When the train has passed, the sound waves reaching us are spaced farther apart, the wavelength is increased and the pitch of the note is lowered. So we detect a sudden drop in pitch.

Astronomers use the same principle to measure the speed with which a star is moving on the line of sight towards us or away from us. If the star is moving towards us, the wavelengths of all the radiations in its light are shortened; if it is moving away from us, the wavelengths are all increased. The island universes can be studied in the same way; the wavelengths of the light they send us are all increased, or, in other words, reddened. We naturally interpret this effect as due to a recession of the universes.

THE GREAT NEBULA IN ANDROMEDA

This giant island universe is the nearest and the most conspicuous of the great nebulæ, and consists of glowing wisps of gas set with stars. Some conception can be gained of the immense distances of outer space when it is realized that light, travelling at about 6 million million miles per year, takes 750,000 years to reach us. The vast size of the nebulæ is revealed by the fact that light takes nearly 100,000 years to cross from one side to the other. Our own galaxy is no doubt a system with a similar structure, but as the sun lies practically on the plane of the Milky Way, it is not possible for us to observe this structure.

Accepting this interpretation as correct, we find that the distances we have determined by assuming that the universes are standard articles—alike in size and in luminosity—and so nearly proportional to the speeds with which they are moving away that the result cannot be an effect of chance. There must be some underlying reason for it. Whatever the reason it provides us with a new and more accurate method for determining their distances. For we can measure the speed of motion in the line of sight with much greater precision than we can estimate actual size or luminosity, and, moreover, we can extend the scale of distance to the most remote universes that we can detect.

It is found that the most distant systems that have been detected are receding from us with immense speeds of the order of 47,000 miles a second, about one-quarter of the speed of light, and that they are at a distance of about 500 million light-years. This estimate of distance is, of course, quite independent of the validity of the interpretation of the changed wavelengths of the light-radiations as being due to a motion of recession. The light by which these remote systems are photographed has been travelling through space for some 500 million years, an appreciable portion of the lifetime of our earth; the light had almost reached the end of its long journey before ever man appeared on the earth.

THE SIZE OF THE UNIVERSE

Out to this distance of 500 million years, the farthest depth of space to which we can yet probe, there are somewhere about 100 million universes. At this distance we can find no evidence of any thinning out in the distribution, such as we find in the case of the stars towards the limits of our galaxy. The separate universes are fairly uniformly spaced at an average distance apart of about 2 million light-years. A scale model can be obtained if we represent each universe by a dinner plate and imagine these to be scattered through space at a distance apart of about 20 ft. and oriented at random. Each universe contains sufficient material to make from one to two hundred thousand million stars like our sun.

Many questions are raised by this picture of the portion of the universe as a whole—the universe of separate stellar universes or galaxies—which is within the reach of our most powerful telescopes. Are the galaxies themselves members of a larger system, which is merely one of many that lie beyond our power of detection? Or are the galaxies the largest units and infinite in number? Are we correct in concluding that the other galaxies are all receding from us, or is there some other intepretation?

Let us take the last question first. If the galaxies are all moving away from us it might be thought at first sight that our own galaxy must be at the centre of all the galaxies. We have seen that it was for long believed that our earth was the centre of the universe. It was displaced from that position by Copernicus, who put the sun in its place. The sun was next dethroned from the central position. We should feel inclined intuitively to distrust any picture which now places our galaxy at the centre. But we must remember that the velocities of recession are proportional to the distances: the farther away any galaxy is, the greater is its speed of recession. It follows at once that the distance between any two galaxies must be increasing at the same proportional rate.

This can be readily seen if we think of a rubber balloon, on which a large number of dots have been marked, being inflated. As the balloon increases in size the distance between any two dots increases at precisely the same rate, the rate at which the size of the balloon is increasing. In this way we arrive at the conception of the expanding universe; that there is a uniform expansion of the whole of space, carrying all the galaxies with it, just as the expansion of the balloon carries all the dots on its surface with it. The relative positions remain the same; it is only the scale that changes.

ALTERNATIVES TO THE THEORY OF THE EXPANDING UNIVERSE

We must pause a moment to consider whether we may have followed a false scent, whether we may not, in fact, have been mistaken in interpreting the reddening of the light of the distant galaxies as the effect of a velocity of recession. It is true that there has never hitherto in astronomy been any reason to question the validity of the interpretation of a change in frequency of light radiations as an effect of motion; the applications of the principle in astronomy have been numerous and consistent. But suppose that in course of time all the atoms of every substance are continually diminishing in size. Within our own galaxy we can only look back in time for a mere 100,000 years or so, but when we look at the very distant galaxies we are looking back through 500 million years.

The atoms in that remote past may have been larger than they are now; their vibrations would then have been slower or, in other words, the light they emitted would have been of longer wavelength. There is no reason to suppose that the atoms are actually diminishing in size. The possibility is mentioned merely to illustrate that there may be an alternative explanation to the one we have adopted.

Another suggestion which seems more plausible is that the light waves in the course of their long journey through space may gradually lose energy, in proportion to the distance they travel. This would give the observed effect, an apparent recession of the source of light, proportional to the distance.

We can look at the problem from another point of view which, however, takes us into rather deep water. Mention has already been made of the view of gravitation which follows from the theory of relativity, that in the proximity of matter space becomes curved so that a freely moving body no longer moves in a straight path. The amount of matter in any region of space determines the curvature of that space. If there is enough matter, the total curvature in the whole of space might be sufficient to close it up into a finite universe, finite but without any boundary, just as the surface of a sphere is finite but unbounded. Einstein supposed that there was just enough matter for this to happen, but a few years later it was shown by the Abbé Lemaître that such a space could not

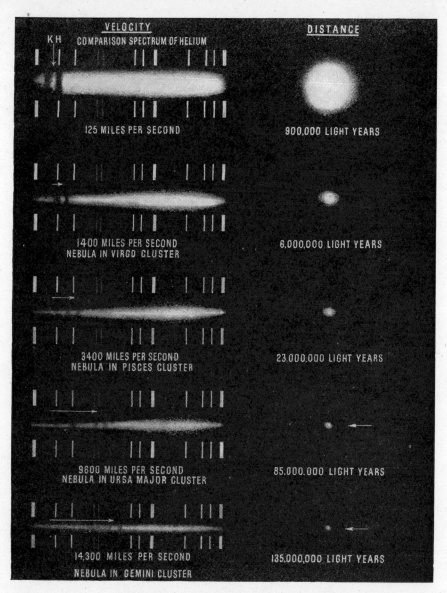

VELOCITY

DISTANCE

K H   COMPARISON SPECTRUM OF HELIUM

125 MILES PER SECOND

900,000 LIGHT YEARS

1400 MILES PER SECOND
NEBULA IN VIRGO CLUSTER

6,000,000 LIGHT YEARS

3400 MILES PER SECOND
NEBULA IN PISCES CLUSTER

23,000,000 LIGHT YEARS

9600 MILES PER SECOND
NEBULA IN URSA MAJOR CLUSTER

85,000,000 LIGHT YEARS

14,300 MILES PER SECOND
NEBULA IN GEMINI CLUSTER

135,000,000 LIGHT YEARS

EVIDENCE FOR THE EXPANDING UNIVERSE

These examples of nebular spectra show clearly the displacement towards the red end of the spectrum; the spectrum of helium is used to compare the displacement. It will be noted that the displacement increases as the distance increases. From a study of the spectral lines it has been found that the most distant galactic systems are receding from us at a speed of about one-quarter the velocity of light. On the basis of this theory it has been suggested that the separate island universes are the fragments of one large universe which exploded.

43

remain in equilibrium. Any movement of matter from one region to another would change the curvature of both regions, and the forces drawn into play would not restore the equilibrium but would upset it still further. The space would be unstable, like a stick balanced on its point; it would begin either to expand or contract. From this point of view a universe that is either expanding or contracting would be more natural to expect than one which is in a state of constant equilibrium.

Now let us endeavour to work backwards in time. The age of the earth, from the time when the solid crust first formed, can be determined with considerable accuracy (Chapter 2, page 79). The ages of a number of meteorites which have fallen on the earth have been investigated in a similar way; the meteorites are of about the same age as the earth. It is pretty certain that the planets were born out of the sun, so that the sun must be older than the earth. We might expect it to be very much older and that the birth of the planets might be a comparatively recent event in its life-history. It was at one time thought that the age of the stars was several million million years. But as new facts have come to light such a great age proves to be impossible, and the evidence now points to the age of the stars not being greater than about 10,000 million years.

DISTRIBUTION OF MATTER IN THE UNIVERSE

The observed rate of expansion of the universe is such that it doubles in size in 1,300 million years. If we go backwards in time for some 10,000 million years we find that the size of the universe, assuming the rate of expansion to have been uniform throughout, was very much smaller than it is at present; only, in fact, about 1/250th of its present size.

We can only date our time-scale from the epoch when the stars were born. Before then we can do little more than speculate on the course of events. It is supposed that if we go far enough back in time the matter in the universe was scattered uniformly through space, the density being extremely low, about 1 oz. in a cube with a side of 100,000 miles. Some slight disturbance might have produced a local increase of density. Under appropriate circumstances a condensation could form and grow; there is a minimum possible value for the quantity of matter in such a condensation, below which the gravitational attraction could not hold the matter together against the tendency of the molecules to fly outwards. It is a problem in mathematics to calculate what this minimum quantity would be. It proves to be many tens of million times that of the sun. The only bodies known which have masses at least equal to these values are the island universes or galaxies. If, therefore, condensations have formed out of an initial primeval gas, they must have been galaxies. Under the influence of the mutual gravitation of these systems, they would be set in motion and also in rotation. As each one condensed more and more, its rate of rotation increased, and it gradually assumed a flattened shape. Eventually the rate of rotation increased to such an extent that matter was thrown off from opposite ends,

NEBULAR CAULDRON

The Virgo spiral nebula, seen edge-on. The dark enclosing line is caused by opaque matter which prevents light emanating from the nebula.

forming the spiral arms which are characteristic of the very remote galaxies.

These spiral arms were at first gaseous, but they would tend to become unstable, and to break up into condensations or nuclei under their own gravitation. It can be shown that these nuclei have a mass comparable with that of the sun, so that they must be individual stars. It is from this epoch that we reckon the age of the stars.

A theory of a very different type has been suggested to account for the expansion of the universe. Suppose that initially the matter in the universe were highly concentrated and that a violent explosion occurred which sent fragments flying in all directions, some with very high speeds, others with smaller speeds. At any subsequent time the outermost fragments will be those which have the greatest velocity, and those with the smallest velocities will be nearest the centre. The behaviour of such a system would bear a very close resemblance to the observed behaviour of the actual universe, the velocity of each fragment being proportional to its distance from the centre, with all the other fragments apparently receding from it at speeds proportional to their distances.

Our observations tell us mainly about the present, except in so far as the remote galaxies enable us to look backward in time. We have little to guide us except conjecture or, maybe, intuition, assisted by the power of mathematical analysis, when we endeavour to reconstruct something of the past history of the universe, and to probe into the beginning of time. There are many things which today we see darkly, but which tomorrow may be clear. The excitement of this quest for knowledge lies in the fact that there is much to be discovered about the structure of the universe and, more particularly, the interior structure of the stars.

RECORDING THE CURVATURE OF THE EARTH'S SURFACE

A section of the earth's surface photographed from a height of 57 miles by a rocket-borne camera. The inset, which shows the curvature of the earth's surface over a distance of 1,400 miles, was photographed in sections and then pieced together into a composite picture. The area shown includes Mexico, Texas, Rio Grande River, Franklin Mountains, Oregon Mountains and areas of Upper Wyoming. This technique, will be used to map the surface of the earth.

CHAPTER 2 The earth we live on

COPERNICUS' great work on the motions of the heavenly bodies was published just over four hundred years ago. Before that, knowledge of the solar system and of the earth on which we live was negligible. It should be noted, however, that two Greek thinkers of the Ionian School, Xenophanes and Herodotus, made geological observations. In the years which have elapsed since Copernicus died, knowledge about the solar system and the earth's structure has increased apace. The advance in knowledge of the physical nature of the earth was undoubtedly the result of man's greater demands for raw materials to meet his increasing needs in a rapidly expanding industrial society.

There are still many points which defy exact knowledge, such as how our earth came into existence; but we are now able to say with some certainty of what elements it is composed, and how its present surface has been evolved through hundreds of millions of years, though the actual age of the earth as such is still one of the crucial points of dispute among scientists.

The study of the earth has helped our knowledge of other subjects; the theory of evolution, and all that it implies, rests partly on evidence collected from the fossils which occur in various strata of the earth's crust. The story of evolution indeed may be regarded as a kind of very ancient archæology.

Geology has helped us to explain many of the phenomena of nature, phenomena which until quite recent times were regarded as evidences of divine wrath, and incapable of explanation in scientific terms. Hot springs, geysers, volcanic eruptions, and the most terrible of all natural phenomena, earthquakes, are all adequately explained by reference to the nature of the earth on which we live, and of the physical changes and movements which it undergoes from time to time, changes which are not yet complete.

In recent times new sciences have grown up closely related with geology, sciences of strictly practical application which have helped mankind draw greater and still greater wealth from the earth's crust. For two thousand years and more the mineral wealth of the earth has contributed to man's prosperity. Now, with a more detailed and more accurate picture of the manifold layers or strata which make up the crust of the earth, we are able by scientific methods to predetermine where such minerals as coal and iron are likely to be found,

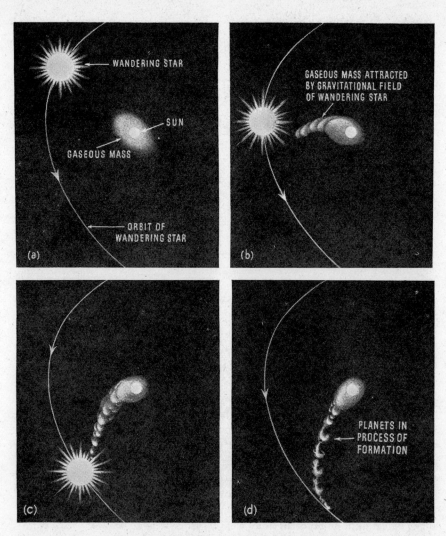

HOW THE PLANETS MAY HAVE BEEN FORMED

This drawing presents pictorially one of the theories that attempts to explain the formation and evolution of the solar system. (a) A great mass of gaseous material was torn away from the surface of the sun by the superior gravitational attraction of a wandering star passing perilously close to the sun. (b) and (c) show how the mass was drawn off into whorls and eddies in the track of the star. (d) The detached portions slowly cooled and condensed to form the earth and other planets. It has been calculated that this complete process would require a period in the neighbourhood of 7,000 million years. Concerning magnitude, it has been estimated from a study of radio-active rocks that solidification took place about 1,500 million years ago. It is quite possible that the gaseous mass pulled from the surface of the sun has not yet disappeared; the particles which reflect the zodiacal light may well be the remains of this.

where it is worth prospecting for gold or any other source of mineral wealth. Even though today no man can say with certainty that rich reserves of oil, for instance, lie under this or that particular spot, the possible field of inquiry is narrowed down to such an extent that prospecting in definite localities is a practical proposition.

Still more recently again, geology has been linked with a science still in its infancy, which has as its goal the enriching of the land for agricultural purposes, and the transformation of areas of the earth's surface which are at present barren, into a countryside which will bear crops and sustain a self-supporting population. Water is sometimes potentially as great a source of wealth as oil or coal; the discovery of underground water supplies in places which from time immemorial have been barren may result in fertile fields taking the place of arid sand, and increase the areas of cultivation in desert parts of the world.

This is only one side of the picture. We shall see later how the soil is deficient, in some regions, of the elements which are necessary for the cultivation of crops, and how by introducing these elements into the bad lands, good soil has been produced which has revolutionized the economy of many districts, and brought new sources of wealth to their communities.

So we see that geology, and the many subjects of study which have sprung from it, is a science which embraces a great deal besides the theoretical study of rocks and one which has immense practical application to the affairs of mankind.

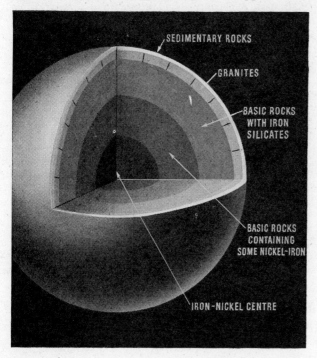

SEDIMENTARY ROCKS

GRANITES

BASIC ROCKS WITH IRON SILICATES

BASIC ROCKS CONTAINING SOME NICKEL-IRON

IRON-NICKEL CENTRE

The core or centre of the earth consists of a solid, iron-nickel core at a very high temperature. The successive layers of rock have been broadly divided into groups. In practice, the divisions between the layers are seldom well - defined and regular owing to volcanic eruptions, the crinkling of the earth's surface, and the development of cracks and faults in the strata.

49

When an earthquake occurs the resulting waves are recorded by the sensitive seismograph, shown on the right. A pivoted aluminium rod has at one end two brass weights which remain stationary when the concrete base of the instrument is vibrated. At the outer end of the boom is a slot through which a bright spot of light, reflected by a mirror, strikes the sensitized surface of a sheet of photographic paper wrapped around a drum. This is rotated, and also moved a quarter of an inch to the left, once in four hours by a clockwork mechanism. The movement of the paper beneath the spot of light passing through the end of boom prints a record which is subsequently developed. The light is cut at hourly intervals to provide a time record.

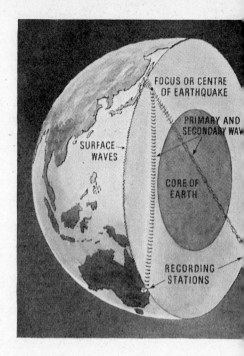

The theory now generally accepted about the origin of the earth is that it was originally a seething gaseous mass. According to one theory, it was a mass thrown off by the sun in the course of some gigantic solar eruption, or perhaps detached from it through attraction by another star passing unusually close to the orbit of the sun. In just the same way it has been maintained that the moon was originally part of the earth and was thrown off from it during the time that the earth's crust had not yet been solidified. Another theory was that the earth and other planets started from solid nuclei which attracted widely dispersed, but already cooled, material, and so developed from the beginning as solid bodies.

It is at least highly probable that the earth was originally molten, and that in the course of time it cooled to such an extent that its outer edges formed a more or less solid crust. It has been considered that the centre of the earth is still in a molten state. Just as the temperature of the atmosphere decreases as measurements are taken at increasingly great heights, so the temperature of the earth increases the farther into its interior measurements are taken. The temperature at the bottom of a coal mine is appreciably higher than on the surface of the earth, and this increase seems to continue indefinitely. There is evidence of this in the nature of the discharges from volcanoes and hot springs; a freshly erupted volcano may throw out lava at a temperature of 1,200 deg. C.

The positive evidence levelled against the hypothesis of the molten state of the interior of the earth at the present time includes the proved high density and rigidity of the interior—a density which is thought to be inconsistent with liquid or molten material. Moreover, compression waves arising from earthquake

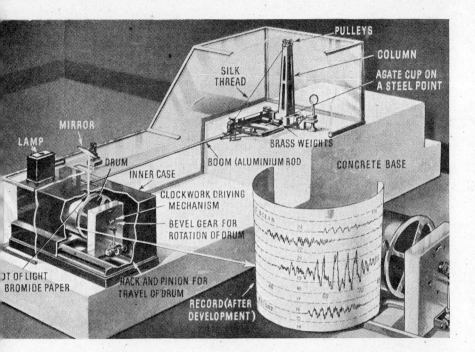

PULLEYS
COLUMN
SILK THREAD
AGATE CUP ON A STEEL POINT
MIRROR
LAMP
BRASS WEIGHTS
DRUM
BOOM (ALUMINIUM ROD)
CONCRETE BASE
INNER CASE
CLOCKWORK DRIVING MECHANISM
BEVEL GEAR FOR ROTATION OF DRUM
JT OF LIGHT
BROMIDE PAPER
RACK AND PINION FOR TRAVEL OF DRUM
RECORD (AFTER DEVELOPMENT)

tremors are conducted straight through the earth, and it is difficult to see how this could happen unless the centre were solid; reader is referred to the diagram above (left), which shows a section through the earth, and the path of earthquake shocks.

The original crust of the earth is not at all the surface of the earth as we now know it. Although parts of it may yet be found, there are no rocks so far discovered which can be dated with any degree of certainty to this first outer shell. What happened was that as the earth cooled still further, gases from the interior of the earth were constantly seeking ways of escape through the crust. Having found the weak spots they erupted through, and carried with them a good deal of molten material, a process which on a tiny scale is repeated in volcanic eruptions. The molten material cooled quickly after it had emerged through the crust, and it is this material which composes what are called the igneous rocks which are found at or near the surface of the earth in many regions.

These include the oldest rocks known and some of the hardest; in places they have resisted strongly the constant forces of erosion and stand exposed. One of the places where this has happened is at Charnwood Forest, in Leicestershire, where the rocks exposed are the oldest in England. There are also some very old rock formations in the Highlands of Scotland and in Anglesey. Among the most frequently found igneous rocks are granite and basalt, the latter well illustrated in the Giant's Causeway on the coast of Ireland and at Fingal's Cave, Isle of Staffa, see page 53.

The main difference between granite and basalt is that basalt is formed more or less precisely in the way described above, that is to say, it is lava poured out on

COAL MEASURES AT SANDERFOOT, PEMBROKESHIRE

Exposed coal measures unfolded to form an arch-like structure, and termed an anticline. These are so called because the measures incline away from the rest.

the surface of the earth's crust and cooled there rather rapidly. In the course of this rapid cooling it has solidified into the characteristically aerated appearance of pumice and basalt, because the escaping gases made vents for themselves and these remained in the solid rock as regular indentations.

The rock that we call granite is always found in large masses, generally in the core of a mountain fold. Cooling very slowly and under pressure, the gas vents were evened out so that the appearance of granite is quite smooth and even, a quality which, allied with its hardness and water-resisting qualities, makes it an ideal building stone. It varies in the relation between the various minerals which compose it, a variation best seen in the differences of colour of granite found in different parts of the world. Even within the small confines of a country like Great Britain there is one kind of granite found in Devon and Cornwall, where it is exposed on the tors of Dartmoor and on the rocks at Land's End, another kind in Cumberland, and yet another kind in east Scotland, where it has been used to build most of the great public buildings in Aberdeen.

These igneous rocks we may regard as the basis of the earth as we know it today, even though they form a comparatively small part of the earth's present crust. How long ago the earliest known rocks acquired their present form is still not known. Certainly 1,000 million years is unlikely to be an overestimate, and is still a topic which is actively engaging the attention of geological research.

The lapse of time may have been considerably greater, but even 1,000 million years is a period which practically defies the imagination to grasp. All through that incredible time nature has been at work changing and modifying to such an extent that even the general outline of the earth's crust has changed out of recognition, not once but many times. It must be remembered, too, that although igneous rocks include the oldest rocks yet discovered, igneous rocks as such are not necessarily old, for fresh areas of igneous rock are being laid down even now in the vicinity of active volcanoes.

Before we go on to consider how other rocks have been formed we must regard briefly the various natural influences which have had a share in reshaping and moulding the earth as we know it. The first and most important of these is the process of further cooling of the earth itself. As the crust decreased in temperature and, later, when the original crust had been replaced by a new crust of lava and igneous rocks, the earth continued to cool and shrink. Now shrinkage involves distortion, as anyone can prove for himself by compressing any hollow article such as a rubber ball, or a ball of paper with a hollow centre, or by looking

THE FORMATION OF THE GIANT'S CAUSEWAY

This close-up of a part of the Giant's Causeway shows clearly the formation and jointing of columns of basalt, also the fine grain of the rock. The columns are polygonal in section and, as can be clearly seen, usually six-sided.

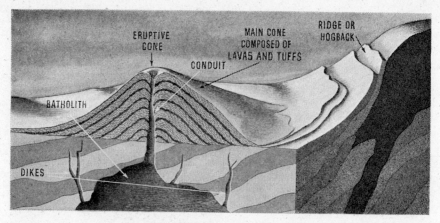

ERUPTIVE
CONE

MAIN CONE
COMPOSED OF
LAVAS AND TUFFS

RIDGE OR
HOGBACK

CONDUIT

BATHOLITH

DIKES

SECTION THROUGH A VOLCANO

A volcano is caused by the eruption of gas, ash, and lava from a pocket of molten rock beneath the crust of the earth, owing to gas pressure forcing the material upwards through cracks to form an eruptive cone fed from the conduit. Sometimes the dykes act as feeders for small eruptions on the side of the main cone.

at a very old orange, or indeed a human face. The tendency is to crinkle and crumple, and that is precisely what happened to the surface of the earth. In the great natural contortions of shrinking mountains were thrown up into high relief. Mountains such as the Andes, the Rockies, the Himalayas, the Alps, and the Highlands of north-west Scotland were thrown up at vastly different periods. Many of the oldest mountain systems have been worn away, while some of the highest mountains of today are of comparatively recent origin.

At one period in the history of the earth some mountain ranges were standing far higher than they do now, while large parts of the present earth were under the sea. To translate this general statement into a specific instance, there was a time when the greater part of what is now England had not appeared above the surface of the sea, while the area which is now north and west Scotland was part of a much larger island or sub-continent stretching west, north and east across the present North Atlantic and the northern North Sea.

When we come to investigate what causes have brought about this vast change we find that the principal agent is the natural force of the atmosphere, exerted in the form of water. Directly a land mass has been thrown up it is subject to a process of erosion or weathering which gradually wears it away. The sea itself is a great agent of erosion. Where today the softer and more recent rocks are exposed to the action of the sea, as along the east coast of England, erosion is something that can be seen taking place from year to year, almost from day to day. Where the cliffs are of harder rock, as in Scotland and Norway, the process is infinitely slower, and may not have any visible effect for hundreds of years.

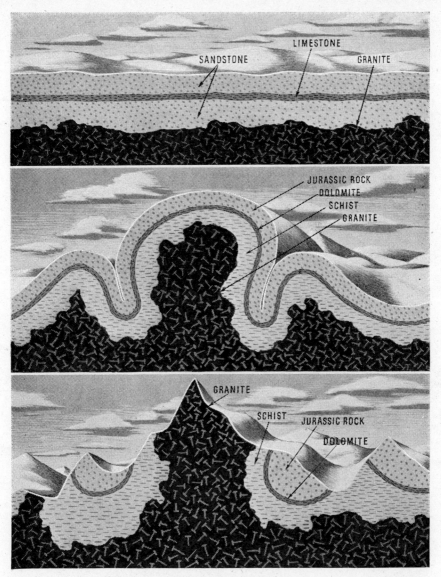

HOW THE ALPS WERE FORMED

Like many other mountain ranges, the Alps began life as comparatively level layers of sandstone and limestone above a hard granite bedrock. The wrinkling and crumbling of the earth's surface as it cooled and contracted threw these layers into great folds, the uppermost points of which were attacked by ice, snow, and rain until the softer rocks had been worn away from the peaks, exposing the harder granite ; erosion had also exposed the edges of the other various strata. Many older mountain ranges have been completely worn away, and it is quite possible that the same forces will eventually wear away the Alpine peaks.

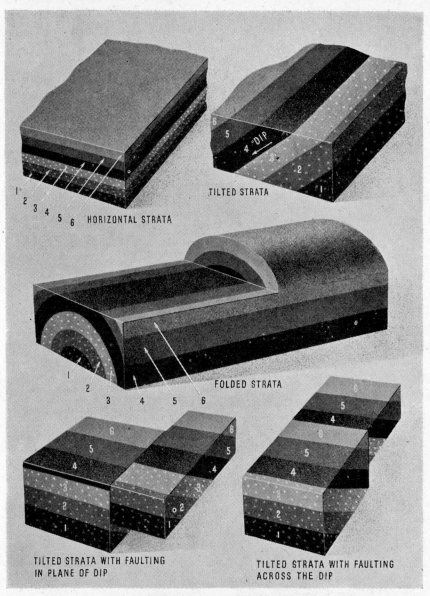

HORIZONTAL STRATA

TILTED STRATA

FOLDED STRATA

TILTED STRATA WITH FAULTING
IN PLANE OF DIP

TILTED STRATA WITH FAULTING
ACROSS THE DIP

HOW TO RECOGNIZE FAULTS IN ROCKS

Tilted, folded, raised, or lowered strata can be recognized by examining the edges of rocks exposed in quarries or cliff faces. The strata may simply be tilted or folded. One section which has fallen in relation to another is termed a fault. Faults can also occur in tilted or folded strata, either across the layers, or in the same plane as the tilt or fold, when one section will have slipped. The attitude or position of an inclined bed is described in geology as "dip" (top right), and is both the direction of the slope and its angle with the horizontal.

THE GRANITE CLIFFS OF LAND'S END

This view of the weathered and castellated cliffs of Land's End, Cornwall, shows the jointing in granite rock formations.

So gradually shrinkage takes place and all the time that this sea erosion goes on there is equal or greater activity inland. Rain-water is here the principal factor, for it contains acids drawn from the atmosphere which tend to dissolve even the hardest rocks. The rain which falls on the high ground flows down towards the sea as a river, and cuts itself a constantly deeper channel. Every drop of water which flows down carries with it some fragment of the rocks over which it flows. When snow takes the place of rain, and the snow by constant compression forms glaciers instead of rivers, the effect is greatly enhanced.

When a glacier flows down a valley, and it flows very much in the same way as a river only infinitely more slowly, it exerts a tremendous pressure on the sides and the base of the valley. It scours out the sides and constantly deepens the floor. It carries with it not only the minute debris and little pebbles that flow down with a river, but large chunks of rock which it first breaks off and then carries down to the point where the glacier melts. If the glacier ends at sea-level it forms icebergs, and the rocks it carries are then borne far over the surface of the sea until the ice breaks up. Thus they are dropped on to the floor of the ocean, perhaps thousands of miles from their point of origin. There will be a time, millions of years hence, when nothing remains of the Highlands of Scotland except a low, flattened range of hills, and when the peaks of the Himalayas have been brought down to the level of the plain. In the absence of any further great convolutions of nature all the hills and mountains of the world would gradually be levelled out, and at the same time the depth of the oceans would grow less, until finally there would be a tendency for the seas to cover the land all over the globe.

Even so, at the present time, side by side with this great process of erosion, there is new land being built up. Deltas are being formed at the estuaries of rivers by the debris deposited there by the rivers themselves, shingle banks are being built up by the sea currents in various places round the coasts of all the continents. In Britain, the Dungeness promontory has been built up in this way in comparatively recent years. Ultimately the shingle which composes it will become more fruitful and habitable.

All the time, too, potentially new land is being built up under the sea. The majority of the younger rocks, the sandstones, the clays, the chalks and the limestones, have, in fact, been created in the first case on the sea-bed or on the beds of large lakes. Their very name, sedimentary rocks, is self-explanatory. The nature of this sediment varies, and we will consider first those rocks which are inorganic in nature, i.e. those which are not partly composed of the remains of living organisms, such as, for example, carboniferous limestone.

EFFECTS OF COAST EROSION

View of the coastline south of Lowestoft, Suffolk, showing the erosive action of the sea on the cliffs composed of glacial sands and gravels.

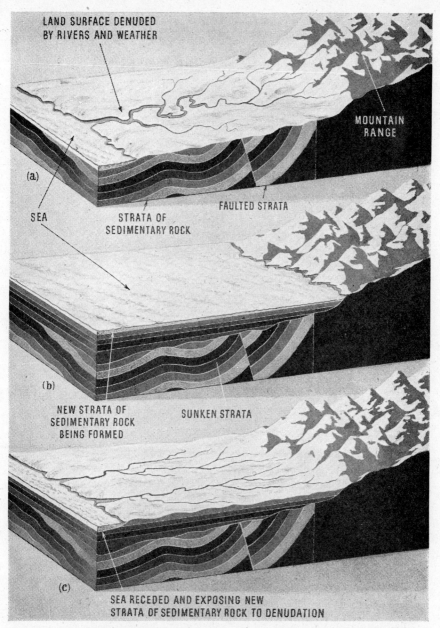

Labels within image:
LAND SURFACE DENUDED BY RIVERS AND WEATHER

MOUNTAIN RANGE

(a)

FAULTED STRATA

SEA

STRATA OF SEDIMENTARY ROCK

(b)

NEW STRATA OF SEDIMENTARY ROCK BEING FORMED

SUNKEN STRATA

(c)

SEA RECEDED AND EXPOSING NEW STRATA OF SEDIMENTARY ROCK TO DENUDATION

DENUDING AND REBUILDING OF LAND SURFACES

The view (a) shows a flat coastal plain denuded by the action of weather and rivers. In (b) the whole plain has sunk, allowing the sea to reach up to the mountains. During this period new strata of sedimentary rocks are being laid down. (c) Shows the sea returned to its previous position, and the land forming a coastal plain which is again subject to denudation by weather and rivers.

A FOLD IN SANDSTONE ROCKS

To the south of the breakwater of Bude harbour, in Cornwall, can be seen this excellent example of a synclinal fold or dip in the Culm measure sandstone.

The inorganic sedimentary rocks are mainly the clays and the sands. Roughly speaking, these are composed of fragments torn off the older rocks and carried along by rivers into the sea, as we have described above. But in the course of their journey they lose some of their elements and are further modified by the action of chemicals held in suspension in the water. The larger fragments are dropped on to the sea bed in the form of sand, a sand which is identical with that which lies along the edge of the sea all round many of the coasts of the world.

Any visitor to the seaside will have noticed that the colour of the sand varies. It varies according to the nature of the rock from which the tiny fragments have been torn, and this difference in coloration persists when the sand is turned into solid stone. It is, in fact, a difference of chemical composition.

Smaller fragments settle on the sea-bed as mud or ooze and it is this which is the basis of the rocks which are known as clays. The difference between ooze and sand is another fact which is readily observed by visitors to the seaside. In many places the sands go out for about a quarter of a mile, but at low tide a layer of mud is exposed at the edge of the sea. In some districts near the estuaries of rivers, such as Southend-on-Sea, there is little sand and wide stretches of mud.

One of the characteristics of sand is that it is very porous. It dries quickly because its moisture content flows through the tiny particles and escapes, and also because the clearly separated particles allow the air to penetrate, so that evaporation is more rapid. By contrast mud and ooze is very retentive of moisture. It is clearly less porous and the moisture evaporates from it less rapidly.

These qualities remain when the sands and the ooze are turned into rocks. Sandstone is a very porous rock, and where sandstone is near the surface of the earth the land is always relatively dry. Only such plants flourish on it as can sustain life with a minimum of moisture. By contrast the clays always make wet and heavy lands which are productive of crops, because they retain their moisture through long dry periods.

Although sandstones and clays are the most frequent sedimentary rocks, they are not by any means the only ones, nor for that matter the most important ones. Their interest, and the factor which gives them a unity, is that they are composed in the main from the decomposition of existing rocks, and that most of them would never have come into existence but for the part played in transporting their integral fragments by rivers flowing out of the land masses.

LIMESTONES AND CHALKS

Another group of sedimentary rocks which appear in many parts of the world, including the British Isles and the Continent of Europe, owe their origin to factors other than the mere decomposition and breaking down of the older rocks of the land masses. These are the limestones and chalks which, like the sandstones, have been laid down under the sea, but, unlike sandstones, are built up in part from organic materials.

Everyone has heard of the coral islands of the Pacific Ocean and of coral formations such as the Great Barrier Reef off the eastern coast of Australia. These coral islands and coral reefs are essentially limestone rock layers in course of formation.

There is a tiny living creature called a polyp which lives in the sea. Essentially it consists of a small body with many tentacles attaching themselves to any convenient platform. The polyp feeds on minute living creatures and absorbs from them a quantity of lime which it secretes and uses to build a kind of shell. New births of the polyp are rather like buds which grow out of the parent organism and remain permanently attached to it. When the creature dies, its lime-encrusted skeleton remains and so the coral reef is gradually built up and forms a small land mass.

The polyp only flourishes in warm seas. The process of coral building is at present only going on in the Pacific and Indian Oceans, and in a few restricted localities such as off the coast of Florida. But millions of years ago there were seas of tropical temperature washing across the area which is now northern Europe and England, and coral formations were built up in those seas over thousands of years; the Cotswolds and the Pennines show remains of coral reefs.

It is not accurate to state that limestone formations are made exclusively of coral, for a high proportion of the bulk of limestone is composed of shellfish and foraminifera. Some of the minerals in the earth's crust, in fact some of the minerals present in the granite formations, can be changed into limestone through the action of the carbon dioxide which is found in the earth's atmosphere. Once changed into limestone, these minerals are soluble in water and are carried away from the hills, down the rivers and into the seas, in just the same way as the elements of other sedimentary rocks. But the lime is carried farther away, because the sea holds it in solution until it reaches a part of the world where the temperature of the water is relatively high, since it cannot be held in solution by water above a certain temperature. When the sea exceeds that temperature it deposits the limestone, and helps to build up the coral formations. An everyday example of this is the fur on the inside of a kettle. The water from the domestic tap has a good deal of lime in solution. When the water is boiled inside the kettle it precipitates this lime; the fur, so called, if left long enough, becomes surprisingly hard, it is, in fact, the first stage in the formation of limestone rock.

Chalk is often described as a kind of limestone because its chemical composition consists largely of carbonate of lime. Under the microscope a section of chalk shows thousands of minute shells of vastly differing texture and shape. These are the skeletal remains of living organisms called foraminifera, creatures which, like the coral polyp, live in shallow seas, but unlike the polyp they still

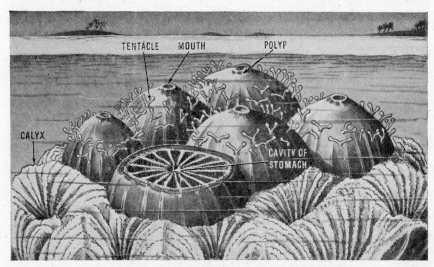

THE FORMATION OF CORAL REEFS

Coral reefs are formed by the skeletons of millions of minute creatures called polyps. They live in tropical waters, and feed on even smaller creatures from which they absorb lime. Atolls and barrier reefs are formed by the same process. Also present in the formation are molluscs, calcareous worms, and bacteria.

CLIFFS AT CAILLEACH HEAD, ROSS-SHIRE
A bed of Torridon sandstone which illustrates what is described in geology as "dip,"
that is, the position in the ground of an inclined bed.

live in the shallow seas bounding the shores of Europe and largely compose the South and North Downs and the cliffs of Dover. In stormy weather millions of them are thrown up on the beach; though they are rarely noted, because of their microscopic size, they can be studied easily with the help of a microscope or magnifying glass.

The foraminifera do not build platforms or grow out of each other like the polyp; they move freely and are separate from each other. When they die their shells sink to the sea bottom and form a kind of ooze. It depends on how deep the sea is where they fall whether the shells are broken and crushed or remain intact. In the swirling currents just off the beach they inevitably lose their form; but in slightly deeper water, where the currents do not extend with such strength and where the effects of storms are not felt so much, the shells often remain intact.

Thus we have sketched the outlines of the picture which has been drawn by a hundred years of research into the formation of the principal igneous and sedimentary rocks. Each of the ones we have described is a type with many variations, but the majority of the rocks which form the present crust of the earth belong to one or other of these groups. A section across southern England, which is composed almost entirely of sedimentary rocks, will reveal more than a

BLASTING AT A LIMESTONE QUARRY
Because of the useful elements it contains, limestone is a valuable mineral to modern industry ; one of the principal elements is calcium, see Chapter 3.

dozen separate strata. Different kinds of limestone and different kinds of sandstone, and so on, were built up in varying conditions at widely differing times in the history of the earth. One of the duties of the science of geology is to classify the relative age of the various rocks; although the length of the periods represented by each is still only approximately known, there is agreement about which kind of rock was formed first.

It was for long one of the great puzzles of geology how the various strata were laid down in such regular order, a layer of sandstone, then a layer of limestone, and so on. That these rocks are in regular layers, even though the layers are often, as it is said, contorted, that is to say, twisted out of the horizontal plane, is perfectly obvious to anyone who has studied a quarry. The answer to this puzzle lies in the vast differences of climatic and other conditions which have succeeded each other in an often repeated cycle since the earth came into existence. One or two instances will make this clear. Sandstones cannot be laid down in the seas bordering the land masses if the climate is very dry, because it is largely the action of rain or snow which causes the igneous rocks to disintegrate, and forms the rivers which carry them down to the sea. So it will be principally in periods of high rainfall that this particular kind of rock will be built up. Similarly, as we have seen, coral limestone will only be formed when the sea is unusually warm.

Particular conditions then favour the formation of particular rocks. When conditions are favourable at one and the same time for the formation of two or more kinds of rocks, one would expect their formation to go on, as it were, side by side, and research has proved this actually to be the case. Some rock strata are of mixed composition, and this fact further strengthens the hypothesis put forward to explain the formation of individual kinds of rock.

The hardening of the constituent elements into actual rock is another problem which has for long defied an exact answer. In this the principal factor is now known to be pressure. As one stratum is laid down upon the top of another, the weight exerted on the lower layers constantly increases. When this happens at the bottom of the sea there is added the weight of the sea on top; the sea itself exerts an enormous pressure. If we add to these factors the influence of certain elements which are held in suspension in the sea, and which act as a kind of cement to bind the other elements together, we have found adequate explanation for what is strictly a natural and inevitable phenomenon.

FORMATION OF SEDIMENTARY ROCKS

There remains the problem of how sedimentary rocks, which, as we have seen, have been built up under the sea, have been raised to form hills, often exceeding a thousand feet in height above sea-level. To this question the answer which geology gives is less precise. Although there is not the slightest doubt of the actual fact that they have been raised, there is still doubt whether the raising was a sudden or gradual process. We have seen how the igneous rocks must have been thrown up by vast crinkling processes of the earth's surface, and the same process is probably responsible for the throwing up of most of the sedimentary rocks. But what causes the crinkling? Is it just the cooling of the earth, or is it, as is more probable, the result of other factors at work?

The actual crinkling is another of the interesting facts of geology which can be observed by the casual wayfarer. Evidence of it in the form of contorted strata is not confined to quarries; it can often be found by the sea, as in the cliff face near Lulworth, to name one conspicuous example. Moreover, if we bore into the earth we find that the sedimentary strata are not lying one on top of the other like sheets of paper, but lie in successive undulations called synclines and anticlines. Each strata rises to a peak, then dips down into a hollow, then rises to a peak again, and so on. This means that the actual lateral extension of each stratum is a great deal more than if it were lying level.

One theory is that the sheer weight of strata plus the overlying weight of water has at times compressed the crust of the earth in one part, and this compression has caused a corresponding area adjacent to it to rise. Another theory is that the continents are in a constant state of gradual motion, with the inference that this movement (which some scientists claim can be measured over a period of a very few years) has been going on ever since there were continents in existence. The effect of a continent in movement would be to press forward the sea

THE GREYWETHERS OF DARTMOOR

These are residual boulders left on the surface of the ground after the denudation of the surrounding earth as a result of weathering and erosion. From a distance they are often mistaken for grazing sheep.

bed in front of it; this, it can readily be imagined, would lead to a collapse of the earth crust at some point, and would explain alike the raising of the sea bed and its distortion into synclines and anticlines.

Most probably major earth movements have been of two kinds, one gradual and the other sudden, and this conclusion is borne out by the experience of historic times. Within the last hundred years at least one fair-sized South Sea island has blown up and disappeared entirely, while others have appeared between one charting of the seas and the next. These may be said to be representative of sudden changes, even though they are on a very small scale compared with the vast cataclysms which resulted in the formation of the Alps or the Himalayas. However, within recorded time it has been proved that the Pacific coast of America is rising by a small fraction of an inch every year, while the Atlantic coast is sinking by a similar amount. There is evidence, too, of gradual changes of level around the coast of Britain; for instance, there are still signs of a submerged forest off the coast of Norfolk at exceptionally low tide, while many parts of the coast show unmistakable signs of raised beaches; that is to say, beach formation which within near-historic times must have been washed by the sea are now several feet above the level of the sea and some distance inland.

The compensatory forces of nature are well illustrated by examples taken

KING'S THRONE ROOM IN THE CARLSBAD CAVERNS

The upward-reaching pillars, termed stalagmites, and the formations which hang from the roof, called stalactites, are formed by deposits of carbonate of lime. In time these unite to form pillars of fantastic shapes.

from the east and south coast of England. The port of Dunwich, on the Suffolk coast, was a flourishing commercial port in the early Middle Ages. Today every sign of it has disappeared, for, like so many other east-coast towns and villages, it has gone "down cliff", and its harbour has been swallowed up in the sea. The eroding action of the sea can be seen in its full effects near Lowestoft, where part of Pakefield nearby has gone "down cliff," while other parts stand precariously on the very brink of the low cliffs.

At the other end of the scale, medieval ports like Rye and Winchelsea in Sussex have been left high and dry miles away from the sea which six hundred years ago was the mainstay of their prosperity. Here it is a matter of the forces of nature building up new land by a mixture of deposits carried down the River Rother, and the depositing of thousands of tons of shingle carried on the tides which sweep down the south-east coast.

DEPRESSION AND ELEVATION

Even though it is difficult to predict any cataclysm sufficient to raise great mountain chains, we have seen that constructive processes are going on all the time side by side with the wearing away of the land. And granted the truth of one or more of the hypotheses we have discussed to explain the raising of the sedimentary strata, it would seem that the process of depression and elevation would continue indefinitely. If the age of the earth is 3,000 million years, as one estimate put it, it is reasonably safe to predict that the earth in some recognizable form has at least another 3,000 million years to go. We must remember, too, that human life has only been associated with the earth for a tiny fraction of time.

Once the sedimentary rocks have been elevated from the sea bed they decline more rapidly from the forces of nature's erosion than do the harder igneous rocks.

Southern England is a good example to illustrate this. The structure of south-eastern England today is predominantly chalk. There is a chalk plateau centred on Salisbury Plain and covering a large part of Wiltshire and Hampshire. From this, like the spokes of a wheel, there radiate a number of chalk ridges, including the South Downs, which traverse Sussex and are broken off at the sea at Beachy Head; the North Downs, which run in a long line through Surrey and Kent and are broken off at the Shakespeare Cliff at Dover; and the Chiltern Hills, which extend from the point where the Thames has cut a gorge separating them from the Berkshire Downs at Goring, through Buckinghamshire and Hertfordshire to Bedfordshire. The line continues thence under various names, through Cambridgeshire and on into Suffolk and Norfolk, where the chalk is clearly exposed at Hunstanton. On the other side of the Wash it continues as the Lincolnshire Wolds, and after the break of the Humber estuary as the Yorkshire Wolds to end at Flamborough Head. Smaller arms point westward and south-westward from Salisbury Plain.

This is vastly different from the configuration of the land when the sedimentary

THE CREEPING DUNES OF CULBIN SANDS, MORAY
This view shows the forward drift of the Culbin Sands, Moray. This natural process, when allowed to persist, is very destructive of valuable agricultural land, and can obliterate villages and farms. This process can be checked by planting binding grasses such as marram or bent.

strata, of which the chalk is now the uppermost, were first elevated. Then the whole of the area comprehended by these present chalk ranges was covered by the chalk, while above it there appears to have been a layer of sandstone which has almost entirely disappeared except for the "greywethers," those large slabs of grey stone which look like sheep at a distance; there are still a number of these to be seen in the Salisbury Plain area. The great stones of Stonehenge appear to have been taken nearly four thousand years ago from this previous covering of sandstone. When the forces of erosion had been at work for a few million years, not only had the upper layer of relatively soft sandstone practically disappeared, but many of the underlying strata had been exposed as well in places, especially in the valley which is known as the Weald of Kent and Sussex, between the chalk of the North Downs and the chalk of the South Downs.

This area was originally an anticline, i.e. an area in which the strata were elevated above the general level and consequently more exposed to the effects of the weather. It will be noticed that the North Downs have a steep drop to the south, while the South Downs have a steep drop to the north. Originally the

INTERIOR OF A ROCK SALT MINE

Salt occurs in nature in the form of rock salt, or halite. Such deposits as those in Cheshire, England, were laid down during the Permian and Trias Ages as a result of the drying up of inland seas; the salt being in solution in the sea water. In addition to its domestic uses, salt is indispensable in the ceramic, tanning, coal-tar dye and fertilizer industries, to mention only a few.

chalk bridged the gap between these two points and was uplifted into a dome. In the course of time the headwaters of the Medway, and the other rivers which flow through the Weald, bit down through the chalk successively to a layer of sandstone (called the Upper Greensand), another layer of sandstone (called the Lower Greensand), which is exposed at points such as Leith Hill in Surrey and Toys Hill and Ide Hill in Kent, a layer of clay (called the Wealden clay), exposed at a large number of points all over the Weald, and finally to another layer of sandstone (called the Hastings sands), which is exposed now in the ridge called the Forest Ridge, which includes Ashdown Forest and St. Leonard's Forest.

Between the North Downs and the Chiltern Hills there was a syncline, and the chalk does, in fact, dip down underneath the Thames basin, and here, of course, the chalk has not been eroded away. Rather, a layer of clay which is called the London clay has been built above it, partly covered by alluvium of the Thames and the material that is carried down with it from the hills. Once the Thames was a far mightier river than it is today, and the gravel terraces which mark its former boundaries have been discovered in some cases several miles from its present course. Hills such as Blackheath were formed from gravel deposits carried down by the river.

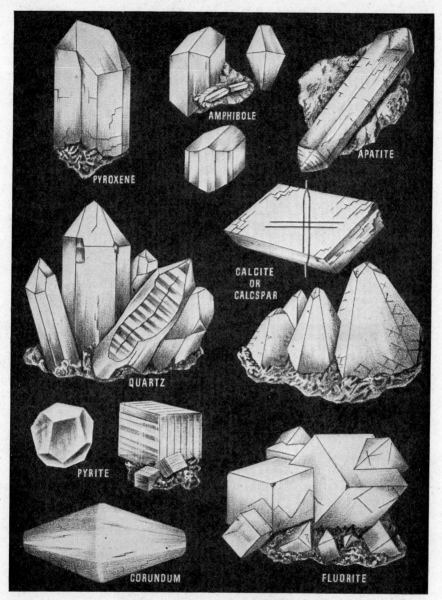

AMPHIBOLE

APATITE

PYROXENE

CALCITE
OR
CALCSPAR

QUARTZ

PYRITE

CORUNDUM

FLUORITE

THE STRUCTURE OF MINERAL CRYSTALS

A selection of some of the mineral crystals mined from the earth. Most solid substances, in their pure state, are found to have a crystalline form, that is, they conform to a definite geometrical pattern. This regular structure is a result of the orderly arrangement of the atoms composing the crystal. The various kinds of atoms being constructed in definite repeated patterns, very much like a wallpaper pattern. During recent years a technique employing X-rays has been used to study and photograph the internal structure of crystals.

This is just one example in which it has been possible to trace in the light of modern research with some exactness the various stages in the growth and gradual denuding of the land and the formation of the scenery as we know it. In many districts the processes uncovered have been far more complex, but they all yield to the same kind of analysis.

An interesting group of rocks not so far discussed is that known as metamorphic. Metamorphic means changed or transformed by natural agencies, and that is precisely what this group of rock is. They started life as sedimentary and igneous rocks, limestones, sandstones, clays, granites, etc., and have been changed by the influence of great heat arising from igneous material, that is, lava which has been poured over them or has been forced in between their layers by pressure during folding.

To get a clear picture of this we must imagine layers of sedimentary rocks built up under the sea, and then raised above the surface of the land with faults in their structure allowing the escape of volcanic materials. This group of rocks includes various kinds of marble, slate, and the natural brick such as that found in Derbyshire. These and other metamorphic rocks are necessarily always found on the edges of granite or other igneous rock.

Flint is another substance found in many parts of the earth's crust; and it is in connexion with flints and their story that the sciences of geology and archæ-

WHEN NATURE AND MAN CO-OPERATE

This aerial photograph, taken in the Loess Region of the Province of Kansu in China, shows a series of terraces on which rice is grown in semi-flooded fields— an example of how natural features can be utilized to the best effect.

CLUES TO THE AGES OF STRATA

Fossils often give clues to the ages of rock strata, as in the case of these fossilized trilobites, a form of crustacean which lived during the Palæozic period and which evolved into the three different types shown.

ology meet. Flint is composed of a solution of silica and water; although the precise nature of the formation is unknown, it seems probable that the silica in its composition is derived from the remains of the living creatures which help to build up the layers of chalk. At any rate, flints are always found in association with chalk and in particular with the more recent layers of chalk. In chalk cliffs such as those of southern England they appear themselves in layers dividing one thin layer of chalk from another.

As the weathering process goes on and the layers of chalk are gradually washed away, the flints necessarily come to the surface. They are themselves harder than the substance of the chalk, and consequently resist erosion more successfully. We have seen above that many of the chalk anticlines have been worn away completely. During the vast length of time involved in this process the flints which have been exposed have been carried along the beds of streams and by the sea currents to districts far from their point of origin. This explains why flints are not only found many miles away from the nearest layer of exposed chalk, but in many different forms; the small pebbles such as those commonly found in gravel pits are as much flints as the flint nodules which any wayfarer may find in the course of his wanderings over the chalk downs. But they have been rubbed and scraped and battered, and in many cases broken by the forces of sea and weather during their long journey until they have taken on the comparatively small, rounded, and often coloured form that they have today.

Thus, there is a family connexion between the flint nodules of the chalk downs, the pebble that we find on the beach and the stones taken from a gravel pit to mend the roads. Many of the flints have been fractured by natural causes, by being crushed and ground together in the course of their travels, and many of the stones found in gravel pits are only fragments of the original flints. It has been proved that not all the fractures are of natural origin, but that many are the result of human work.

This discovery revolutionized ideas about the history of the human race. It all started with the discovery of beautifully worked flint weapons and implements exposed on or near the surface of the chalk downs. Almost every museum in Britain, and in particular the British Museum, has hundreds of examples of these delicately fashioned weapons and tools of long ago. They include arrow-heads, spear-heads, hand-axes, scrapers, borers, and almost every variety of tool which primitive man required to enable him to rise superior to the forces of nature; to kill the wild beasts which would give him food and clothing; to cut down the timber with which to build himself rude shelter; or to clear areas in the forest where he could pasture his cattle or at a later period cultivate crops.

EARLY EXAMPLES OF MAN'S CRAFTSMANSHIP

The systematic study of these flints and the human remains found in associa-tion with them is still in its infancy. It is only within the last hundred years that knowledge has advanced to a point where the newer can be distinguished from the older, and some sequence of ages propounded to cover the development of human work and craftsmanship during the last ten thousand years. It seems to be a fact that flint is the very earliest material used for manufacturing weapons and that the emergence of *homo sapiens*, that is to say, man as we known him, can be dated virtually to the beginning of the manufacture of flint weapons.

Almost all the beautifully wrought products of flint which have been dis-covered on the surface of the earth are dated with reasonable certainty to a period not exceeding seven thousand years ago, while most of them are probably not much more than four or five thousand years old. For long it was thought that this represented about the limit of the history of civilized man. Knowledge might have remained thus incomplete had it not been for the fact that scientists noted that flints which had been used for the manufacture of weapons exhibited a characteristic marking at the point where flakes had been struck off them with a hammer or some other striking implement. This characteristic marking is a depression in the flint, with, of course, a corresponding bulge known as the "bulb of percussion." The existence of the bulb of percussion is taken as a sign of human workmanship, and flints which have been cracked by natural means do not show this marking. Examination of gravel pits revealed a very large num-ber of flint fragments which showed these signs and a number of flint cores, too, which bore the unmistakable traces of man's handicraft.

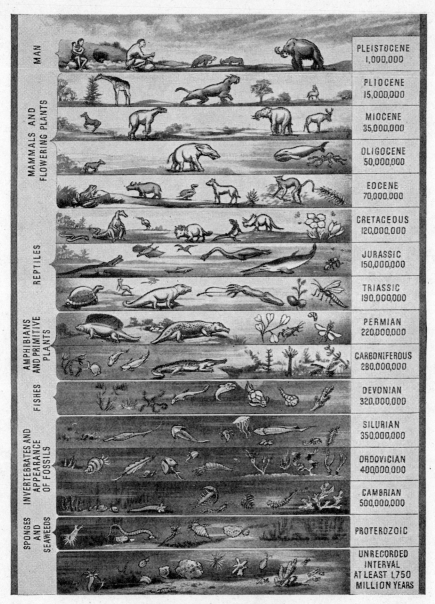

MAN		PLEISTOCENE 1,000,000
MAMMALS AND FLOWERING PLANTS		PLIOCENE 15,000,000
		MIOCENE 35,000,000
		OLIGOCENE 50,000,000
		EOCENE 70,000,000
REPTILES		CRETACEOUS 120,000,000
		JURASSIC 150,000,000
		TRIASSIC 190,000,000
AMPHIBIANS AND PRIMITIVE PLANTS		PERMIAN 220,000,000
		CARBONIFEROUS 280,000,000
FISHES		DEVONIAN 320,000,000
INVERTEBRATES AND APPEARANCE OF FOSSILS		SILURIAN 350,000,000
		ORDOVICIAN 400,000,000
		CAMBRIAN 500,000,000
SPONGES AND SEAWEEDS		PROTEROZOIC
		UNRECORDED INTERVAL AT LEAST 1,750 MILLION YEARS

THE GEOLOGICAL TIME SCALE

The age of the various strata that compose the crust of the earth can be established by the fossil remains embedded in them. Conversely, it enfolds the wonderful story of the evolution of life from very primitive forms. As fossil remains of plants and animals are found in the rocks in regular sequence it is possible to divide the stratified rocks into appropriate periods covering a time interval of at least 1,750 million years. The names of the main geological periods are given in the right-hand column, together with the estimated age.

WORKED FLINT FROM SUB-CRAG BED
NORFOLK COAST

QUARTZ TOOL OF PEKIN MAN

WORKED FLINT FROM
NORTH DOWNS, KENT

PEBBLE TOOL FROM
EAST AFRICA

TOOLS OF PRIMITIVE MAN

A selection of very early tools or eoliths used by our primitive ancestors at the dawn of the Stone Age. Of particular interest is the quartz tool used by Pekin Man (Sinanthropus pekinensis).

The science of geology had definitely dated the life of some of these gravel deposits to a period far earlier than had previously been thought to mark the period of human activity. So what was a revolutionary theory became substantiated, that mankind had lived and worked on the face of the earth for many thousands of years longer than had ever been supposed before. A distinction was thus drawn between the New Stone Age of human activity, represented by the polished stone celt usually of volcanic lava or other igneous rock, and the Old Stone Age period, represented by finds in the gravel deposits and also in caves.

There is still controversy as to the length and the relative antiquity of the Old Stone Age, but it is clear that the period is not that of one race of mankind, but a succession of many. Further research has proved that different kinds of flints existed in different kinds of deposit representing different ages, and some attempt has been made to classify these, reaching back, according to some estimates, more than fifty thousand years.

But even that is not the end of the story. Once the scientists were convinced that traces of human workmanship were to be found in deposits earlier than the rocks exposed in near historical times, search has constantly been made for traces of man in older deposits still than those represented by the gravel pits so far excavated. And in the last twenty years definite traces have been found dating back to a still earlier time, particularly in England, in the cliffs of East Anglia, which are rapidly being eroded owing to their comparative softness.

The flint industries associated with these early strata are different again either from those of the New Stone Age or the Old Stone Age. They bear the distinguishing name of eoliths, from the Greek words *eos,* meaning dawn, and *lithos,* meaning stone, i.e. dating from the dawn of the Stone Age. Oddly enough, the first eoliths were discovered at Oldbury Hill in Kent, on or near the surface of the earth, but most discoveries of this kind have been well buried. That, of course, makes it all the harder to distinguish flints which have been broken by natural causes from those definitely of human origin, and it is only in the last few years that eoliths have been accepted by the majority of scientists as definitely the work of human beings. The effect of this discovery is to take back the story of mankind at least a hundred thousand years and probably much more.

Human remains have been found occasionally in association with the flints. Remains, of course, are only skeletal, often only a single bone, but they have been enough to allow of credible reconstructions of the appearance of early man. In general, the appearance has not differed very much over the years. Two of the earliest human remains discovered are the Piltdown skull (cap and jaw bone fragments), discovered at Piltdown in Sussex, and the Heidelberg skull, discovered near the town of that name in Germany.

These human remains may be regarded as a special type of fossil. What are fossils ? The human bones we have referred to above are in a special sense fossils, but of a very rare kind. Briefly it may be said that fossils are the hard parts of living things preserved in rocks. However favourable the circumstances, the softer parts invariably decay to leave no record of their form.

FOSSILS OF EARLY MARINE LIFE

Inevitably the vast bulk of fossils are of creatures that live in water—in the sea, in lakes or in rivers, which became trapped as the layers of sedimentary rocks were being built up under the water. The foraminifera which form such a striking part of the composition of chalk are in another sense fossils.

There are fossil remains, too, of plants and parts of plants of every description; even pollen grains have left perfectly formed fossils. These fossils are rather different, because ordinarily they consist only of the outline of the plant indelibly marked on the rock and visible only when the rock is split.

To understand how fossils, other than those of marine creatures, occur it is necessary to appreciate the only possible means by which land animals or men could be found in fossil form in the sedimentary layers. A large number of possibilities have been worked out, the most credible of which are as follows. A land creature might come down to the seashore and die there and its remains be swept out to sea, or it might come down to a riverside to drink and fall into the river and be carried away by it, or, of course, it might be involved in a cliff fall, or even fall over the side of a cliff. These and many other accidental circumstances suggest themselves, but all of them represent rare happenings as opposed to the inevitable and constant formation of fossils of marine creatures.

The study of fossils has brought fresh knowledge in two directions. It has helped scientists to work out the relative age of different kinds of rock, and it has yielded an important part of the evidence in support of the hypothesis of evolution.

If the fossil remains in different strata of rocks in close juxtaposition are studied it will be found that the fossils are quite different in one stratum from those found in another. By repeated study of the fossils found in various layers of sedimentary rock it has been proved beyond any shadow of doubt that the variations in the conditions of life at various times in the history of the earth were far-reaching and affected all parts of the earth's surface. There have been periods of great heat and great cold, periods of heavy rainfall and of prolonged drought, and these variations have occurred all over the globe at different times. Now different conditions are favourable to the life of various creatures; we have seen, for instance, that the coral organism can only live in warm seas. Consequently it follows that if the coral organisms are found in fossil form in areas where the seas are now relatively cold, these seas at some past time when the rocks were being built up must have been correspondingly warm.

Similarly, if fossilized plants which could only have grown in tropical conditions are found in rocks that form the crust of the earth in Europe, it follows that at some time the land masses of this part of the northern hemisphere must have been covered in tropical forest. We shall find plants analogous to those found in these rocks in the present-day forests of the Amazon valley.

FOSSILS AND THE AGE OF ROCK STRATA

As regards the age of the rocks, it has so far proved impossible to give any precise estimate of actual age. But if geologists find one layer of sedimentary rock on top of another, it is a fair inference that the lower one is the earlier, because although strata have become contorted in the uplifting and folding of the earth's crust, they have very rarely been displaced entirely. If, then, fossils of a type "A" are found in the rocks, for instance, of France and fossils of the same type in similar rock found in Wales, it is a fair inference that the relative age of these two strata, unconnected though they seem to be, is similar, i.e. that they were being built up at the same time and may have formed part of the same original layer.

As different parts of the sedimentary strata of the earth's crust have been uplifted at different times and to a varying extent, and as the long-term effects of weathering are imponderable, comparison of fossils is often the only method by which to discover with certainty that, for instance, the old red sandstone of Devonshire belongs to a vastly earlier age than the sandstone of the Weald of Kent. In Britain the Geological Survey has drawn up tables of the relative age of all the rocks so far identified. Similar work is being done in many other countries of the world.

To date the rocks which do not contain fossil remains, i.e. igneous rocks, the geologist has solicited the aid of the physicist and his specialized knowledge of radioactive elements.

Although igneous rocks do not contain fossils it sometimes happens that they contain radioactive minerals. Now, a radioactive element is one which disintegrates by giving off particles and rays; a well-known example is radium.

The radioactive elements present in the minerals contained in igneous rock are principally uranium, thorium and actinium. During disintegration helium gas is liberated, but is of no value to the geologist as it escapes. The stable endproduct, i.e. the product left after the process of disintegration has finished, is the metal lead; the process is diagrammatically shown in Chapter 10. The rate at which lead is formed from uranium is known and it is, therefore, possible to determine the age of the rock containing it if the proportion of uranium to lead is known; this proportion is found by chemical analysis. This method has revealed the age of the oldest rocks as at least 1,750 million years.

THE THEORY OF EVOLUTION

As regards evolution, Darwin in the second half of the last century collected and codified a great deal of evidence pointing to the truth of a theory that all the creatures that live on the face of the earth today, whether on land or in water, are derived ultimately from a common ancestor which probably lived in water. That part of the theory of evolution which has received most popular attention is the hypothesis that man and the anthropoid apes are derived from a common ancestor, but that is only part of a theory which embraces all living organisms.

The evidence of the fossil record shows beyond a doubt that evolution has occurred in the sense that there have been changes in the form of various living creatures, partly in the way of adaptation to changing conditions. There are few who will deny that the horse is derived from the same ancestor as the fossil remains known as *eohippus* (the horse of the dawn of time). Similarly, there is little doubt that mankind has changed slightly, as we have indicated before, even within comparatively modern times. The fossils show, too, that many animals strange to modern experience have roamed the face of the earth from time to time and have become extinct.

The theory of evolution as a whole is no more than an inference based on evidence not so far complete, and evidence, too, which in the nature of things can never be complete. The fossil record is only part of that evidence. The fossil remains go back over eons of time, but at a given point they stop, and in the oldest rocks no fossil remains have been found. It has been argued that this implies that when the oldest rocks were being formed no life existed on the earth. Equally well it may be true that there was life on the earth at that time, but that the fossil remains have been destroyed in the immeasurably greater span of time involved in the case of the oldest rocks.

Further research may bring to light fresh evidence. It is even possible that fossil remains will ultimately be found in the oldest rocks. If a fossil were discovered which linked the amœba-like fossils and the most primitive living organisms of today with the earliest vertebrates, part of the chain of evidence would be complete. Similarly, if skeletal remains of a vertebrate from which both the anthropoid apes and man might be derived, then this disputed part of the evolutionary hypothesis would be established beyond reasonable doubt.

THE FERTILE SOIL

A layer of fertile soil is mainly composed from decayed vegetable and eroded or deposited material which lies above the infertile subsoil and bedrock. The depths of the soil and subsoil vary greatly, as does the fertility of the top layer.

Geology and agriculture are closely linked for the simple reason that what we call the soil, which is, as it were, the top dressing on the surface of the earth, is directly related with the underlying rocks. Soils are of two kinds, those which are formed on the spot and those which are carried to their present position from places more or less distant. We have seen that all rocks break up as the result of erosion and chemical activity. It is, in fact, the particles or fragments of rock which are carried by water to form new layers of sedimentary rocks under the sea. But clearly not all the rock fragments are carried away at once. If the slope of the land is only gentle the carrying-away process is far slower than if the slope is steep. That is why the steep sides of hills are seldom suitable for intensive agriculture, while the fertile and extensive areas of agricultural land are always, or nearly always, gently undulating stretches of countryside.

Soils vary very much in their depth. When they are formed on the spot, or *in situ* as it is called, they are usually fairly shallow. In this case they are composed literally of the material of the underlying rocks. They consist of bits and pieces of the rocks themselves mixed with decaying vegetable matter. Often in thin soils it is possible to dig through the top layer and come to a layer which is increasingly filled with stones until a little later the solid bedrock is reached. In

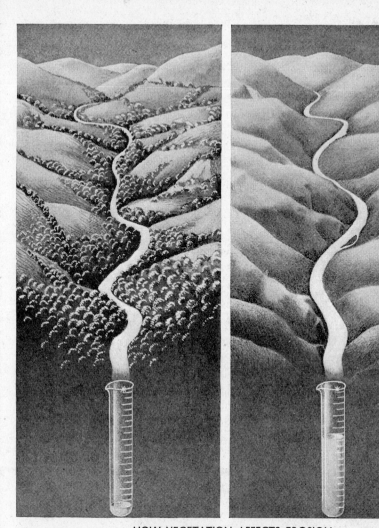

HOW VEGETATION AFFECTS EROSION

The water needed by vegetation for healthy growth is very considerable, and must be absorbed through the roots from the moisture in the soil. It is for this reason that every effort has to be made to retain sufficient water in the soil. For example, in a well-wooded valley the forests and woods act as a sponge to retain the rainfall, so that the water runs off very slowly, and erosion of the land is reduced; rainwater is distributed by run-off, that is, direct flow down surface slopes, percolation to bedrocks and direct evaporation. Lack of vegetation causes a heavy run-off (right), which carries away the top soil. In Great Britain the rate of run-off may be reduced by 70 to 80 per cent at first, that is, until the forest and soil are saturated, and then it reduces to about 30 to 40 per cent. In many countries attention has been directed to the adverse effects of excessive run-off, and afforestation is being carried out to replace trees that have been felled or where none existed before. This conserves the soil, and ensures future timber stocks.

these thin soils quite obviously agriculture is more difficult than when the soil layer is thicker, because the growing of crops uses up the vitality of the soil. In areas of thin soil, once the vitality of the top soil is used up there is nothing to fall back upon. In thicker soil the layer is turned and a new layer of fresh vitality comes on top.

When soil is formed from an accumulation of material carried down by water and wind from high ground to lower, it may lie several feet thick and the mixture contains a much larger proportion of decaying vegetable matter or "humus." Then the land is much better for agriculture. This is proved by the healthy and fertile soil found in mountain valleys.

Soils differ also in their porosity, that is to say, in the extent to which they retain moisture. Sandstone and limestone soils commonly do not retain their moisture for long. Clay soils, on the other hand, are relatively non-porous and retain their moisture for a long time. This ordinarily is an advantage, but may be a disadvantage if the soil is so retentive of moisture that it becomes waterlogged in winter. Wet soil is cold, and consequently autumn-sown corn does not flourish in very heavy clays.

The nature of the soil determines very largely the kind of vegetation which grows in it. In the dry sandy soils we often find nothing but heather, rank grass and perhaps bracken, all plants which are peculiar to heathland and require very little moisture. In this type of soil, too, evergreen trees, which are much more hardy than deciduous trees and capable of storing more water, stand a good chance of surviving, whereas the forest oaks and ashes would inevitably die.

SANDSTORM APPROACHING PORT SUDAN
Sandstorms are features of the weather over desert areas during the hot season, and consist of a curtain of relatively coarse grains of sand.

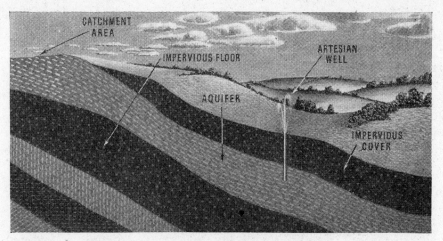

GEOLOGICAL FORMATION OF ARTESIAN WELL

Artesian wells occur when the underground water is subject to hydraulic pressure sufficient to force it to the surface. The aquifer (an inclined water-bearing strata) is sandwiched between impervious strata which prevent the water escaping, and its rim exposed to a catchment area which provides an hydraulic head. An example of these conditions is the London Basin, in which the aquifer is chalk enclosed by impervious strata of London clay above and Gault clay below. The catchment area is the chalk exposed along the Chilterns and the North Downs.

The relatively light clays are the finest for agriculture, and the corn lands of East Anglia, the granary of Great Britain, are almost all on light clay soils. Oak trees, the traditional tree of British forests, cannot have too much moisture; consequently we find that the medieval oak forests and the traces of them that remain are mainly in the heavy clay soils of the river plains or at least in valley country.

The lowland soils contain a large mixture of humus, and of marl, which is the name given to a mixture of clay and limestone, and of loams, which are a mixture of clay and sandstone. The great Midland Plain of England mainly consists of marl soil. This is suitable for all types of agriculture, both arable and pasture. It should be appreciated, however, that frost and rain are important factors in the formation of rich soils.

Modern science has been directed to evolving means by which soils which are relatively poor can be enriched. One way which has been widely adopted is by the addition of lime, which has the effect of removing the acid from soils which have overmuch of the impurities of the rock from which they have been formed. This allows the bacteria which exist in their myriads in all soils to do their work of changing the nitrogen of the air into plant food.

Another method of enriching the soil is by adding humus, the substance of

THE RAVAGED EARTH

Once fertile, arable land now lacerated with gullies which not only carry away rainwater, but the valuable top soil as well. Today these areas are being reclaimed by large-scale projects such as the Tennessee Valley Authority.

many commercial manures, for this decayed matter gives plants destined to grow in this soil ready-made food material. Most plants, including the corn crops, require some phosphorus and iron for their proper growth. These can be added to soils that are deficient in them. Research is still going on actively to discover other ways in which poor or thin soils can be made more suitable for intensive cultivation, and in various parts there are specialized agricultural research stations designed primarily to investigate these possibilities.

The greatest single factor in determining the fertility of a country is water. In general, those parts of the earth's surface which have a temperate or sub-tropical climate, and which have a relatively high rainfall, are fertile, those which have a low rainfall are unfertile. Some places, of course, have too much rain for the growth of specialized crops such as wheat, but these are in a minority and even there something will grow satisfactorily, if only rich pastures, as in the west of England, where the rainfall is rather too high for the cultivation of wheat.

A few examples will make the matter clearer. The rainfall of the eastern districts of England averages between twenty-four and twenty-eight inches a year, and this amount, in relation to the average cloud-cover of the district (cloud, of course, helps to slow up the process of evaporation), is very nearly ideal for the principal corn crops and for many root crops as well. The western districts of England and Wales average forty inches a year and upwards. This amount, allied with a greater cloudiness than in the east, proves rather too high for wheat, though oats, which require more moisture than wheat and less sunshine to ripen, can be grown in most of the valleys. But, in general, the west is the area of pasture land and the pastures here are much richer and more reliable than in eastern England.

At the two extremes of the scale there are many places in the mountainous districts with more than a hundred inches of rain a year, while at one point on the south-east coast, Shoeburyness, records an average of only about twenty inches a year. The former, quite apart from considerations of soil, makes corn cultivation impossible. The latter, however, comes within the range of adequate rainfall, and south-east Essex is, in fact, famed for its fertile soil that produces rich harvests of wheat, barley, and oats.

In some years the rainfall is less. In one particularly dry year Margate recorded less than ten inches of rainfall. If this were repeated over a number of years and affected large parts of the country, the fertile fields of Great Britain would

SOIL EROSION IN EAST AFRICA

A close-up of a shelf of eroded soil of the type found in Uganda, East Africa. Anti-erosion schemes are now in operation to prevent the further spread of this land rot, and to regain those areas already affected.

85

POWER GENERATION

WHEELER DAM

NEW CHEMICAL INDUSTRIES

RURAL ELECTRIFICATION

Nashville

Cumberland

Ohio River
Paducah
KENTUCKY DAM

Cairo

Mississippi River

Tennessee River

T E N N E S

Duck

Buffalo River

PICKWICK DAM

MISSISSIP

HARNESSING THE POWER OF TH

The vast Tennessee Valley Authority project was initiated by the Congress of the U.S.A. to develop the resources of the regions covered by the Tennessee River and its tributaries. Before the project, the river was a yearly threat to all the farms and industries on its banks. Today these waters which once flooded and denuded valuable land are being directed to productive uses. The project consists of twenty-one dams on the Tennessee and its tributaries. In its construction more than 170,000 acres of land were cleared, 1,200 miles of roadways and almost

The map shows the Tennessee River and its tributaries, with dams labelled: SOUTH HOLSTON DAM, WATAUGA DAM, CHEROKEE DAM, DOUGLAS DAM, GLENVILLE DAM, FONTANA DAM, NORRIS DAM, CHEGAN DAM, NANTANALA DAM, FORT LOUDOUN DAM, CALDERWOOD DAM, HIWASSEE DAM, CHATUGE DAM, SANTEETLAN DAM, WATTS BAR DAM, NOTTELY DAM, CHICKAMAUGA DAM, OCOEE DAMS, BLUE RIDGE DAM, HALES BAR DAM, GUNTERSVILLE DAM, WHEELER DAM, WILSON DAM, WILSON STEAM PLANT. Cities: Bristol, Knoxville, Chattanooga. States: KENTUCKY, VIRGINIA, N. CAROLINA, TENNESSEE, GEORGIA, ALABAMA. Rivers: Holston River, Hiwassee River, Elk River. APPALACHIAN MOUNTAINS. Inset pictures labelled MALARIA RESEARCH, RECREATION, REAFFORESTATION.

TENNESSEE RIVER AND ITS TRIBUTARIES

140 miles of rail-road, and nearly 30 million cubic yards of rock and earth excavated. These figures serve to show the vast extent of the project. The hydro-electric power stations generate 1,200 million kilowatt hours of electric energy. The T.V.A. is not only a power-producing scheme, but it enters into every sphere of modern industry and agriculture; in fact, it is the result of the collective endeavours of manual workers, engineers, scientists, farmers, architects, foresters, and public-spirited individuals, and is an outstanding example of collective effort.

disappear. The top soil would disintegrate, the desiccated fragments of soil would become airborne and disperse with the slightest breeze, ultimately to settle as layers of sand in the lee of the nearest hill. The soil would thus grow thinner and thinner until ultimately the underlying rocks would be exposed. By then the green crops and grass so typical of a fertile countryside would have disappeared and with them most of the trees, though they, because their roots are deeper, would have greater resistance and continue to grow for a number of years.

Though rainfall is the principal factor in determining water supply, it is not the only one. Rivers flowing through desert country from regions of moister climate can by their own stream and by artificial canals used for irrigation transform arid into fertile country. The best example in the northern hemisphere is the valley of the Nile, the most fertile part of Egypt, yet a district which but for the river would be as unfruitful as the wastes of the Sahara.

UNDERGROUND RESERVOIRS

There is one other source of water, and it is here that geology has been of great value. We have most of us seen springs issuing from the ground at high levels, springs which are often the sources of rivers, and which represent rainwater which has flowed through the rocks from higher levels. But springs do not only occur on high ground. Underground reservoirs of water have been discovered in many parts of the world and in some cases these have been tapped to bring fertility to arid country. Of course, underground reservoirs cannot exist unless they are fed indirectly by rainwater, but they are often found at some distance from the actual source of the precipitation.

What happens is that rain falls on the relatively high ground (and there is frequently an adequate rainfall on hills when nearby valleys are subject to drought) and seeps through a porous layer of rock until it comes to an impervious layer. So rainwater will seep through the sandstones but not through clays. If, as is usually the case, the layers of rock are inclined at an angle, the water will flow down the layer of clay under the layer of sandstone to the foot of the syncline. It will be trapped here and form a reservoir. One such reservoir, very well known, is that which exists under London, a reservoir which still supplies by wells a fair proportion of the water needs of the City of London. When it is remembered that nearly half of the total rainfall sinks into the earth's crust, it will be appreciated how large such reservoirs can be in suitable conditions. The water is most securely trapped in the trough of a syncline when a porous layer or rock lies between two impervious layers. In the London basin the chalk, which is the porous layer, dips down from the North Downs and the Chilterns with a layer of impervious clay below and the layer of the London clay above it. Geology has helped by mapping out the rocks of the earth's crust and so giving a pointer to where it is worth boring for artesian wells, as these wells are called. Up to date many square miles of the arid part of Australia and the southern United States of America have been made fertile by just this means.

HARVESTING IN THE TEIGN VALLEY, DEVON

Part of the Teign Valley, showing the rich crops and woodlands that grow in this fertile, red soil of Devon. Compare this with the ravaged earth on page 84.

The story of oil is similar, for it is now known in what kinds of strata oil is likely to be found, and by the geological survey of wide areas it can be predetermined where these strata occur in the earth's crust. So it is known where it is worth making trial borings for oil. Many of the great wells of the Middle East have been discovered in this way and also the smaller deposits of oil in the British Isles. These latter were for long unsuspected and their working is not a profitable commercial undertaking. Even so, they are a valuable reserve for emergency, as has been proved by the several wells which have been worked successfully during the past few years.

These are just a few of the ways in which the science of geology has assisted in the enriching of the earth and its people. Its scope in these directions for the future is almost without limits. Meanwhile there are three unsolved problems which are the subject of continuing and intensive research. One is the age of the rocks, for more knowledge of this will give knowledge of the age of the earth itself. The second is the manner of formation of the earth and its original composition. The third, perhaps of the most practical importance of them all, though not a problem of geology alone, is the uncovering of the mystery of life itself.

MODERN SCIENCE IN THE FOUNDRY

No branch of industry can isolate itself from the forward march of science. In the view above is seen the application of the science of high-frequency electric currents to foundry practice. The operator on the right is filling ingot moulds from a tilting high-frequency induction furnace. In this type of furnace the metal is melted by the heat produced by high-frequency electric currents induced in the charge itself. The current consumption is in the region of 700–900 kilowatt-hours per ton of steel. Steel produced in the electric furnace is characterized by its purity and for this reason the process is used for making special steels.

CHAPTER 3 Materials from the earth

THE function of the chemist is to check the efficiency of many processes and by the regular testing of raw materials to ensure a uniform high quality of finished products. There are today few industries where chemists are not employed to control all operations where chemical changes are known to take place; this they do by carrying out individual tests or devising special automatic means of determining the chemical condition of the gas, liquid or solid being processed. In large bakeries chemists are helping to produce better bread. They test the purity of the yeast and flour used for making the dough, watch and control the fermentation and ensure that the dough is really ripe and ready for bread-making. Chemists have devised many ingenious dough-testing machines which estimate the bread-making value of doughs and so ensure a more appetizing and health-promoting bread. They are also able to advise on the addition of vitamin concentrates and minerals used to enrich flour.

The chemical industry employs a large number of chemists, some of them on shift work so that throughout the twenty-four-hour day continuous processes are kept under constant observation. Many of these are so finely adjusted that the most meticulous control has to be exercised so as to avoid complete stoppages or even serious explosions. In the manufacture of ammonia from the nitrogen in the air, the chemist must first separate and purify the nitrogen from the oxygen and traces of other gases present in the atmosphere. Hydrogen obtained from coke-oven gases is then mixed with the nitrogen and heated together under pressure in the presence of a catalyst, or substances, usually metals, capable of promoting a chemical change. Unless the chemist is present to control the purity of the reacting gases, to regulate the flow of gases and their pressure and temperature, it is impossible to obtain a continuous high output of ammonia gas, which today is one of the most important inorganic chemicals produced by our chemical industry. This process, known as the Haber-Bosch process, is one of the triumphs of chemistry in winning raw materials from the air.

As the chemical industry develops, the role of the chemist becomes more important. Frequently he has to collaborate closely with the engineer to ensure that machines are built so that chemical reactions take place with the maximum efficiency. He needs also to work closely with instrument makers in devising

At the present time large quantities of crude coal-tar are treated in continuous pipe stills. The crude tar is first heated in the lower coil of pipe in the furnace. As soon as the heated tar passes into the dehydrator, the water and gases in it evaporate, and pass to the condenser. Meanwhile the purified tar passes to the furnace, where it becomes vaporized. The vapour begins to condense on reaching the first cooling coil, although this, unlike the remainder, is steam-heated. In this manner the various oils are effectively separated from one another, and can be drawn off from the base of each tower.

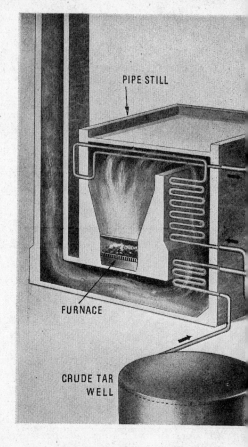

PIPE STILL

FURNACE

CRUDE TAR WELL

new means of controlling chemical processes which may have to be carried out at very high pressure or temperature, perhaps both.

In many cases the chemist can find no answer to problems in any text-book and he needs to approach new tasks with imagination as well as knowledge. The chemist has never been faced with greater difficulties than during the early stages of preparing fission products from uranium in making the atomic bomb. Here he was called upon to devise entirely new processes of separation and purification of elements, such as, for example, pure carbon for use as a moderator to slow down nuclear processes in atomic piles, new control methods and new means of protecting workers from the lethal effects of radio-active rays, see Chapter 7.

COAL AND ITS BY-PRODUCTS

One important section of the chemical industry is based on the distillation of coal, from which are produced large quantities of substances required for the manufacture of a wide range of chemicals.

The coal is heated in closed retorts in gasworks and crude gas is driven off. This crude gas is cooled, washed and purified and during these processes crude substances are removed. On its first cooling, tar and ammoniacal liquor condense into wells; washing removes more of the ammonia; iron oxide removes the sulphur compounds, and a further process takes out the benzole.

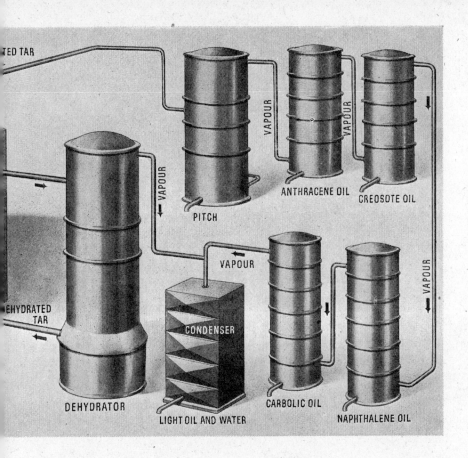

The crude tar is the most complex, and on fractional distillation it splits up into several different liquids and a residual solid, pitch; the whole range of products obtained from coal-tar is illustrated on page 95.

The liquids are light oils which include benzoles, toluoles, xylols and solvent naphtha; then carbolic oil, which gives phenol, cresols, xylenols, and pyridine; then naphthalene oil, which gives in turn pure naphthalene and light creosote. The next is creosote oil, from which various grades of creosote are made; and, lastly, anthracene oil, from which alizarin is derived.

Benzene (or pure benzole) is a very volatile, inflammable liquid which can be converted readily into aniline, the starting point of many dyes. Carbolic acid (or phenol), which most people know by the smell, is the starting point for certain plastics like nylon, dyes, drugs and explosives. Yes, that aspirin you probably took this morning for your headache came out of a lump of coal; and vitamin B2 can be made up from a member of the phenol family. The gasworks today cannot produce enough phenols to meet the enormous demands that are being made by the rapidly expanding plastics industry.

The range of modern dyestuffs derived from coal-tar is very extensive, numbering some three thousand actual colours and shades, each one fulfilling a definite need or possessing special characteristics of interest for specific applications. There is no perfect dye; indeed, it is unlikely that there ever will be one; but meanwhile the search for improved colours proceeds.

Colours are special chemical substances designed for particular types or kinds of materials, although, perhaps, serving many purposes. A dyestuff used for dyeing wool may be successfully employed for colouring leather, but is of little use for calico printing or colouring anodized aluminium. The chemist in the colour industry is, therefore, concerned with supplying the needs of many different trades, each one presenting individual problems. It may be that a harmless, but fast dye is needed for a particular type of foodstuff, a non-rubbing and light-fast dye for spirit varnishes, a colour for calico printing that will fade less than any other dye when exposed to tropical sunlight, or a sensitizing dye for photographic emulsions. The list is almost endless.

MANUFACTURE OF DYES FROM COAL-TAR

The manufacture of man-made dyestuffs is completed in three main stages. First of all there is the production of the raw or fundamental chemicals, such as benzene, anthracene and naphthalene, toluene and xylene, from coal-tar, by distilling this substance at temperatures at which these various constituents boil; this is known as fractional distillation, or fractionating. The principle of it is very simple. Suppose the chemist has a mixture of ether and chloroform and wishes to separate the two. The mixture is placed in a distillation apparatus and heated. It begins to boil at about 35 deg. C., the boiling point of ether, and consequently it is only the ether that distils over, forming the first fraction of distilled liquid. As heating is continued beyond this, the temperature rises and a mixed fraction is obtained until at 61 deg. C. only the chloroform distils over. The mixture has been fractioned.

When the fundamental chemicals are prepared of a sufficiently high standard of purity, their conversion into dyestuffs can be carried a stage further by changing them into intermediate chemicals. This may involve several chemical processes or be accomplished in one step, depending entirely on the type of dye to be made. Thus benzene can be treated with nitric acid to give nitro-benzene, a liquid which smells strongly of almonds. Nitro-benzene may then be converted into the well-known intermediate, aniline, by heating it with iron and a little hydrochloric acid, whereby hydrogen is produced which combines with the oxygen present in the nitro-benzene to form aniline and water. By means of further chemical action it is possible to change aniline into several other intermediates, including naphthol, probably the most famous of all dye-making chemicals.

These intermediates, of which there are many thousands, are generally colourless chemicals, but all of them are characterized by the fact that they can be changed into vividly coloured compounds. The actual conversion of the inter-

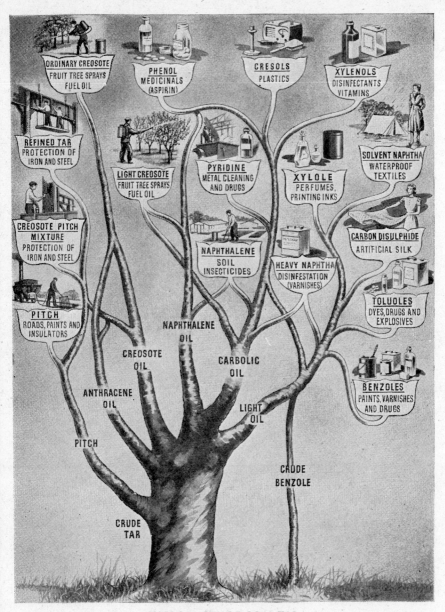

ORDINARY CREOSOTE
FRUIT TREE SPRAYS
FUEL OIL

PHENOL
MEDICINALS
(ASPIRIN)

CRESOLS
PLASTICS

XYLENOLS
DISINFECTANTS
VITAMINS

REFINED TAR
PROTECTION OF
IRON AND STEEL

LIGHT CREOSOTE
FRUIT TREE SPRAYS
FUEL OIL

PYRIDINE
METAL CLEANING
AND DRUGS

XYLOLE
PERFUMES,
PRINTING INKS

SOLVENT NAPHTHA
WATERPROOF
TEXTILES

CREOSOTE PITCH
MIXTURE
PROTECTION OF
IRON AND STEEL

NAPHTHALENE
SOIL
INSECTICIDES

HEAVY NAPHTHA
DISINFESTATION
(VARNISHES)

CARBON DISULPHIDE
ARTIFICIAL SILK

PITCH
ROADS, PAINTS AND
INSULATORS

TOLUOLES
DYES, DRUGS AND
EXPLOSIVES

NAPHTHALENE
OIL

CREOSOTE
OIL

CARBOLIC
OIL

ANTHRACENE
OIL

LIGHT
OIL

BENZOLES
PAINTS, VARNISHES
AND DRUGS

PITCH

CRUDE
BENZOLE

CRUDE
TAR

BY-PRODUCTS OF COAL-TAR

Once considered of very little value, coal-tar is now the source of an abundance of important raw materials for the chemical industry. There are, in fact, some three thousand different compounds derived from this by-product of coal. As will be seen from the above diagram, these have application in domestic life, industry, agriculture and medicine. It should be appreciated that these valuable materials are obtained after the coal-gas has been extracted from the coal.

Labels on diagram: HYDROGEN AND HYDROCARBON GASES; GAS SEPARATOR; RECOVERED HYDROGEN; HYDROGEN; HYDROGEN COMPRESSOR; RECOVERED HYDRO-CARBONS; HYDROGEN GENERATOR; HYDROGEN UNDER HIGH PRESSURE; GAS; COAL CRUSHER; HEAVY OIL; STEAM; MIXING TANK; CONVERTER; COAL AND OIL PASTE; HEATING ELEMENTS; COAL ELEVATOR; PUMP; HEAVY OIL

mediate into the dyestuff is fairly simple and is achieved in most cases by combining together two or more intermediate chemicals; for example, the range of synthetic colours, the nigrosines, which are very dark blue dyes, are made by heating nitro-benzene, aniline and aniline hydrochlorides with iron filings.

PETROL FROM COAL

In America, where large quantities of petroleum and natural gas are used, supplies are dwindling, and proven reserves are only given a lease of life amounting to twenty years or so, consequently coal is assuming a much greater strategic importance. It is estimated that only 0·5 to 2·0 per cent of the original supply of bituminous coal has been consumed and the estimated reserves are more than three trillion tons of all grades, including lignite. Although the supplies of coal in the United States of America are ample, the cost of producing oil from coal to meet the drying up of petroleum reserves would greatly exceed the price of petrol. Moreover, one to three times the present annual United States' production of coal would be needed to yield the present annual requirements of petroleum motor fuel. Coal can provide the answer to most problems in organic chemistry, but at a price. The extent of this price can best be realized when it is stated that four to five tons of coal are required to make one ton of petrol.

The modern process of hydrogenation can be followed in this diagrammatic illustration. First the coal is pulverized and mixed with oil and a catalyst, a compound of tin, which makes the subsequent reaction possible. As the paste is pumped into the converter tower, hydrogen gas from a generator is mixed with it. In the tower the mixture is maintained at a temperature of 400–480 deg. C., and under a pressure of over 3,750 lb. per sq. in., for about two hours. The hydrogen combines with the coal, forming a mixed gas, which is taken to a still, or cooling tower, where the gas condenses and the medium-heavy diesel oil, tar acid and petrol separate out.

High-grade petrol can be made from coal or creosote by hydrogenation (treating with hydrogen gas under pressure) or from gases derived from incomplete combustion of coal. The latter process, known as the Fischer-Tropsch synthesis, can convert a mixture of hydrogen and carbon monoxide into petrol fuel by passing it over a special catalyst at a temperature of 200 deg. C.

PRODUCTS OF PETROLEUM

Crude petroleum is a dark-coloured mobile or viscous liquid which occurs in many parts of the world, including America, Russia, the Middle East, West Indies, Burma, East Indies, etc. It is generally associated with natural gas, which is made up of varying proportions of methane (better known as firedamp or marsh gas), ethane, butane and propane. Crude petroleum and natural gas consist very largely of hydrocarbons, i.e. compounds made up of hydrogen and carbon, but in most crude oils there are also compounds which contain sulphur or oxygen or nitrogen in addition to the hydrogen and carbon.

The hydrocarbons themselves differ both in respect of the size of the molecules and in chemical type, depending on the way in which the carbon atoms are joined to each other, in straight chains, branched chains or in rings. Crude oils vary both in respect of the proportions of the different types of hydrocarbons present (i.e. some may be predominantly aromatic or others predominantly paraffinic) and in respect of the proportions of light and heavy hydrocarbons present (i.e. some may give high yields of motor spirit, others low or none at all). For nearly a century crude petroleum has formed the basis of a number of industrial products, and the number and variety is increasing daily.

AERIAL VIEW OF A HYDROGENATION PLANT

This aerial view shows the layout of a modern hydrogenation plant for the large-scale production of petrol from coal. The physical and chemical processes in this type of plant are illustrated on pages 96 and 97.

There are broadly two ways in which industrial products are derived from petroleum. Firstly, the hydrocarbons present in crude petroleum and natural gas can be grouped into fractions possessing the required characteristics for certain purposes, that is, by separating all the comparatively light or volatile hydrocarbons motor spirit is obtained, and by separating all the heaviest hydrocarbons bitumen is obtained. This process is known as distillation and gives a range of products of varying boiling point, such as motor spirit, white spirit, kerosene (paraffin oil), gas oil, lubricating oils, waxes, bitumens, etc. This is a purely physical process.

Another physical process is solvent extraction in which all the hydrocarbons of a certain type, i.e. aromatic or paraffinic, can be removed. This is generally applied to the refining of lubricating oils, and the by-products, aromatic extracts or paraffin waxes, themselves give rise to useful industrial products.

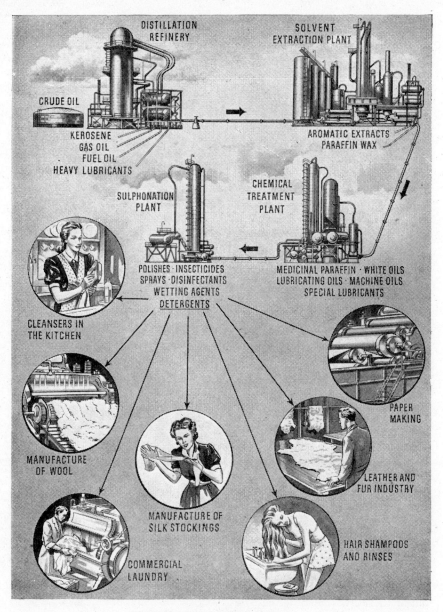

DISTILLATION
REFINERY

SOLVENT
EXTRACTION PLANT

CRUDE OIL

KEROSENE
GAS OIL
FUEL OIL
HEAVY LUBRICANTS

AROMATIC EXTRACTS
PARAFFIN WAX

SULPHONATION
PLANT

CHEMICAL
TREATMENT
PLANT

POLISHES · INSECTICIDES
SPRAYS · DISINFECTANTS
WETTING AGENTS
DETERGENTS

MEDICINAL PARAFFIN · WHITE OILS
LUBRICATING OILS · MACHINE OILS
SPECIAL LUBRICANTS

CLEANSERS IN
THE KITCHEN

PAPER
MAKING

MANUFACTURE
OF WOOL

LEATHER AND
FUR INDUSTRY

MANUFACTURE OF
SILK STOCKINGS

HAIR SHAMPOOS
AND RINSES

COMMERCIAL
LAUNDRY

BY-PRODUCTS OF PETROLEUM

*At the refinery the crude oil is heated to obtain various grades of oil and paraffin.
The remaining compounds are then treated with solvents, leaving behind waxes
and pitch. The soluble products are next treated to give various oils, and finally,
in the sulphonation plant, a range of useful chemicals is prepared, many of
which were originally obtained from coal-tar. In addition to meeting our fuel
needs, petroleum is becoming a valuable raw material.*

The second type of treatment given to petroleum is chemical processing for the purpose of manufacturing either special fuels for aviation purposes, or chemical products for industry. This type of processing started about twenty-five years ago and is now a very large feature of the petroleum industry. As has been previously mentioned, the main constituents of petroleum are hydrocarbons and in the case of crude petroleum and natural gas these are not particularly reactive to chemical treatment. However, a process known as cracking was evolved some thirty years ago for the purpose of increasing the supply of motor fuel to meet the expanding automobile industry. This process consists of breaking up the large molecule present in the heavier petroleum fractions such as fuel oil into the lighter molecules suitable for inclusion in motor spirit.

CHEMICALLY UNSATURATED PETROLEUM GASES

At the same time, a range of gases is produced which differ chemically from those present in natural gas in being very reactive towards chemicals. They are termed chemically unsaturated. Owing to the fact that some of the carbon atoms of which they are composed are not completely combined (or saturated) with all the hydrogen possible, it is a comparatively simple matter to add other chemical groups in the positions where the hydrogen atoms would normally occur. These cracked gases have formed the main basis of the petroleum chemical industry, and from gases, such as ethylene, propylene, butylene, have been produced a wide range of chemicals, such as alcohols, ketones, aldehydes, etc.

In addition to these cracked gases it has been found possible by special processes to treat the stable gases occurring in natural gas by chemical means and to form from them compounds containing chlorine or oxygen or nitrogen, such as formaldehyde, chloroform or nitro-methane from methane, the lightest gas present in natural gas. Natural gas is also burnt under conditions of incomplete combustion to provide carbon black, a kind of soot, used for the reinforcing of rubber for motor tyres. Sometimes it is cracked to provide the cracked gases for chemical processing mentioned above. A further important raw material for production of chemicals is the cracked distillates produced during cracking operations (in addition to the gas). By recently developed processes these can be converted to synthetic detergents, alcohols, etc.

As mentioned above, the chemical processes can be applied to the production of special grades of motor and aviation spirit. This was of extreme importance during the last war. Some of these processes were aimed at producing iso-octane, a hydrocarbon of remarkably high anti-knock value, either by combining two molecules of iso-butylene and hydrogenating the resulting compound or by a process known as alkylation, in which the same hydrocarbon is produced by combining an unsaturated hydrocarbon, iso-butylene, with a saturated hydrocarbon, iso-butane.

Chemical processes such as polymerization, hydroforming, polyforming, etc., have been evolved with the aim of tailoring the molecules to give the properties required for high-grade aviation or motor spirits. Yet another source of petroleum chemicals is the by-products from the refining of petroleum products with sulphuric acid or soda. From this it will be seen that in petroleum the chemist has a raw material of very great potential value. By the straightforward physical processes he can obtain motor spirit; special dry-cleaning spirits and rubber solvents; kerosene (paraffin oil) for stoves, tractors, lamps, etc.; fuels for light and heavy diesel engines; lubricating oils of all kinds, even medicinal oils; waxes for making floor polish, boot polish and candles; and bitumen for road-making, roofing felt, etc. By chemical processes he can produce either special fuels for incorporation in motor spirit or aviation spirits or a whole range of products of value to industry either as solvents for paints and lacquers, intermediate products for the manufacture of drugs, pharmaceutical products, plastics and synthetic rubbers, synthetic fibres, synthetic glycerine, carbon black for motor tyres, etc.

The petroleum industry is thus making very great strides in the chemical field and in many cases is producing chemicals originally obtained from coal-tar. In fact, practically every chemical derived from coal-tar is capable of being produced from petroleum. So far, the petroleum chemical industry has been largely based on the unsaturated hydrocarbons, but with modern processes which produce aromatic hydrocarbons such as benzene, naphthalene, anthracene, etc., interesting possibilities of a new chemical industry are being opened up.

HEAVY CHEMICAL INDUSTRY

So far mention has been made only of the chemical industries based on coal and petroleum, these being mainly responsible for the bulk production of dye-stuffs, drugs and pure chemicals, synthetic rubber, plastics, synthetic fibres, detergents, explosives, insecticides and many other chemicals. There are, however, other important branches of the chemical industry, such as that concerned with the production of heavy chemicals like sulphuric acid, washing soda and bleaching powder, and the nitrogen industry which makes fertilizers, explosives, and special nitrogen-containing substances.

The heavy chemical industry is so called because it is concerned with the large-scale manufacture of acids, alkalis, and other compounds from raw minerals and gases. Sulphuric acid, the most important chemical used in modern industry, is produced at the rate of some eleven million tons a year, and washing soda at about five million tons a year, whereas dyestuffs and drugs are only made in pounds and ounces as compared with tons. Although the heavy chemical industry mainly uses inorganic or mineral raw materials, such as common salt, lime, sulphur, and phosphorus, it requires very large quantities of coal for fuel and also depends upon it as a source of hydrogen which is needed for certain manufacturing processes.

It is no exaggeration to say that the heavy chemicals are vital to the prosperity of modern industry. Without sulphuric acid it would be extremely difficult, if not impossible, to manufacture artificial silk, dyestuffs, explosives, refine oil or clean metal sheeting, to name only a few well-known materials. A shortage of washing soda has an immediate effect on the soap, artificial silk and glass industries which use very large quantities of this alkali. Chlorine, made from common salt or sodium chloride, is not only essential for making bleaching powder, large quantities are required by the textile industry, but it is widely used in the manufacture of dyestuffs and in the processing of rubber.

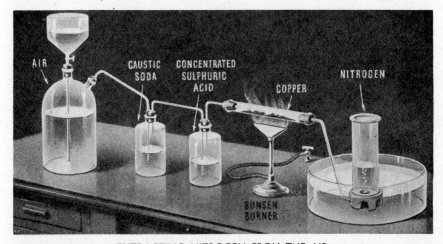

EXTRACTING NITROGEN FROM THE AIR

This simple experiment illustrates how nitrogen is obtained from the air. It is interesting to compare the simple apparatus used in the laboratory with the industrial apparatus illustrated on the facing page.

Air is a mixture of several different gases, the most important being oxygen and nitrogen, which are present in the proportions by volume of 78·08 per cent nitrogen and 20·94 per cent oxygen.

Oxygen is separated from the other gaseous constituents of air, purified and, in the highly compressed liquid form, bottled in steel cylinders. It is in the gaseous form that oxygen finds its greatest use, being of importance in medicine, metallurgy and various chemical processes. In some countries where coal is gasified underground instead of at the gasworks, large quantities of oxygen are pumped into the mine so as to enable incomplete combustion to be carried out at the coal face which will produce a mixture of valuable gases. These gases can be burned as fuel or used in the synthesis or building-up of many organic or carbon-containing chemicals. In metallurgy, the availability of cheap and abundant oxygen enables large-scale welding and metal-cutting processes to be carried out, and the gas is also of value in the smelting of iron ores and the refining of iron in Bessemer converters and open-hearth furnaces.

GAS SUCTION AND
DELIVERY PIPES

CYLINDER COOLING
WATER TANK

CONSERVED
PISTON
LEAKS PIPE

STEAM TURBINE GOVERNOR

GAS PRESSURE GAUGES

ATMOSPHERIC NITROGEN PLANT

The giant compressor shown here is used to compress atmospheric nitrogen combined with hydrogen to about 250 atmospheres to form ammonia.

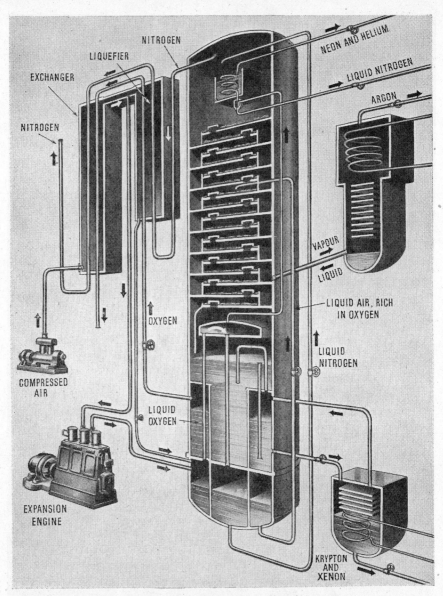

NITROGEN

LIQUEFIER

NEON AND HELIUM

EXCHANGER

LIQUID NITROGEN

NITROGEN

ARGON

NITROGEN

VAPOUR

LIQUID

LIQUID AIR, RICH
IN OXYGEN

OXYGEN

LIQUID
NITROGEN

COMPRESSED
AIR

LIQUID
OXYGEN

EXPANSION
ENGINE

KRYPTON
AND
XENON

OBTAINING GASES FROM THE AIR

When compressed air has been liquefied it is split up into its various gases by allowing the nitrogen, neon and helium to evaporate from the liquid air in the left-hand compartment at the base of the column, and subsequently evaporating the less volatile gases from the remaining liquid mixtures of argon, oxygen, krypton and xenon. The most volatile gases are drawn off from the highest points in the column, while the less volatile gases are drawn off at progressively lower levels. Helium, neon, argon, krypton, and xenon are present only in very small proportions.

Nitrogen, which plays such a vital part in plant life, is an inert gas and, in its gaseous form, finds comparatively few industrial applications. To make nitrogen serve its full purpose as a fertilizer it is necessary to "fix" it or combine the gas with other elements so as to produce nitrogen compounds, of which ammonium sulphate is the best known. The nitrogen fixation process forms the basis of a large section of the chemical industry and supplies many thousands of tons of fertilizers, such as ammonium salts, sodium nitrate, and nitro-chalk, as well as large quantities of nitric acid for explosives manufacture. In addition, nitrogen from the air can be converted into many so-called speciality chemicals, such as urea, from which drugs, detergents and insecticides may be produced.

There are several methods of converting nitrogen into nitrogen chemicals,

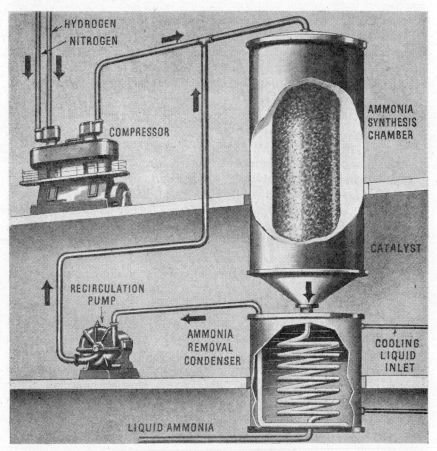

THE HABER-BOSCH PROCESS

A pictorial representation of how hydrogen and nitrogen are treated in the Haber-Bosch process to produce large quantities of liquid ammonia.

some of which require the use of water in the form of steam, while others utilize only air itself. Air is drawn into the gas plants by huge blowers, and steam from the boiler plant is passed over beds of heated coke in large closed vessels, resulting in two mixtures of gases, one called "N" gas, containing a large proportion of nitrogen, and the other "H" gas, consisting mainly of hydrogen. When these two gases are mixed together and heated under pressure in the presence of a catalyst, ammonia is formed. This fixation process is known as the Haber-Bosch method, and is the most important method of "fixing" the nitrogen in the air.

The ammonia made by the direct method is fixed or combined with other chemicals to give soluble salts. One interesting and important method of converting ammonia into ammonium sulphate consists of passing carbon dioxide gas (another constituent of the air) into a solution of ammonia in water in the presence of finely ground anhydrite (calcium sulphate). The solution of ammonium sulphate is filtered and evaporated, while the precipitate of chalk is removed, dried and used in the manufacture of nitro-chalk. An interesting point in connexion with the use of ammonium sulphate in agriculture is the attention now given to the value of the sulphur element present in the fertilizer. It has been shown that unsuspected sulphur deficiency is sometimes the cause for poor crop yield, a low sulphur content in the soil restricting chlorophyll (the green constituent of plant life) formation and retarding the vital process of cell division.

THE CHEMISTRY OF FERTILIZERS

Ammonium nitrate, a high-nitrogenous-content chemical, is used in large quantities in the manufacture of nitro-chalk, which is much prized by the farmer as a top dressing for grass-land and arable crops. One method of making this fertilizer is by use of a process somewhat similar to the time-honoured process for making lead shot. The hot thick pasty mixture of chalk and ammonium nitrate solution is sprayed down a 200-ft. tower and thereby converted into granules, which are dried, screened to uniform size, coated with chalk dust and then packed. The physical mixture of calcium carbonate and ammonium nitrate overcomes one disadvantage of the latter chemical, namely, its moisture-absorbing property.

The availability of nitro-chalk, which contains 15·5 per cent nitrogen, for British farmers, has helped to make good a national deficiency of sodium nitrate (16·0 per cent nitrogen content) obtained hitherto from South America. For a number of years the need for nitrogen chemicals in Britain has been satisfied by ammonium salts, principally ammonium sulphate, which is the cheapest and most economical of this class of artificials. There is, however, growing evidence that the farmer of the future will be supplied with more balanced nitrogen fertilizers derived from ammonia which overcome some of the serious disadvantages of ammonium sulphate. Urea made from ammonia and carbon dioxide may possibly form the starting-off point for a new series of organic nitrogen chemicals, which, while supplying much-needed nitrogen to the living plant, might also contribute in the building up of humus, which is the fibrous

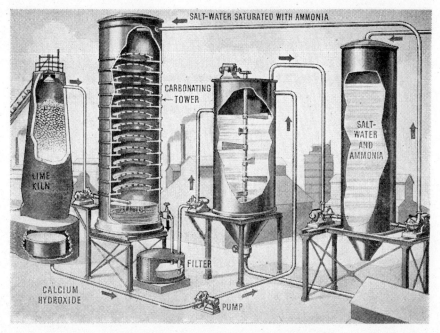

THE SOLVAY OR AMMONIA SODA PROCESS

This chemical process consists of making sodium bicarbonate by treating an ammoniacal solution of common salt with carbon dioxide made by the action of acid on lime. When this bicarbonate is heated it yields sodium carbonate (soda); the carbon dioxide gas is collected and used again for the primary reaction.

constituent of the farmyard manure and compost, and used as a fertilizer.

In the modern chemical industry a large percentage of the ammonia produced by one or other of the fixation processes is utilized in the manufacture of nitric acid and its derivatives, the most important being those suitable for use as fertilizers. Nitric acid is generally made by burning ammonia in air in the presence of a platinum catalyst. The mixture of gases so formed is absorbed in water to produce nitric acid, some of which is used to make ammonium nitrate, while sodium nitrate is also made in large quantities.

The production of nitric acid from ammonia is generally preferred on account of its greater economy to the various arc processes in which ordinary air is passed at rapid rate through a broad or long arc. It was Henry Cavendish who first caused nitrogen and oxygen to combine to form a nitrogen oxide by means of an electric spark in 1780. Many years later, Sir William Crookes, to be followed by McDougall and Howles of America and Birkeland and Eyde in Norway, elaborated the method of making nitrates, such as those of sodium, calcium, and ammonium, from the nitrogenous content of the air. Calcium nitrate was first

STIRRER DRIVE

VAPOUR MAIN

EVAPORATOR DOME

INSTRUMENT DIALS

BRINE FEED

BATTERY OF VACUUM EVAPORATORS

This view shows the domes of the vacuum evaporators in which the brine solution is evaporated to separate the salt from the impurities in the brine.

produced by the Birkeland-Eyde process in Norway in 1905. The method, although only assuming commercial importance where there is plentiful and cheap hydro-electric power, consists of heating air in a specially designed electric furnace in which the arc is made to assume a diskous shape by a special arrangement of an electro-magnet. The nitrous oxide produced as the result of the discharge is further oxidized to higher oxides, which are allowed to combine with the appropriate bases to form salts.

A new method of nitric-oxide production consists in blowing large quantities of air through a hot bed of refractory pebbles, then through an extremely hot gas-fired furnace, and finally through a second pebble bed, where the gas is chilled rapidly and the heat released and stored for use in pre-heating the incoming air when the flow is reversed. By pre-heating, the flame temperature of the gas reaches 4,200 deg. F.; moreover, one bed of the furnace is cooled and the opposite one heated. Thus by periodically reversing the stream of air it is possible to heat the nitrogen and oxygen to the temperature at which they will combine and almost immediately to chill the resulting nitric oxide to prevent decomposition.

Salt, which is either dug out of the earth in the form of rock salt or pumped up as brine, is the mainstay of the important alkali industry. Alkalis, so necessary for the production of glass and soap, viscose rayon, and many other goods, are derived from common salt and lime, by the well-known ammonia soda or Solvay process. Briefly this consists of making sodium bicarbonate by treating an ammoniacal solution of common salt with carbon dioxide made by the action of acid on lime. When this bicarbonate of soda is heated it yields sodium carbonate, or common washing soda, while the gas, carbon dioxide, is collected and used again for the primary reaction. Soda may, of course, be produced by other methods, such as the electrolysis of brine, which produces sodium bicarbonate. This is then dried and calcined to give sodium carbonate (sometimes known as soda ash). The success of the method depends on the availability of cheap electrical power and a ready market for the large quantities of chlorine produced as a by-product.

Apart from supplying the alkali industry with its vital raw material, salt is used for making a wide variety of sodium salts, including sodium sulphate, acetate, bichromate, chlorate, bromide and chromate. From sodium sulphate, which is either made synthetically from common salt, or obtained as a natural product from the earth, the chemist is able to make the

Hot water is pumped down to the level of the sulphur-bearing rocks and dissolves the sulphur. It is pumped to the surface by compressed air, and then conducted through pipes into tanks where it is allowed to solidify.

The pyrites burner produces sulphur dioxide gas, which rises through the Glover Tower, and is sprayed with weak acid to form nitrogen oxides from the gas. It next passes to the lead chambers where it mixes with water injected in the form of steam. Weak sulphuric acid is formed, and accumulates in the bases of the chambers, to be returned to the Glover Tower; nitrogen oxides are reclaimed in the Gay-Lussac Tower. The concentrated sulphuric acid is drawn off from the base of the Glover Tower.

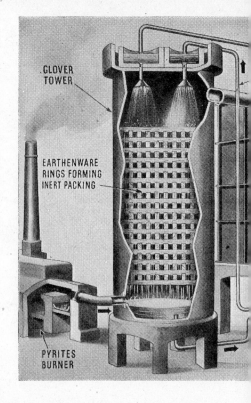

metal sodium. This is a silvery white substance which possesses a great attraction for water and when in contact with it gives off hydrogen gas. Sodium is used in large quantities in the manufacture of coal-tar dyes, tetraethyl lead, the anti-knock agent in motor fuels, and many organic chemicals. Pure sodium sulphate is also widely employed in the production of glass, paper, such as the familiar kraft paper used so extensively for packing purposes, dyestuffs, and many textiles.

Sulphur, either in the form of natural sulphur, or as sulphur containing minerals like sulphate of calcium (gypsum and anhydrite) and iron pyrites, is a key element, for without it the entire chemical industry of the world would be at a standstill. As previously mentioned, sulphur forms the essential raw material for the manufacture of sulphuric acid, a very large tonnage of which is used in making fertilizers, dyes and general chemicals. Some authorities go so far as to say that a nation's consumption of sulphur forms the index of its industrial prosperity. Apart from sulphuric acid, sulphur is also widely used in the synthesis of many organic and inorganic chemicals, including dyestuffs, pharmaceuticals and synthetic rubber. Sulphur chemistry serves dozens of important industries, from those concerned with the refining of oil to the purification of water, from the tanning of leather to the making of matches. Great Britain is almost entirely dependent on the sulphur recovered from sulphur-containing minerals, coal, and various industrial gases. Ordinary coal-gas as it leaves the retorts in the gasworks contains about 2 per cent of the unpleasant-smelling gas, hydrogen sulphide. At one time this impurity was left in the gas, and caused the burning gas to give off sulphur dioxide and sulphuric acid, both of which are highly corrosive

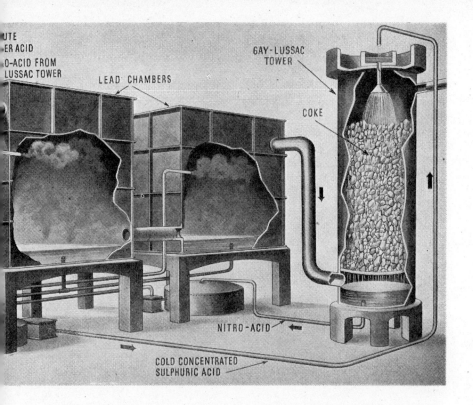

LEAD CHAMBERS

GAY-LUSSAC
TOWER

COKE

NITRO-ACID

COLD CONCENTRATED
SULPHURIC ACID

and have a choking smell. Nowadays the objectionable hydrogen sulphide is removed from coal gas and the sulphur recovered for further use.

Lime is not only a very valuable mineral for the farmer, enabling him to correct acid conditions of the soil, but it is vital to the building trades, where large quantities are required for making cement and mortar, the latter being a mixture of water, lime, and sand. In addition, lime is essential to the chemical industry for producing calcium carbide, bleaching powder, calcium cyanamide, made by heating calcium carbide with nitrogen gas in the electric furnace, and many other chemicals. Lime, the chemical name of which is calcium oxide, is obtained by heating limestone or calcium carbonate in kilns so as to drive off the carbon dioxide gas and leave behind the calcium oxide or quicklime. Fortunately, Great Britain has extensive deposits of limestone or chalk, and although large quantities are needed for making cement (obtained by heating in a furnace a mixture of limestone or chalk with clay) there is sufficient to serve all the needs of industry. Apart, of course, from the use of lime for making specific compounds, such as bleaching powder, lime fulfils a major purpose in chemical manufacture by taking part in many reactions so as to enable specific products to be made. Limestone is, for instance, necessary in the production of washing soda, as it provides the carbonate part of the sodium carbonate, the common salt providing the sodium. In dyestuff and fine chemical manufacture limestone acts as a link

BATTERY OF LIMEKILNS

Limestone is processed in the kilns shown above to give lime, which is a valuable mineral to the farmer, and is essential to the chemical industry.

by giving up the carbonate portion of its structure, and so makes available to the chemist a convenient means of completing certain difficult and perhaps incomplete reactions. When lime is treated with water it becomes slaked or converted into calcium hydroxide or hydrated lime, which is the familiar white powder used by the gardener for dressing the soil.

There is also the carbide chemical industry which uses coke and lime as raw materials. These two substances are heated together in the electric furnace to form calcium carbide, which, when placed in water, gives off the gas acetylene. This unpleasantly smelling gas can be converted into a large number of important chemicals, such as plastics, new fibres, adhesives, lacquers, pharmaceuticals, and even dyes. As the economical manufacture of calcium carbide requires cheap electrical power for the electric furnaces, large-scale manufacture of carbide can only take place where there is abundant hydro-electric power.

Potash or potassium carbonate is one of the most valuable of the natural salts, and is used as a fertilizer. Other potassium salts include the chloride and sulphate. Originally formed by evaporation of sea-water, potash deposits are found in many parts of the world, particularly Germany, New Mexico and Texas in the United States of America. The principal use found for potash is in the manufacture of fertilizers, and crop husbandry cannot be successful without adequate potash replenishment of the soil. Unfortunately, Great Britain is devoid of potash and the home requirements for fertilizer and chemical manufacture have to be satisfied by imports from Spain, Germany, and Palestine. From the last-named country large quantities of potash are recovered from the Dead Sea. The recovery plant is situated at the mouth of the River Jordan, water being drawn from the Dead Sea at a depth of 175 ft., and evaporated by the sun in a series of pans. A similar plant is in operation at the southern end of the Dead Sea, and the production of high-grade potash salts (principally the chloride) will, it is claimed, soon exceed 100,000 tons a year.

Potash in the form of sulphates and chlorides is generally incorporated with nitrogen and phosphorus-rich chemicals in making compound fertilizers. By varying the proportions of the three mineral nutrients, a complete diet for specific crops can be made up. A granular form for the final product makes application to the land easy and accurate for the farmer.

In addition to its use for making fertilizers, potash is needed for glass manufacture and the production of caustic potash, a necessary ingredient of soft soap, certain types of explosive, and chemicals such as potassium chlorate. This last-named product is required in the manufacture of fireworks and matches.

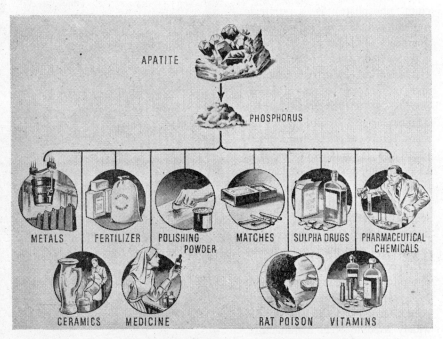

EVERYDAY PRODUCTS CONTAINING PHOSPHORUS

The chief source of phosphorus for industrial purposes is the mineral apatite, which is to be found in most types of igneous rock. In addition to the range of familiar articles pictured in the insets above, phosphorus is essential for plant and animal growth, hence its use as a fertilizer.

The isolation of metallic magnesium consists of filtering the brine to remove the impurities, and mixing the sea-water with milk of lime to form magnesium hydroxide. This compound is then treated with hydrochloric acid to produce magnesium chloride. The last step in the process is the evaporation of the magnesium chloride and electrolysing the fused salt. This separates the metal from the chlorine gas. The metal is skimmed during the electrolysis process and cast into pigs.

Phosphate rock or apatite (calcium phosphate) is a strategic mineral which now supplies vast quantities of elemental phosphorus and phosphorus salts to the fertilizer and chemical industries. Another and indigenous source of phosphorus for fertilizers is basic or Thomas slag, a by-product in the manufacture of steel from phosphatic ore. It contains not less than 12 per cent phosphoric acid and is generally used as a fertilizer in its finely ground form. Apatite is the sole commercial source of industrial phosphorus and increasing quantities are required today by the fertilizer industry for making superphosphates by treating the ground rock with hydrochloric and sulphuric acids. Phosphorus is also widely used in steel manufacture, ceramics, medicine, and polishing powders. Elemental phosphorus is of considerable value in foundry

OYSTER SHELLS

SETTLING TANKS

FLOCCULATOR

SEA WATER

FILTERS

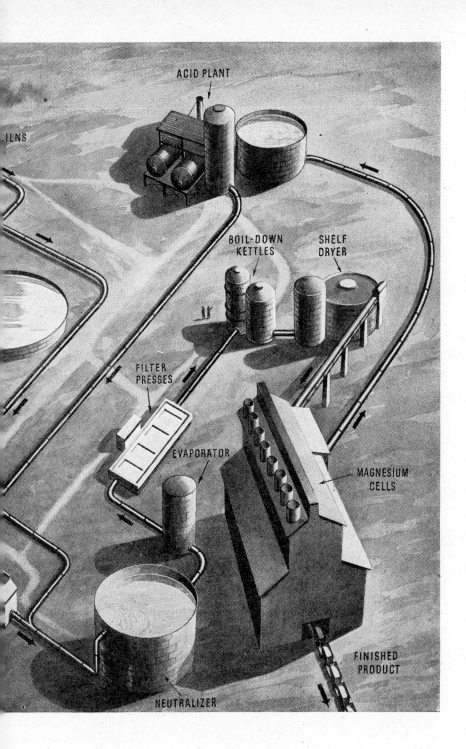

KILNS

ACID PLANT

BOIL-DOWN
KETTLES

SHELF
DRYER

FILTER
PRESSES

EVAPORATOR

MAGNESIUM
CELLS

NEUTRALIZER

FINISHED
PRODUCT

work for making special alloys, such as phosphor copper, phosphor bronze, phosphor tin, and improving the corrosion resistance of steel. Other uses for pure phosphorus include match production, rat poisons, and the production of sulpha drugs, vitamins, and several pharmaceutical chemicals.

MAGNESIUM FROM SEA-WATER

The sea, which contains $3\frac{1}{2}$ per cent mineral matter, can be made to yield a rich harvest of chemicals. These include bromine, a dark-brown, pungent-smelling liquid, used for making anti-knock compounds to be added to petrol, iodine for medicinal purposes, and many other salts.

The method employed for isolating and purifying magnesium from sea-water is, in principle, fairly simple. First of all the brine is filtered so as to remove all the seaweed, sand, and other impurities. Milk of lime, obtained by calcining or burning oyster shells, is then mixed in with the sea-water. This causes the formation of magnesium hydroxide, a gelatinous substance which is allowed to thicken, and then filtered and treated with hydrochloric acid to produce magnesium chloride. The final step in the process consists of evaporating the magnesium chloride and electrolysing the fused salt so as to separate the magnesium metal from the chlorine gas. During electrolysis the pure metal can be skimmed off the electrolytic vessels and cast in pig form.

In peacetime it is generally considered to be uneconomical to produce magnesium metal from sea-water, as the method, although continuous, is much more costly to operate than the extraction of the metal from magnesium ores, such as magnesite or dolomite, which are the principal raw materials.

MAGNESITE AND FLUORSPAR

Magnesite or magnesium carbonate is the chief source of magnesium metal and magnesium salts. It occurs as a natural mineral in various parts of the world, extremely rich deposits being found in Austria, Greece, Canada, and the United States of America. Another magnesium mineral, brucite, or natural hydrated magnesium oxide, is mined in Canada. Both magnesite and brucite are used in the manufacture of bricks for basic refractory furnace linings, recovery of magnesium metal, and the manufacture of Epsom salts (magnesium sulphate), building materials, fine chemicals, and rubber.

Fluorspar is assuming growing importance to the chemical industry, as it is the main source of the gas fluorine, which is highly poisonous and corrosive. Although it was discovered in 1886 by the French chemist Moissan, this highly reactive gas has never been more than a laboratory curiosity. Work carried out during the past few years on fluorine chemicals for aircraft petrol, uranium hexafluoride, used in the separation of U.235 (see Chapter 7), and the propellant gas for insecticide atomizers, increased the tempo of research. The availability of fluorine gas for the chemical industry opens up a new chapter—one might almost say, a new volume—in modern industrial chemistry. Not only is fluorine

SCIENTIFIC RESEARCH AND THE DOMESTIC CONSUMER

A tea-service made from opal glass with opalescent flutes. This exemplifies the developments being made in glass technology for domestic purposes.

the most reactive of all gases, but fluorides and fluorine compounds generally are noted for their high stability and inertness to chemical attack. A number of chemical manufacturers have already announced their intention to produce fluorine compounds for use in refrigerating systems and fluorine plastics.

Great Britain is well supplied with fluorspar and fluorite, substantial deposits of which exist in Derbyshire and Durham. The largest deposits in the world are, however, in Illinois and Kentucky, in the United States. The bulk of the fluorspar mined has been used as a flux in the basic open-hearth steel process and only a small proportion used for making hydrofluoric acid and fluorides. Elemental fluorine is derived from hydrofluoric acid and potassium bifluoride.

SILICATES AND THEIR USES

The element silicon is one of the most important constituents of the earth's crust. Combined with oxygen as in silica it forms the bulk of the sands by the seashore, quartz and rock crystal, and also makes up many precious and semi-precious stones, such as amethyst, jasper, onyx, and opal, as well as many common stones like agate and flint. It is estimated that about 60 per cent of all rocks, stones, clays and sand consist of silica, or to give it the chemical name, silicon dioxide.

Silica is one of the most inert materials in the world, being insoluble in all acids, except hydrofluoric. Fused silica is used for making chemical plant where exceptionally high temperatures have to be employed and where vessels, pipes, valves, and other parts have to withstand the action of concentrated sulphuric acid and other corrosive acids. The production of fused silica pipes and other parts is difficult, as pure fused silica has a melting point of 1,750 deg. C.

The most important application of silica is found in the manufacture of glass, which is a fused mixture of various silicates, such as potassium calcium silicates. Ordinary plate glass is made by heating a mixture of silica, soda ash or sodium carbonate, and calcium carbonate. A new type of high-heat and shock-resisting glass is made from 96 per cent silica. It can withstand sudden extremes of hot and cold without breaking, and temperatures up to 1,100 deg. C. without melting. It is one of the hardest, most acid-resistant and electrically resistant glasses known. An application found for this new glass is as a burner plate on the modern gas range. The smooth glass plates distribute heat more evenly and give firm support to even the smallest utensils. They can also keep spilled food from clogging burners.

Apart from the use of silica for making glass, it is also of importance for ceramics, cements, abrasives, and building stones. Finely ground silica finds many important applications in industry. It is, for instance, chosen as an insulator in some refrigerators and as a filler for certain kinds of moulded plastics, especially those required to withstand very high temperatures. Silica is also an ingredient of many different kinds of paints where hard, flat surfaces are required.

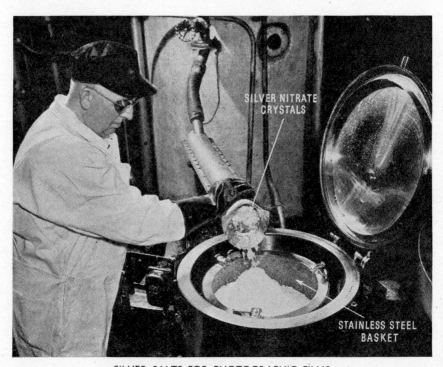

SILVER SALTS FOR PHOTOGRAPHIC FILMS
A stage in the process of making photographic film emulsions. The crystals being pumped into the basket are a compound of silver and nitric acid.

Sodium silicate, or water-glass, is one of the best-known silicon chemicals. It is produced by fusing a mixture of white sand and soda ash with a small quantity of carbon in a tank furnace. The cold glassy mass is then extracted with water and the syrupy liquid sold for use in industry as an adhesive in the production of corrugated paper boxes, as a filler in soap manufacture and for making non-porous bricks and cements. Sodium silicate is also widely used as a preservative for keeping eggs, in the dyeing and textile finishing of silk, the clarification of fruit juices and the fireproofing and preservation of wood.

The element silicon is a brown-coloured powder which is never found in nature in its pure state, but always combined with oxygen. It can, however, be prepared by heating together a mixture of potassium fluosilicate and metallic potassium. During the heating, the potassium replaces the silicon which is thus set free, and obtained by dissolving out the potassium fluoride with water. Pure silicon is used in metallurgy for producing special alloys, such as ferro-silicon, for admixture with molten steel, and for the reduction of oxides to their metals.

When acid is added slowly to a solution of sodium silicate a jelly-like form of silica, known as silica gel, is formed. This substance finds several quite important applications in industry, being used for the removal of hydrogen sulphide from gas, the refining of mineral oils by removal of sulphur and for iceless refrigerators.

Of growing industrial importance are the new silicon plastics and synthetic rubber made from silicon tetrachloride. This is a colourless volatile liquid which can be chemically treated so as to yield various kinds of highly complex compounds built up from silicon, carbon, oxygen, and hydrogen, known as silicones. These differ in properties according to their composition. Some of the silicones are used as high-temperature greases in engine lubrication, others as insulating varnishes and impregnating agents, and one at least as an entirely new kind of heat-resistant rubber which possesses an exceptionally high elasticity or rebound.

METALS IN INDUSTRY

In the extraction and refining of metals from their ores chemistry plays an important part. The chemist works side by side with the metallurgist in the development of efficient and economical methods of production.

Iron is obtained from its ores, which consist mostly of oxides and carbonates, that is, compounds formed as a result of the iron combining with oxygen or carbonic acid. The metal is extracted from these ores in the modern blast furnace, where a mixture of clean and finely ground ore, coke, and limestone is heated together in the upper part of the furnace. As the charge of ore descends from the top of the furnace to the bottom it is subjected to increasing temperatures and comes in contact with various reducing gases, mostly carbon monoxide, which combine with the oxygen of the iron oxide to form carbon dioxide. In this way iron in a rather impure form known as pig-iron is produced in very large quantities. Many of the impurities present in the ore combine with the lime to form blast-furnace slag, which is used in road construction.

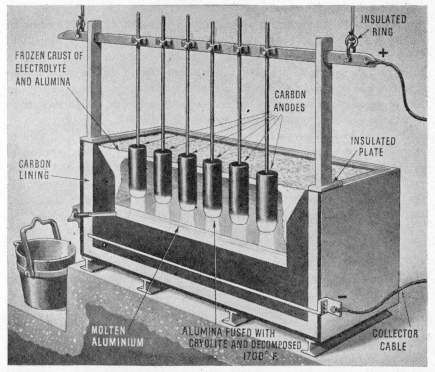

THE ELECTROLYTIC PRODUCTION OF ALUMINIUM

Alumina, or aluminium hydroxide, is mixed with cryolite, which acts as a flux, and packed into a carbon-lined trough into which a number of carbon anodes project. A very heavy electric current passes from the anodes to the lining of the trough, melting the alumina and driving off the oxygen. The metal collects on the floor of the furnace and is then run off for casting into ingots.

Steel is made from pig-iron in the Bessemer furnace, which is an egg-shaped converter designed so as to blow air through molten iron. The oxygen in the air combines with the excess of carbon in the pig-iron to form carbon monoxide, an inflammable gas, which burns at the mouth of the converter. The elements silicon, manganese, and phosphorus, as well as traces of other elements, are converted into their oxides and form a mixture known as basic slag. This is a very valuable fertilizer in great demand by the farmer. Stainless steels are alloys of steel and chromium or nickel.

Although at one time the bulk of the steel was made by the Bessemer process, today the open-hearth method has assumed greater importance. The hearth is actually a shallow trough lined with refractory materials able to withstand the high temperature of molten iron (maximum 1,630 deg. C.). As in the Bessemer method, the carbon-monoxide gas formed from the carbon in the pig-iron and the oxygen in the iron oxide or ore added to the charge burns at the top of the furnace with a blue, almost ghostly, flame.

Light metals, and particularly aluminium, are of great importance in the engineering industries, owing to their lightness in weight, good strength-to-weight factor and ease of fabrication. Known as silver in clay, aluminium is the most common metal in the world, being present, in the form of silicates, to the extent of 80 per cent of the earth's crust. The most important source of aluminium is bauxite, an impure form of alumina, and cryolite or sodium aluminium fluoride. Bauxite is mined in various parts of the world, particularly France, U.S.A., British Guiana, Dutch East Indies, etc., and cryolite is found in Greenland, where there are enormous deposits.

Aluminium was named by Sir Humphry Davy, inventor of the famous Davy lamp for use in the mines. This British scientist produced the first iron-aluminium alloy in 1809. It was not until the electrolytic method of recovering aluminium from its ore was discovered in 1883 that the manufacture of this

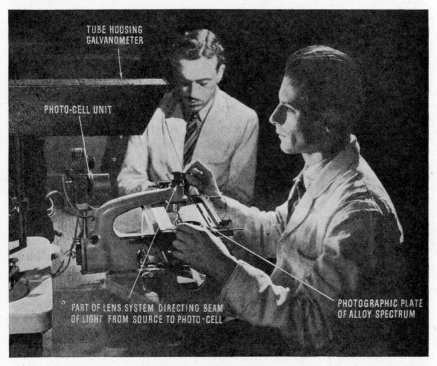

TUBE HOUSING GALVANOMETER

PHOTO-CELL UNIT

PART OF LENS SYSTEM DIRECTING BEAM OF LIGHT FROM SOURCE TO PHOTO-CELL

PHOTOGRAPHIC PLATE OF ALLOY SPECTRUM

MEASURING SPECTRUM LINES

A microphotometer being used to measure the percentage of alloying elements contained in a sample of aluminium alloy. This method of analysing the composition of metals is being increasingly adopted in modern industry.

metal became a practical proposition. The process is completed in two stages. First of all, pure alumina has to be prepared from bauxite by chemical means, this being known as the Bayer process. The crude ore is crushed, ground to a fine powder and boiled with strong caustic soda, at a temperature of 160 deg. C. and a pressure of about four or five atmospheres. By this means the alumina goes into solution to form aluminium hydroxide, while all the impurities, such as a small amount of iron and titanium, collect as a red mud at the bottom of the vessel. The aluminium hydroxide is separated from the water by filtration, dried and finally roasted or calcined at a high temperature in rotary kilns to form pure aluminium oxide or alumina.

ELECTROLYTIC PRODUCTION OF ALUMINIUM

The electrolytic process of making aluminium metal from the oxide is carried out in a large rectangular iron bath or furnace lined on all sides with carbon, which acts as a cathode of the cell at the beginning of the electrolysis; later on the metal itself becomes the cathode. The furnace is then packed with a mixture of alumina and cryolite, the latter acting as a flux or means of dissolving the alumina. Carbon electrodes forming the anode of the cell are next placed in position in the mixture so that they dip right down from above to the floor of the furnace. When the current is switched on the temperature rises to 1,700 deg. F. and the alumina dissolves in the cryolite. Under the conditions of this great heat oxygen is driven off, leaving the aluminum, and the metal collects on the floor of the furnace; a sectional view of this plant is shown on page 120. It is then run off for casting into ingots.

Aluminium in its pure state is a somewhat weak metal and it needs to be alloyed to other metals to make it suitable for general engineering purposes. It was in 1910 that the first important aluminium alloy, Duralumin, was introduced into Great Britain and gave an impetus to the use of light metals in engineering. Duralumin is made by adding small quantities of copper and magnesium to molten aluminium. Other alloys can be produced by adding nickel, manganese, and silicon to pure aluminium. In most cases the strength of the alloys is greatly improved by suitable heat treatment. The alloys of aluminium are particularly suitable for die-casting, which is now a fairly common method of mass-producing small metal shapes by moulding. The metal is first melted, forced by plungers into steel moulds and finally ejected.

Aluminium alloys have excellent hot-working properties and are, consequently, particularly suited to the extrusion process which is widely practised today. Briefly, the process consists of forcing the metal through a die in which an opening has been cut conforming to the cross-section of the finished rod or tube required. The pressure needed to force the metal through the die is naturally high, and modern extrusion presses are capable of producing pressures up to 5,000 tons. A wide variety of shapes can be obtained by this method, and have wide application in the light-metal industries.

MICROCHEMICAL ANALYSIS OF ALUMINIUM ALLOYS

The above type of analysis is used where the quantity of the sample available is restricted to less than 10 milligrammes. The samples are weighed on a microchemical balance, completely dissolved in small platinum beakers, and then known volumes of these solutions are treated with selected chemicals; these produce specific colours proportional in intensity, that is, depth of colour, to the amounts of alloying elements present in the specimen being analysed.

Practically all the metals, including the radioactive rare metals, can be chemically treated to yield salts, and many of these find applications in industry, medicine, and the arts. Mercuric salts, such as mercuric chloride, are well known in medicine as antiseptics and in agriculture as fungicides for dressing seeds; copper acetate and carbonate are well-known pigments used in paint manufacture; ferrous sulphate or copperas made from iron is an important ingredient of inks and also is used in water purification; tin oxide is employed in making up ceramic enamels or glazes, and tin chlorides find uses in chemical synthesis. Thorium compounds derived from the mineral monazite, found in Brazil, India, and East Africa, are used in making incandescent gas mantles, and, when alloyed with tungsten, for electric lamp filaments, also for flashlight powders, while uranium oxides are highly esteemed for making glazes in the ceramic industry and as pigments for paints. Mesothorium is used as a substitute for radium.

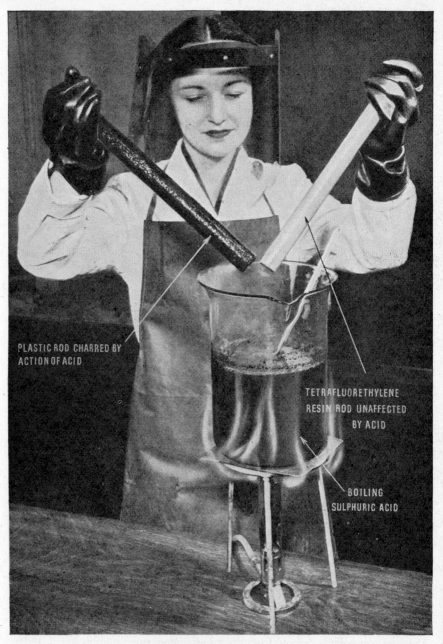

PLASTIC ROD CHARRED BY
ACTION OF ACID

TETRAFLUORETHYLENE
RESIN ROD UNAFFECTED
BY ACID

BOILING
SULPHURIC ACID

A CHEMICALLY INERT PLASTIC

Comparing the action of boiling sulphuric acid on two forms of plastic material. The unaffected one on the right is made of tetrafluorethylene resin, which not only resists the action of concentrated acid, but high temperatures as well.

CHAPTER 4 Creating new materials

MANY familiar products are man-made, and represent triumphs on the part of the chemist in making products to measure, that is, with specific properties destined to meet the most exacting conditions of service.

The first in the field of true synthetic fibres, and still the most important, is nylon, which was put on the market in 1938.

Viscose and acetate rayon cannot be classed as synthetic fibres, as they are derived from cellulose obtained from cotton linters or wood pulp. Today, nylon is a large tonnage fibre finding applications in several textile fields, notably hosiery manufacture, where its gossamer-like fibres, elasticity, and toughness are greatly esteemed properties. There are several different types of nylon, but the best known is 66, the first digit of which is the number of carbon atoms in one of the constituents used for its manufacture, the second digit being the number of carbon atoms in the acid with which the former reacts.

Nylon is the generic name given to a family of fibre-forming synthetic substances known to the chemist as polyamides. They are produced by reacting together an acid, such as adipic acid, which is derived from phenol or carbolic acid, and a base, such as hexamethylene diamine, also made from phenol. The result of heating together these two related substances produces nylon salt. This is a chemical with the long-sounding name, hexamethylene diammonium adipate. When this is heated under pressure in the presence of an inert gas (nitrogen) nylon is formed. This is melted in oil-heated vessels in the presence of nitrogen (all air being excluded) and the molten nylon forced through a spinneret in the form of fine filaments which are brought together and wound on bobbins (see illustration on page 127).

A new synthetic fibre is known as Terylene. This is produced by reacting together terephthalic acid with ethylene glycol. Both of these chemicals can be derived from coal or oil. Terylene, like nylon, is made by melt spinning; the fibre-forming compound, which is used in chip form, is melted at a temperature of 246 deg. C. and, after filtering, extruded through an appropriate spinneret to give the required filament. For the development of the full physical properties, the filaments are drawn to predetermined gauge or denier, and afterwards the yarn plied and twisted into skeins ready for passing to the mill for machining.

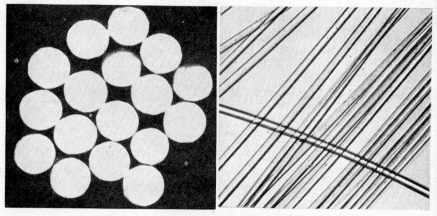

MAGNIFICATION OF NYLON THREADS

Photomicrographs showing the round and smooth cross-section, and translucency of nylon threads used in sheer stockings and fine knit goods.

Other synthetic fibres of growing interest and importance are made from plastics derived from acetylene, e.g. polyvinylidene-chloride and polyvinyl chloride-acetate, while among the semi-synthetic fibres are those based on proteins, such as casein, soya bean, chicken feathers, and alginates from seaweed.

THE ROLE OF CHEMICALS IN FOODSTUFFS

In the manufacture of many of our foodstuffs, chemicals play a vital although often unsuspected part. Not only are synthetic vitamins used to enrich our foods, but health-giving phosphorus salts added to many of them. Cereals, flour, prepared mixes, and food beverages are now boosted up with essential phosphorus, calcium, and iron by the addition of calcium and iron phosphates. Calcium phosphates also provide the necessary leavening acid in prepared flour mixes. Disodium phosphates serves as an emulsifier in the production of processed cheese and condensed milk, while other phosphates are used as ingredients of soft drinks, sugar, imitation jellies, yeast, and many brands of commercial baking powder.

Colouring matters in the form of innocuous coal dyestuffs give an appetizing appearance to many foodstuffs. These synthetic dyes are generally preferred to those of vegetable, mineral, and insect derivation on account of their greater stability, higher tinctorial value, and uniformity of strength. Today, synthetic dyes are used in the manufacture of confectionery, cereal products, canned fruits and vegetables, meat products, preserves, kippers and other cured fish, mineral waters, margarine and butter.

During the war years food chemists paid a good deal of attention to the production of essential foodstuffs, particularly fats and proteins, from home-produced materials, preferably wastes or by-products of industry. In Germany,

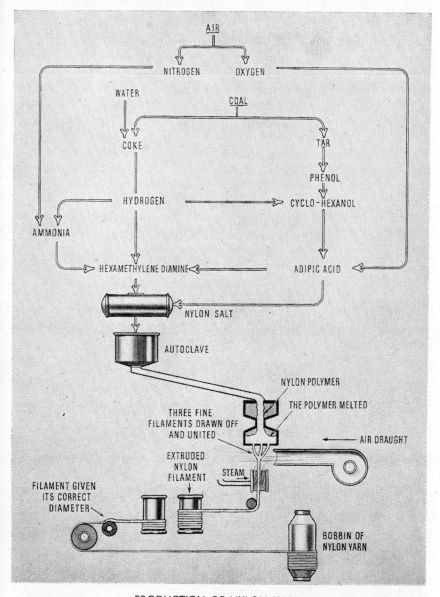

PRODUCTION OF NYLON YARN

From the phenol distilled from coal-tar and ammonia synthesized from the air the chemist can make hexamethylene diamine and adipic acid. These two intermediate chemicals can be made to react together to form nylon salt, which can be converted into nylon polymer. This is a white, horny substance which may be melted and extruded into filaments by forcing the molten nylon through a spinneret. Nylon can be converted into yarn, bristles for brushes, threads for fishing lines, and into a moulding powder.

a successful method was evolved for making margarine from the synthetic fats prepared from paraffin wax, derived from the hydrogenation of coal or the Fischer-Tropsch reaction, by oxidizing it under special conditions. The most successful method of making edible fats from paraffin wax consisted in blowing the molten wax with air in the presence of manganese, which acted as a catalyst. The fatty substance obtained by this process was then combined with glycerine to make the type of fat suitable for margarine and shortenings. From waste sulphite liquor, which formerly was run into rivers and streams, a good-quality yeast can now be made by fermentation of the wood sugar present in the effluent. This yeast is of great value as a cattle food and can also be used for making vitamin concentrates for human consumption.

The food chemist is able to improve the quality of natural fats to make them more suitable for specific applications; for instance, he can make soft fats hard by a process known as hydrogenation. This consists of heating the oil or fat in the presence of hydrogen gas and finely divided nickel or other metal. Fats

AUTOCLAVE IN WHICH NYLON
POLYMER IS MADE

POLYMERIZATION OF NYLON

In the autoclave the polymerization process takes place, that is, the process in which small molecules are joined together to make large ones.

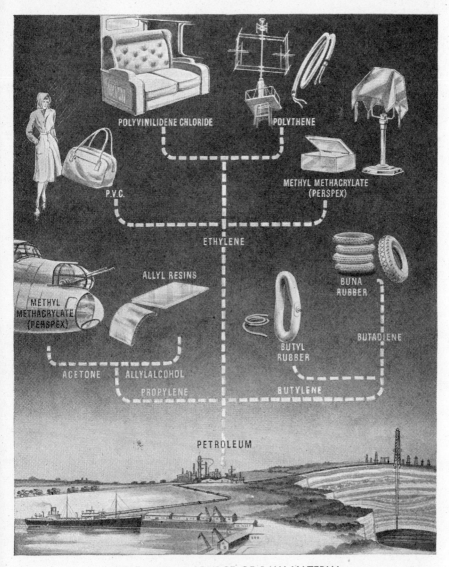

POLYVINILIDENE CHLORIDE

POLYTHENE

METHYL METHACRYLATE
(PERSPEX)

P.V.C.

ETHYLENE

ALLYL RESINS

BUNA
RUBBER

METHYL
METHACRYLATE
(PERSPEX)

BUTADIENE

BUTYL
RUBBER

ACETONE   ALLYLALCOHOL

PROPYLENE

BUTYLENE

PETROLEUM

PETROLEUM—A SOURCE OF RAW MATERIAL

Petroleum to the chemist is a source of raw material of very great value. By straightforward physical processes he can obtain motor spirit ; dry-cleaning spirits and rubber solvents ; kerosene for stoves, etc. ; fuels for diesel engines ; lubricating oils ; waxes for polishes and candles ; and bitumen for road-making, roof felting, etc. By chemical processes he can produce either special fuels for incorporation in motor spirit or a whole range of products of value to industry either as solvents for paints or lacquers, intermediate products for the manufacture of pharmaceutical products, plastics and synthetic fibres, rubbers, glycerine and carbon black for motor tyres. A selection of finished products is illustrated above.

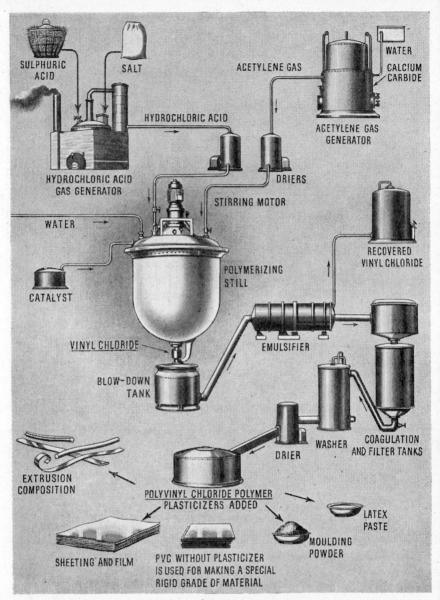

MAKING POLYVINYL CHLORIDE

Polyvinyl chloride is a rubber-like thermo-plastic which is being used in place of fabrics for such items as tablecloths and curtains. Acetylene and hydrochloric acid gases under carefully controlled conditions form vinyl chloride, also a gas, which can be made to polymerize, or form a solid plastic, by heating with a catalyst, such as certain mercury salts. Polyvinyl chloride is a white, odourless, and stable compound which looks something like flour. Its physical properties can be varied by adding different quantities of plasticizer.

which are unsaturated or lack their full quota of hydrogen are able to combine with this gas, thereby becoming hardened and losing any offensive smell they may possess. Whale oil can in this way be converted into a white, practically odourless solid fat suitable for making into margarine. By means of other processes the chemist is able to split natural fats into their constituents, and then to sort these into required groups and re-unite them. In this way food manufacturers are able to make shortening agents and margarine to exact specifications, and to meet recommended dietary needs.

The chemist also contributes to the supply of foodstuffs in designing fertilizers, either of the general type or specialized ones to correct deficiencies of certain minerals in the soil, such as zinc or boron in developing insecticides to reduce the enormous losses caused to foodstuffs by insects, both on the living plant and in stored grain, etc. Further, he is now attempting and succeeding in controlling the growth of the plant cell itself. The more important of the approaches to this problem are to stimulate growth, cause setting of fruit blossoms, restrict growth (during frosty periods) or even kill the cells, as in the case of weeds.

THE RAW MATERIALS OF PLASTICS

Modern plastic materials are the products of chemistry. They consist of two kinds. First of all there are the true synthetics, built up from the simplest raw materials; for example, the manufacture of polyvinyl chloride from acetylene and hydrochloric acid, and urea formaldehyde resin from urea and formaldehyde. Then there are the semi-synthetics, such as the cellulose plastics, e.g. celluloid, cellulose acetate, and ethyl cellulose. These semi-synthetic materials are made by chemical treatment and, therefore, modification of the long and complex cellulose molecule.

Most plastics are carbon compounds, being derived either from coal or petroleum. In addition, there are several important synthetic plastics containing nitrogen obtained from the air, and a new field of plastics is now being explored where inorganic elements, such as silicon and fluorine, are combined with carbon and hydrogen and sometimes oxygen.

One of the most important raw materials for plastics manufacture is phenol, which can be made synthetically from coal-tar benzene (or benzene made from petroleum), or distilled from coal-tar. In Great Britain, resin producers depend largely on the gas industry for supplies of phenol. In high-temperature carbonizations of coal (usual method of making gas) a yield of ten gallons of tar is secured for every ton of coal carbonized, but of this tar only 35 to 48 per cent represents fractions useful to the chemical industry, the residuum being pitch. Crude tar acids containing phenol and cresylic acids, etc., make up about 20 to 25 per cent of the tar distillates.

The importance of phenol to the plastics industry cannot be overestimated. This intermediate is used in the manufacture of phenol formaldehyde moulding powders, laminated materials, adhesives, coatings, plasticizers, and solvents.

STEAM PIPES FOR
HEATING BOWLS

POLISHED STEEL BOWLS
OR ROLLERS

CALENDERED SHEET

PLASTIC SHEETING FOR DOMESTIC USES

Calendering vinyl butyral which has been plasticized between polished steel rollers or bowls. This synthetic material is now being extensively used for making a host of domestic products, for example, hospital sheeting, baby pants, shower curtains, tablecloths, raincoats. This interesting member of the vinyl family is also widely used as an interlayer in the manufacture of shatter-proof safety glass. Although opaque when manufactured, it becomes perfectly transparent when compressed between glass layers. Some of the characteristics which make vinyl butyral an ideal substance for interlayers are its clarity, toughness, adhesiveness, insensitivity to moisture and stability to light and heat.

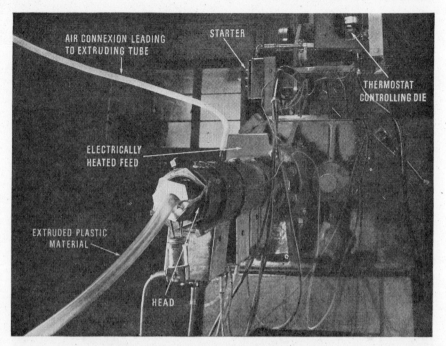

EXTRUDED POLYVINYL CHLORIDE EMERGING FROM DIE
The plastic is fed cold into the extruder and a screw conveys it through zones of increasing heat until it emerges through the die. It is possible to extrude rods and tubes up to six or eight inches in diameter.

It also forms the starting-off point for making nylon. From benzene, which the chemist is able to convert into phenol, it is also possible to make other plastic-forming compounds such as styrene, a clear inflammable liquid used for producing a glass-clear resin, polystyrene. Other derivatives of coal-tar which play an important part in plastics manufacture include naphthalene, which is required for the manufacture of phthalic anhydride, a vital ingredient of the type of resin used in high-grade plastic paints and stoving lacquers, and resorcinol or resorcin. The last named, which is obtained in large quantities from the distillation of tars made from the low-temperature carbonization of coal, is now being used for the manufacture of special adhesives. It is also used as a lotion for certain diseases of the skin.

Ethylene gas, which is made in large quantities during the cracking and refining of petroleum, is of considerable interest to the plastics industry. When the gas is subjected to moderate temperature and very heavy pressure, in the region of 2,000 atmospheres, a wax-like plastic is produced possessing excellent electrical insulating properties, particularly at radio frequencies, and also outstanding resistance to moisture and chemicals. This plastic, known as polythene,

133

is widely used for the insulation of radar cables and accessories, and replaces lead for insulation of heavy submarine cable. As an insulant it has several important advantages, apart from possessing excellent insulating properties. It can, for instance, be easily extruded from a heated die to form sheathing or used to cover copper wire. Polythene may also be moulded to produce various electrical parts.

PLASTICS FOR THE DOMESTIC CONSUMER

These examples of tableware are made from polymethyl methacrylate, the manufacture of which is illustrated on page 138. In addition to white the plastic is made in a wide variety of pleasant pastel shades.

The high chemical resistance of this plastic, which is even unaffected by the highly corrosive hydrofluoric acid, renders it very suitable for applications in the food and chemical industries. In some modern breweries polythene pipe is being used for conveying water and also fermented liquors and has the advantage of being rustless, tasteless, and without any effect on liquids passing through the pipe. Polythene-coated paper and polythene transparent film are of considerable interest to the food industry, which needs tough, water-resistant wrapping materials for perishable foods. Although it is not possible to stick polythene to polythene with an adhesive, it is easy to join together by heat sealing.

The vinyl plastics constitute a large family of modern thermo-plastics and include polyvinyl chloride, or P.V.C., polyvinyl acetate and compounds made up

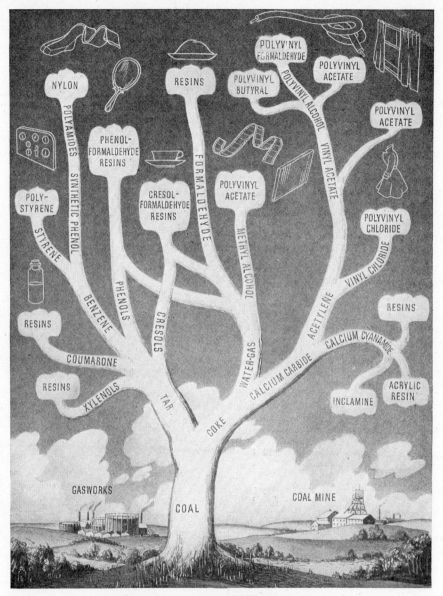

PLASTIC MATERIALS DERIVED FROM COAL

In addition to supplying heat for industry and our homes coal is a source of numerous raw materials. One important section of the chemical industry is based on the distillation of coal from which are produced large quantities of chemicals and these are used to produce a wide range of synthetic compounds, which have many applications in industry, medicine and domestic life. There are in fact about three thousand different compounds, in addition to the primary gas and coke, which are derived from coal when it is carbonized in the gasworks.

of P.V.C., and the acetate, polyvinyl butyral, polyvinyl alcohol, and polyvinylidene chloride. These are all derived from acetylene or petroleum gases and possess different chemical and physical properties. Some of the vinyl plastics can be stretched, folded, moulded, extruded, calendered, and coated on to paper and fabric. In Great Britain, the vinyl plastics, and particularly P.V.C., are made from acetylene, which is converted into vinyl chloride through the action of hydrochloric acid gas. The vinyl chloride, also a gaseous product, is then changed into the familiar plastic, P.V.C., by heating it in the presence of certain mercury salts which act as a catalyst in promoting the chemical change.

P.V.C., or polyvinyl chloride, is a white, odourless, and stable compound which looks somewhat like flour. On processing or compounding it with substances known as plasticizers, the flexibility of the P.V.C. can be increased. Wide variations in the properties of the finished plastic can be achieved by adding different quantities of the right plasticizer. A great deal of thought has been given to the study of these compounds by chemists, and there are today hundreds of plasticizers, each one being suitable for a specific application.

When P.V.C. has been properly plasticized it can be calendered between stainless-steel heated rollers (known as bowls) to form thin sheets, which are made up into rainwear, umbrellas and curtains. Calendering can also apply a thin coating of heat-softened P.V.C., or what is called a co-polymer or plastic made up of polyvinyl chloride and polyvinyl acetate, to a fabric. Extrusion products of P.V.C. and other vinyl plastics consist mostly of flexible tubing, men's belts, tool handles, and sections for draught exclusion. The method entails the feeding of the plastic in granular form from the hopper into the extruding machine, where a screw forces the softened plastic through a die.

MEMBERS OF THE VINYL FAMILY

Another interesting member of the vinyl family of plastics is polyvinyl butyral, which is widely used as an interlayer in the manufacture of shatter-proof safety glass. Although the butyral film is opaque when manufactured, it becomes perfectly transparent when compressed between glass layers. Other topical uses for this plastic include jam-proof coating of tablecloths, flexible film on raincoats and shower curtains.

Polystyrene is another important new plastic. It is made from styrene, a watery liquid made from ethylene derived from petroleum or alcohol by fermentation, and benzene made from coal. The intermediate chemical, styrene, is converted into the plastic by merely heating it, exposing it to light or by chemical means. The plastic is normally a clear rigid material, but it is also made in a wide range of opaque and transparent colours. When produced in powder form it is particularly suitable for injection moulding. This is an operation which consists in feeding the plastic powder from a hopper into a heating chamber, where it is thoroughly softened, and then forced into cold mould cavities, where it hardens. Cycles are fast and a modern injection machine turning out combs

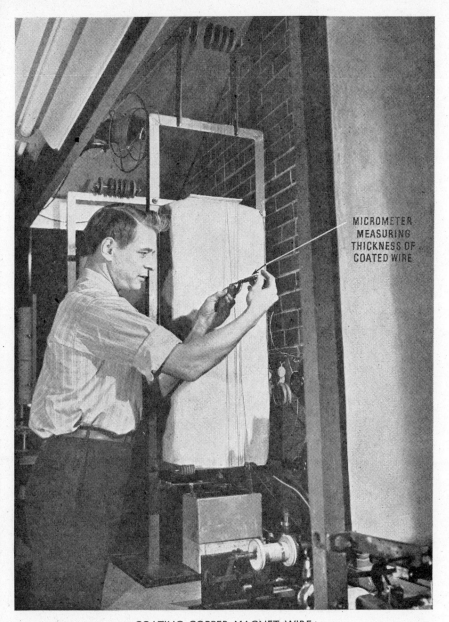

MICROMETER
MEASURING
THICKNESS OF
COATED WIRE

COATING COPPER MAGNET WIRE

An operator measuring the thickness of copper wire coated with silicone enamel.
Silicones are built up from silicon, carbon, oxygen and hydrogen. Some of these
new plastic materials are being used as high-temperature greases in engine
lubrication, others as insulating varnishes and impregnating agents, and one at
least as an entirely new kind of heat-resistant rubber which possesses exceptionally
high elasticity. Also they possess high electrical resistance.

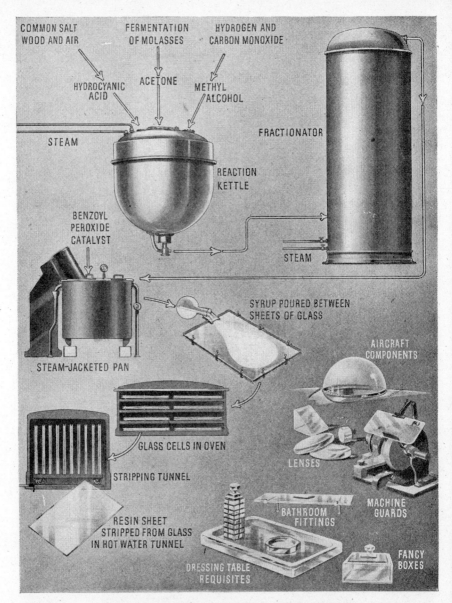

COMMON SALT WOOD AND AIR

FERMENTATION OF MOLASSES

HYDROGEN AND CARBON MONOXIDE

HYDROCYANIC ACID

ACETONE

METHYL ALCOHOL

STEAM

FRACTIONATOR

REACTION KETTLE

BENZOYL PEROXIDE CATALYST

STEAM

SYRUP POURED BETWEEN SHEETS OF GLASS

STEAM-JACKETED PAN

AIRCRAFT COMPONENTS

GLASS CELLS IN OVEN

LENSES

STRIPPING TUNNEL

MACHINE GUARDS

RESIN SHEET STRIPPED FROM GLASS IN HOT WATER TUNNEL

BATHROOM FITTINGS

DRESSING TABLE REQUISITES

FANCY BOXES

PRODUCTION OF POLYMETHYL METHACRYLATE

This flow diagram shows the step by step processes in the manufacture of polymethyl methacrylate, from three simple organic chemicals, hydrocyanic acid or prussic acid, acetone and methyl alcohol. In the form of transparent sheet this plastic is used for making gun-turrets, astrodomes, wind-shields and windows for aircraft. Coloured methacrylate sheet is made into wash-hand basins, kitchen sinks, cups and saucers, machine guards and even lenses for use in television sets. Articles manufactured in this material are illustrated on page 134.

can produce thirty every minute, that is, if it has sixteen mould cavities.

Polystyrene finds many uses, ranging from battery boxes to soap dishes, bathroom tiles to spoons, toys to chemical measuring flasks for hydrofluoric acid.

In the field of modern plastics the acrylics are of interest owing to their glasslike transparency, toughness, moulding properties and resistance to water and many chemicals. The sheet material known as polymethyl methacrylate is made from acetone derived from alcohol, itself a fermentation product of molasses, and prussic acid or hydrocyanic acid obtained from the gasworks. From these chemicals a watery white liquid known as methyl methacrylate is obtained, which can be converted into a transparent solid by heating it with a little benzoyl peroxide, which assists the change-over from liquid methyl methacrylate to solid polymethyl methacrylate; see the flow diagram of this process on the facing page.

USES OF METHACRYLATE PLASTICS

In the form of transparent sheet this plastic is used for making gun-turrets, astro-domes, wind-shields and windows for aircraft, both military and civil. The coloured methacrylate sheet is made into wash-hand basins, kitchen sinks, cups and saucers, machine guards, and even new aspherical lenses used for the optical systems in modern television sets. These lenses are of special interest as it is the first time in the history of the optical industry that it has been possible to make accurate aspherical lenses on a large scale at a reasonable cost. The lenses are actually moulded in optically perfect glass moulds so that they take on the contours of the mould. Apart from the use of plastic aspherical lenses for television, they are finding widening employment as industrial inspection lenses in many industries handling small parts and are also used in railway signalling.

In modern plastics technology research has opened up promising new sources of raw materials; in particular inorganic substances, such as silicon, are assuming growing significance for making plastics possessing special properties. From sand, brine, coal, and petroleum the chemist is now able to make a new range of silicon plastics which possess outstanding resistance to heat as well as excellent electrical insulation properties. Some of the silicon compounds, known as silicones, are of great value as hydraulic fluids or lubricants for use in extreme cold.

PRODUCTION OF SYNTHETIC RUBBER

It was a British chemist, Sir William Tilden, who first made rubber synthetically. Experimenting with turpentine he produced isoprene, which he converted into rubber. That was in 1882. In succeeding years many scientists studied this same problem in an attempt to obtain another source of rubber, but success was achieved only by slow degrees.

Synthetic rubber can be made from three types of raw material, oil, coal, and agricultural materials such as corn. From these the relatively simple gas, butadiene, is produced by a series of complicated reactions. Waste gases from petroleum refining and natural gas are converted into the gases butane and butylene.

It is from the butylene that butadiene is ultimately made by dehydrogenation or the withdrawal of some of its hydrogen. Starting from butane, butadiene is made in two stages. First of all, butane is reduced or hydrogen withdrawn and by this means converted into butylene. Further dehydrogenation produces butadiene. Starting from coal, the first stage in the manufacture of butadiene is the production of calcium carbide by heating together lime and coke. By dropping water on to carbide the gas acetylene is made. Acetylene can also be produced from methane or marsh-gas, from coal by hydrogenation and certain waste matters from the petroleum industry.

In Great Britain only relatively small quantities of calcium carbide are produced, as its manufacture calls for plentiful and cheap electrical power. A modern carbide electric furnace uses 10,000 kilowatts and generates a temperature of 3,000 deg. C. It is estimated that one ton of calcium carbide needs 4,250 units of electrical energy for its manufacture.

Butadiene is made from acetylene, by a series of reactions. First of all, the gas is passed into dilute sulphuric acid containing very small quantities of mercury salts. In this way, acetaldehyde is produced. The next stage consists of changing the acetaldehyde into a chemical known as aldol by means of dilute alkali. The aldol is hydrogenated by passing hydrogen into it at a temperature of 100 deg. C. in the presence of a nickel-alumina catalyst. In this way the familiar liquid butylene glycol is made. By a single-stage chemical reaction the glycol can be changed into butadiene, which is an important compound in the synthesis of rubber.

RUBBER FROM AGRICULTURAL PRODUCTS

Alcohol made from agricultural products, such as corn and molasses, can be made to yield butadiene, but the method is not as economical as the synthesis from petroleum gases. In general, the production of butadiene from alcohol follows the general lines of manufacture from acetylene. The alcohol is oxidized to form acetaldehyde, which is then changed to aldol, and stage by stage to butylene glycol and butadiene.

Butadiene is a highly inflammable, unstable gas. It is liquefied under pressure and stored in large tanks which are sprayed with cold water to prevent premature conversion of the gas into synthetic rubber. The actual manufacture of rubber from butadiene is really quite a simple process. Polymerization, or the linking up of a large number of butadiene molecules to form long chains, can be achieved by merely heating the gas, subjecting it to light or by chemical means, i.e. heating it in the presence of certain catalysts. By varying the conditions of polymerization it is possible to produce synthetic rubbers possessing different properties and, therefore, suitable for special applications in industry.

One famous type of synthetic rubber, known as GR-S or Buna S, is made by combining butadiene with styrene. It is then compounded with carbon black and milled to form sheets ready for the manufacture of rubber tyres and other types of rubber goods. The actual production of Buna S rubber is carried out in

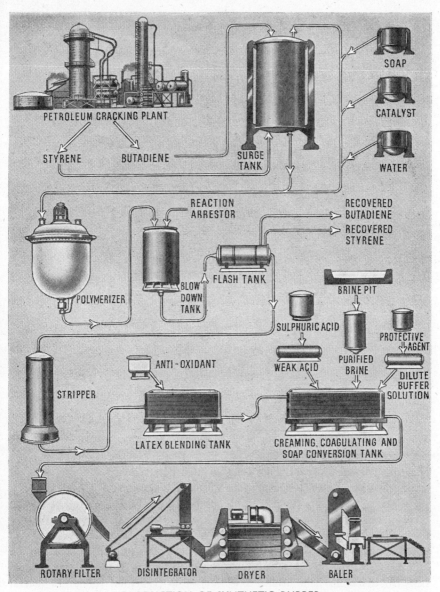

SOAP

CATALYST

WATER

PETROLEUM CRACKING PLANT

STYRENE   BUTADIENE   SURGE TANK

REACTION ARRESTOR   RECOVERED BUTADIENE   RECOVERED STYRENE

FLASH TANK

BRINE PIT

POLYMERIZER   BLOW DOWN TANK

SULPHURIC ACID   PROTECTIVE AGENT

WEAK ACID   PURIFIED BRINE   DILUTE BUFFER SOLUTION

ANTI-OXIDANT

STRIPPER

LATEX BLENDING TANK   CREAMING, COAGULATING AND SOAP CONVERSION TANK

ROTARY FILTER   DISINTEGRATOR   DRYER   BALER

PRODUCTION OF SYNTHETIC RUBBER

From the by-products of petroleum the chemist can produce the liquid styrene and the gas butadiene. The two compounds are highly reactive, and can be made to form a co-polymer which is known as GR-S rubber or Buna S. The synthetic rubber requires vulcanization with sulphur and reinforcing with carbon black before a commercial rubber can be produced. It should be appreciated that its properties are not as good as those of natural rubber. For this reason it is not an ideal material for such products as tyres, which have to stand very hard wear.

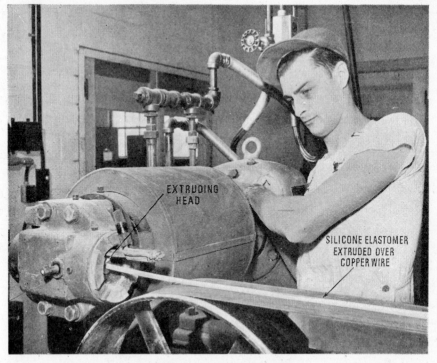

EXTRUDING HEAD

SILICONE ELASTOMER EXTRUDED OVER COPPER WIRE

COVERING A COPPER WIRE
Silicone elastomer is shown being extruded over copper wire to make a flexible and water-repellent insulation resistant to heat and oxidative hardening.

glass-lined vessels, where the styrene, liquefied butadiene gas and soap solution are thoroughly mixed and heated in the presence of a catalyst which brings about the actual conversion of the ingredients into synthetic rubber latex. The rubber is coagulated from the latex by adding acid, washed, dried, and pressed into bales for dispatch to the rubber fabricator, who makes the rubber into tyres and other goods. Buna S resembles natural rubber in some ways; for instance, it can be vulcanized by heating it with sulphur, and possesses several rubber-like properties. On the other hand, Buna S is inferior to plantation rubber in several important characteristics, for example, elasticity and resilience. It is for this reason tyres made of it do not stand up to heavy wear.

The synthetic rubber known as Buna N is also produced as the result of mixing butadiene with another chemical, in this case acrylonitrile. The method of manufacture is somewhat similar to that used for making Buna S, the liquefied butadiene and acrylonitrile being heated together in the presence of a soap solution to form a creamy latex. The rubber is removed by coagulating this with weak acid, drying and compressing into bales. Buna N is useless for rubber-tyre manufacture, but of great value for petrol hose, cable sheathing, and other applications where the outstanding resistance of the rubber to petrol, oils, and chemicals can be exploited.

A synthetic rubber of particular value for inner tubes of tyres is butyl, made by co-polymerizing an olefine such as isobutylene with a small quantity of a diolefine such as isoprene, the latter having a similar effect to the cross linking of sulphur when added to natural rubber in vulcanizing.

OIL-RESISTANT SYNTHETIC RUBBER

Neoprene is a type of synthetic rubber which is well known in Britain on account of its outstanding resistance to oil, petrol and many solvents, general indifference to light, and impermeability to gases. This rubber differs from GR-S as butadiene is not used as intermediate material; instead the gas, vinyl acetylene, a derivative of acetylene, is employed. This is made by passing acetylene into a solution of copper chloride containing ammonium chloride. Vinyl acetylene is treated with hydrochloric acid to form chloroprene, a colourless and pleasant-smelling liquid which can be readily converted by heat into a rubber-like substance, neoprene. This form of synthetic rubber is used for making petrol hose, rollers on various types of machinery including printing machines, balloon cloths, and linings for chemical plant.

Another very interesting rubber-like material, although strictly speaking it is not a true synthetic rubber, is Thiokol, which is made from salt, sulphur, and natural gas or petroleum, which give the chemist the two intermediate chemicals, ethylene dichloride and sodium polysulphide. On mixing and heating these two chemicals a very pungent-smelling rubber-like compound is formed which possesses outstanding resistance to oil, petrol, and other solvents. By varying the character of the polysulphide used for making the rubber it is possible to prepare a wide range of Thiokols, varying from soft cements to ebonite-like mouldings used in the electrical industry.

An entirely new form of rubber is made from silicon and carbon by combining certain organic chemicals with silicon oxide. The finished product possesses good elasticity and the ability to withstand high temperatures, up to about 300 deg. C., for several days without deterioration.

MAN-MADE PIGMENTS

Recent chemical research has placed at the disposal of the paint manufacturer new pigments, resins, and solvents, and British paint technology is becoming less dependent on the importation of foreign raw materials. Among the man-made pigments developed during recent years is a yellow pigment known as lead cyanamide. This is particularly valuable where corrosion-resisting coatings are required for metal-work. Another interesting addition to the range of paint pigments is a new type of titanium dioxide, known as Rutile grade. This differs from the ordinary white pigment by the crystals being a different shape to those of the standard prewar grade. In consequence of the new shape of the crystals, paints are whiter and do not chalk on outside exposure, and less pigment is required than when ordinary titanium pigment is used.

Among the new resins now being used for paint manufacture are those based on pentærythritol, a synthetic resin used instead of glycerine for the production of paints made up largely of synthetic resins (phenol formaldehyde type). This gives a coating with a harder finish. Another interesting development is the reaction of styrene made from coal-tar with linseed oil dissolved in white spirit. The result of this mixture is a paint possessing a high gloss and hard finish. Resins based on silicon are able to give durable, heat-resisting paints that are also unaffected by many corrosive chemicals. Unfortunately, the silicon resins are very expensive and have at present a limited application. An entirely new type of synthetic resins known as urethanes was made in Germany during the last war, their production involving the treatment of chemicals with the poison gas phosgene. The urethanes are of special value for baking or stoving enamels or paints and their use enables a substantial economy to be made in the use of glycerine. This by-product of soap manufacture is an expensive chemical, and is at the present time in very short supply.

Some solvents, which were nothing more than laboratory curiosities during the Second World War, are now in use in paint manufacture. The volatile liquids known as nitro-paraffins, which are produced from simple derivatives of petroleum, find several applications in paint production and are also used as solvents for lacquers.

For distempers, and oil-bound water paints generally, several new kinds of substances are being tried out to give emulsions. One of these is sodium alginate, derived from seaweeds, while another is methyl cellulose, made from cotton waste. An interesting new addition to distempers is D.D.T., which kills flies and other insects landing on the painted surface.

NEW CHEMICAL WEED-KILLERS

Science has given the farmer a revolutionary new weed-killer produced from chemicals based on phenol and is known as the sodium salt of 4–chlor–2–methylphenoxyacetic acid. Some weed-killers, such as those like sodium chlorate and sodium arsenite, sterilize the soil so that nothing can grow in it. Others like sulphuric acid act externally by burning the leaves to which they adhere. These killers are only slightly selective, tending to remain on broad-leaved plants and to run off those with narrow leaves. The new chemical weed-killer is quite different in its action, having a drastic toxic action on all weeds with two-leafed seeds and without serious effect on weeds with seeds possessing one leaf. Tests have shown that the acid salt can eradicate many common weeds, such as white charlock, pennycress, yellow charlock, etc., from the common crops.

Methoxone is really a synthetic hormone which only in heavy concentrations has a damaging effect on certain plants. Farmers are using it in fields of wheat, oats, barley, and rye when infested with annual weeds, such as the various species of wild mustard.

Owing to the acute shortage of natural fats for soap manufacture, great interest is being taken in the production of synthetic detergents or washing compounds from coal and petroleum by-products.

The cleansing action of soap is due mainly to its ability to disperse particles of dust and hold them in suspension in the washing solution. This action, which is known to laundry technologists as deflocculation, depends to a large extent on the ability of the detergent to wet the surface to be cleaned. The synthetic detergents which are now being developed include substances possessing the ability to wet as well as to remove dirt from different kinds of surfaces.

DETERGENTS FROM COAL-TAR AND PETROLEUM

The first real synthetic detergents to be prepared from coal-tar derivatives were made in Germany during the First World War from naphthalene, derived from coal-tar. These first synthetic washing compounds were not very successful, owing to the necessity of using very strong solutions. During the Second World War, German scientists developed new detergents from coal. In particular, great success was achieved by making soap-like material from the simple gases given off by coal during carbonization. The famous Fischer-Tropsch synthesis, whereby carbon monoxide and hydrogen are made to combine to give a series of organic or carbon compounds, produces the starting-off substances known as higher alcohols. These are waxy solids capable of being chemically treated to make them into soluble detergents.

Important developments in the manufacture of synthetic detergents from petroleum took place in America in 1940, and as a result of considerable research a range of sulphuric acid derivatives of petroleum detergents was made by treating petroleum with chlorine gas made from common salt. The product of this reaction was further chemically treated to make the detergent.

New petroleum detergents possess good foaming properties, stability in water and high washing power. Washing powders made from them are white, free-flowing and similar in appearance to ordinary soap powders. A small quantity of the detergent foams up into abundant suds in hard and soft water. These compounds are suitable for cleaning dairy and food-processing equipment and containers and general plant sanitation, also for various processes in leather, textile, pulp, and paper manufacture, and as an ore-flotation medium in mining.

Prominent among new developments in detergents are the so-called quaternary ammonium compounds of complex chemical structure derived from coal-tar. These are not only powerful washing agents, but valuable germicides, which are recommended for such hygienic purposes as cleaning wounds, disinfecting, and washing eating utensils, cold disinfection and storage of surgical instruments, and general washing and cleansing work in many industries.

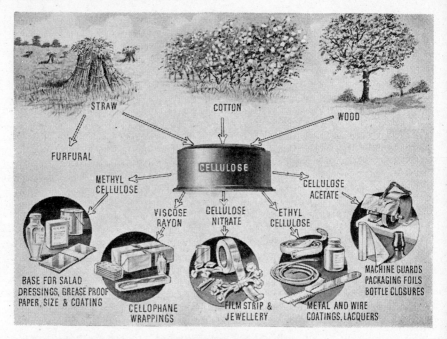

STRAW

COTTON

WOOD

FURFURAL

METHYL CELLULOSE

CELLULOSE

CELLULOSE ACETATE

VISCOSE RAYON

CELLULOSE NITRATE

ETHYL CELLULOSE

BASE FOR SALAD DRESSINGS, GREASE PROOF PAPER, SIZE & COATING

CELLOPHANE WRAPPINGS

FILM STRIP & JEWELLERY

METAL AND WIRE COATINGS, LACQUERS

MACHINE GUARDS PACKAGING FOILS BOTTLE CLOSURES

PRODUCTS OF CELLULOSE

Cellulose which forms the walls of plant cells is, as the diagram shows, a source of very valuable raw materials for the synthetic chemical industry.

The research chemist has learned to make substitutes and equivalents of many natural perfumes and today the synthetics made in the laboratory are often more popular than the rare essential oils and fixatives derived from plant and animal sources, and have a much wider application in modern industry. Man-made perfumes are considerably less expensive than the natural scents. Oil of violets made from coal-tar derivatives is equivalent to the natural flower oil, a pound of which requires the pressing of 35,000 pounds of violet leaves with 2,000 flowers to the pound of leaves.

The essential oils and fixatives from which natural perfumes are made come from many parts of the world—flower oils from the Continent; pine oil from Siberia; oil of geranium and vetiver, a plant root used in perfumery, from the Reunion Islands; musk from the musk glands of a rare species of deer found only in the Himalayas; ambergris, the vomitus of certain whales, which is washed up on the shores of South Sea islands. Synthetics for the perfumery industry are made mostly from similar intermediate chemicals to those used in the manufacture of coal-tar dyes.

The synthetics are often more permanent than the natural scents and are, therefore, particularly useful in food processing, where distinctive odours and flavours have to be retained with undiminished bouquet for long periods. Although such large users as the food and tobacco trades are probably the biggest customers of the perfume manufacturers, very small quantities of the synthetics suffice to scent and flavour large proportions of food, etc. One ounce of imitation butter flavour is sufficient for 100 pounds of margarine and one ounce of a new artificial garlic is equal to 3,200 ounces of genuine garlic.

The blending of synthetics and also natural essential oils to make perfumes is an art of great complexity and skill. So skilful are these perfume blenders that they can produce almost any scent to order; lilac, the scent of new-mown hay, geranium, rose, exotic scents of the East, or perfumes reminiscent of the countryside.

Meanwhile, chemists are carrying out new research to synthesize much-needed but elusive scents, such as the aroma of freshly baked bread and masking perfumes for use in places where large crowds of people congregate, such as underground railways, theatres, cinemas, etc. It is safe to say that practically all manufactured foodstuffs contain artificial flavouring which can be standardized to ensure absolute uniformity. One of the most important of the flavouring agents used in foods is vanilla. This was formerly obtained from a seed pod of the orchid family, but is now produced synthetically from several raw materials, notably eugenol, derived from clove oil, coniferin, a white crystalline material made from the sapwood of the northern pine and waste liquors from paper mills. Today large quantities of synthetic vanilla are produced from paper-mill sul-

EFFECT OF DETERGENTS ON WOOL FIBRES

At the left is an enlarged view showing the greatly reduced surface tension and greater wetting power of wool fibres from fleece after being dipped in a synthetic detergent. To the right are similar fibres dipped in water. As will be seen, globules of water are produced by surface tension and lack of wetting power. Some of the new detergents have foaming qualities equivalent to those of soap powders.

phite liquor, which is evaporated and then oxygen is passed through it at 110 deg. C. for several hours so as to ensure a high yield.

Coumarin is another interesting product, which until a few years ago was derived exclusively from tonka beans, but today is made from a well-known coal-tar chemical, salicylic aldehyde. Musk, one of the most famous ingredients of certain heavy perfumes, is prepared from cresol, a common by-product of coal-tar. One of the most famous examples of man's success in copying nature is afforded by camphor, an important medicinal and perfumery additive which is also used in large quantities in the manufacture of celluloid. Practically every ounce of camphor now used in industry is synthesized from turpentine.

SYNTHETIC PRODUCTS FROM FARM WASTE

The British organic chemical industry is today using large quantities of molasses obtained from sugar-beet and sugar cane which grows in various parts of the world, particularly Java, British West Indies, Cuba, and Hawaii. The molasses is fermented so as to produce alcohol, which can then be distilled and used in the synthesis of many important chemical products. From alcohol it is possible to make synthetic rubber, fine chemicals, and a host of other necessary substances.

In America, interesting experiments are being carried out on the making of synthetic motor fuels from the alcohol produced from farm waste, such as surplus corn-cobs. It is estimated from preliminary work carried out that 1 ton of farm residue will yield 90-95 gallons of motor fuel.

Although primarily considered as foods, the proteins, particularly surplus proteins derived from vegetable sources, have great industrial potentialities; soya-bean and zein proteins are being utilized to an increasing extent for adhesives, coatings and paints, plastics and textiles. The annual capacity for soya-bean protein in the U.S.A. is approximately 15 million pounds and the figure for zein from corn about 333 million pounds. A new artificial wool, Ardil is being made from peanut protein. This new fibre, which is not a substitute for wool but fulfils a role which is supplementary to the natural fibre, promises to have a rich future. It can be used in conjunction with wool to produce lighter fabrics, or in union with cotton or rayon, when it gives warmth, fullness of handle, resilience and crease resistance to the mixture. In Kenya and other parts of Africa vast schemes of peanut development are being pushed forward to supply Great Britain with much-needed oil and also protein-rich meal for Ardil and other products. As the peanut yields a prolific crop it is expected that within five years Britain should be well supplied with this vegetable raw material.

Among the animal proteins some interest is being aroused in wool grease, casein, chicken feathers, and egg white. In Australia, wool grease accumulates in the fleece to the extent of 30,000 tons a year and is used for making cosmetics, ointments and various salves. Casein obtained from surplus milk is used as a basis for invalid and infants' food, soups and various other manufactured food

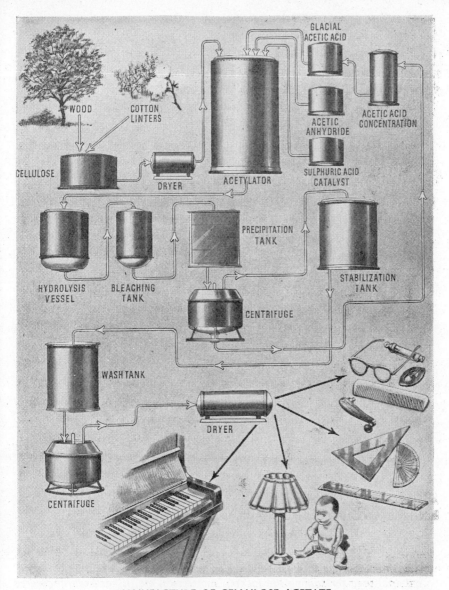

MANUFACTURE OF CELLULOSE ACETATE

Cellulose acetate is the product of the action of glacial acetic acid and acetic anhydride on cellulose, with sulphuric acid acting as a catalyst. Some of its outstanding physical properties are mechanical strength, toughness and low moisture absorption. The cellulose is obtained from organic matter such as wood or cotton linters. The finished product is usually formed into blocks, then machined into sheets; it can, however, be cast or extruded, see illustration on page 133. In the bottom right-hand corner of this drawing is a selection from the very wide range of domestic articles that can be made from cellulose acetate.

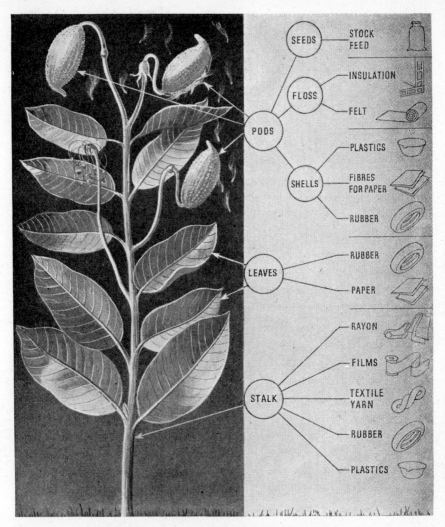

RAW MATERIALS FROM COMMON WEEDS

In America much attention has been devoted to the common milkweed, Asclepias syriaca, since its silky floss was used during the late war as a substitute for kapok, a material used for stuffing life jackets, mattresses, etc. It has been discovered that the leaves and stalk contain 1–4 per cent rubber which, when mixed with a synthetic rubber such as Buna S, gives a product of increased tear-resistance and flex life. The diagram above shows other valuable products that can be obtained from this hardy weed that can live successfully in poor soil, and is immune from insect attack. The branch of science devoted to the uses of agricultural products is termed "chemurgy" and is revealing new sources of raw material for industry. Some of the more interesting of the recent developments facilitated by this new branch of chemical science are the manufacture of paper from straw, textiles, such as rayon, from seaweed, and synthetic wool from peanuts.

products. A large quantity of casein made from milk unfit for human consumption is used in the manufacture of adhesives. Chicken feathers and egg white are assuming some commercial importance as proteins and in those countries where there are large surpluses they are now being made into textile fibres, some of which are similar to artificial wool made from casein.

Waste vegetable matter is now being used in very large quantities for the production of substances from which a wide range of chemicals can be made. Furfural, a sharp-smelling dark-coloured liquid, can be used as the starting point for the synthesis of as varied a range of chemicals as those derived from benzene obtained by distilling coal-tar. To the chemist, the potential importance of furfural cannot be overestimated, as the structure of this compound is of great stability and there is thus readily available a range of many thousands of chemicals, including dyestuffs, solvents, drugs, plastics, synthetic rubber, etc.; in fact, the entire range of chemicals in the aromatic field may once again be explored.

The raw materials capable of producing furfural are inexhaustable and must remain so as long as the earth can sustain vegetable life. The chemical furfural, which is the key to the possible synthesis of so many compounds, can be obtained by a simple chemical reaction involving the action of mineral acid (such as hydrochloric acid) on cereal straws, husks of grain or oilseeds, sawdust and wood waste, in fact all products of agricultural residues. When the heated mixture of acid and vegetable matter is distilled, furfural is produced. It can be collected and purified by re-distillation. Large quantities of furfural can be obtained from surplus organic matter such as straw, oat husks, rice hulls, wattlewood, etc. Furfuryl resins derived from furfural are valuable as casting resins.

ARTIFICIAL SILK FROM SEAWEED

Another very interesting raw material is seaweed or algæ. Large quantities of this are collected, washed, dried and baled for transportation to factories, where it is used in the manufacture of the gum agar-agar. Before the outbreak of war in 1939, agar-agar was obtained almost exclusively from Japan, but when supplies were cut off Great Britain and other sea-bound countries set out to produce their own agar. In Britain it has been found that *Cigartina stellata*, or a mixture of that alga with *Chondrus crispus*, after suitable treatment, produces an agar of good setting point of hardness, being particularly suitable for food manufacture, such as the manufacture of diabetic foods and in the canning of meat and fish, also for thickening soups, creams, ice-cream, puddings, and meat pies. It has also found extensive applications in pharmacy, particularly as a constituent of petroleum agar emulsions. A promising use for seaweed is found in the manufacture of a new kind of artificial silk, this being made from the alginic acid derived from the seaweed. This silk can be made either soluble (capable of being dissolved) or insoluble, the former finding important applications in the textile industry, where there is a great need for soluble and easily removed threads, so as to produce special novel effects in fabrics.

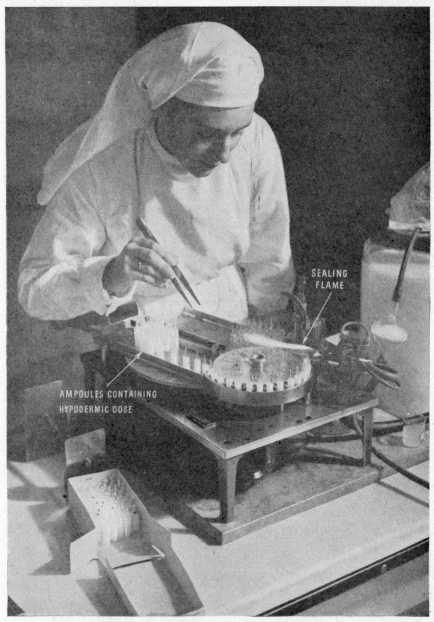

SEALING
FLAME

AMPOULES CONTAINING
HYPODERMIC DOSE

MECHANICS IN THE SERVICE OF MEDICINE

Drugs, vaccines, serums, etc., that are administered with a hypodermic are contained in a small, sealed, glass capsule, called an ampoule, which holds a measured dose. The apparatus shown above is used to fill mechanically the ampoules from the large flask on the right; the open ends are hermetically sealed by the gas flame as the ampoules move round in the miniature conveyer.

CHAPTER 5 Chemistry fights disease

THE chemist and the doctor are firm allies and by their united efforts they are winning many battles in the remorseless war against disease. Chemistry makes three outstanding contributions to medicine:

(1) It helps to explain the working or functioning of the human body in terms of definite chemical reactions, for example, the behaviour of the gastric juices during digestion of food and the effects of certain drugs on the various body organs. In addition, the chemist, and particularly the biochemist, is carrying out research designed to determine the chemical constitution of all the complex protein matter making up the body.

(2) It places at the disposal of medicine an accurate analysis of all the products of human metabolism (sum total of changes in living matter), as well as foods and drugs. This is often of great assistance to the doctor in the diagnosis and treatment of disease.

(3) It makes available a wide range of synthetic and disease-fighting drugs, vitamins, anæsthetics, antiseptics, and many other medicinals. It is in the production of new drugs that the chemist makes his most important contribution to medicine. Often he forms one of a team working to a set programme, which may be the development of a new anti-malarial or a new anæsthetic. Sometimes the chemist is himself a doctor and is able to carry out clinical tests as well as laboratory experiments. It is rare today that great discoveries in chemo-therapy are made by one man, as so many of the problems which arise in the development of new drugs need to be solved by specialists working in different fields. The recognition by Sir Alexander Fleming of penicillin as an antibiotic was only the beginning of the long, and at times baffling, search to find means of isolating, purifying and concentrating the drug.

The mycologist by his study of fungi; the biologist by his appreciation of all questions concerning the growth and behaviour of organism; the biochemist by his detailed knowledge and experience of methods of handling sensitive natural products; the bacteriologist by his study of the effect of penicillin on the growth of disease-causing bacteria and, lastly, the doctor by his clinical tests; all these working as a team made possible the commercial production of penicillin.

Frequently the chemist has to examine hundreds, sometimes thousands, of different chemicals before he finds the one which gives the required results. Paul Erhlich, the great German chemist, prepared and tested 606 arsenic compounds before he found one that was really effective against syphilis. His drug, known as Salvarsan, was also called 606. One of the outstanding triumphs of chemistry is the manufacture of an ever-increasing range of drugs required by the doctor in his fight against disease. Since the beginning of the twentieth century the chemist has been producing man-made remedies as distinct from those extracted from plant and animal sources.

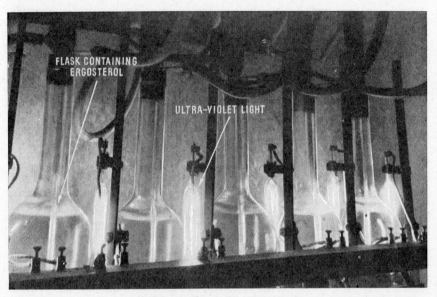

MANUFACTURE OF VITAMIN D

Ergosterol is present in yeast, moulds and diseased rye seed, called ergot, and when subjected to irradiation with ultra-violet light produces vitamin D. This vitamin is known as a fat-soluble vitamin, and usually occurs with vitamin A. Vitamin D is usually given to persons suffering from rickets.

Today a very large number of drugs are being made which have a specific action against disease-causing bacteria and yet are not dangerously poisonous to patients under treatment. In addition, there are chemicals able to dull pain, vitamins and other necessary food-enriching substances, anæsthetics, antiseptics, insecticides, and fungicides. Many of the new medicinal chemicals are derived by synthesis from coal-tar, but there are still quite a large number which are isolated by the chemist from substances of natural origin. When Banting and Best isolated insulin in 1922 a great step was made in the treatment of diabetes. Today several new forms of insulin extracted from the pancreas of various animals have been introduced as the result of research work carried out by

GAS-MASK TO PROTECT OPERATOR
FROM OBNOXIOUS FUMES

STAGE IN THE PROCESSING OF VITAMIN B₁

An important and unpleasant stage in the synthesis of vitamin B_1 is the introduction of sulphur into its molecular structure, and the workers wear gas-masks for protection from noxious fumes which are generated during this stage of the process. The operation is carried out in a separate and specially ventilated building.

medical men and chemists. Some of the new insulin compounds make use of zinc combined with insulin.

In the modern production of drugs for the hospital dispensary and home medicine cupboard, the manufacture invariably calls for considerable technical skill and the closest scientific control so as to ensure the highest possible standard of purity and uniformity. In some cases, such as the growth of moulds to give penicillin, streptomycin, chloromycetin and other antibiotics, the biologist works closely with the chemist in the development of satisfactory techniques which are later translated into works practice by the chemical engineer. Team work has frequently been responsible for overcoming apparently insuperable difficulties.

MANUFACTURE OF SYNTHETIC VITAMINS

Contrary to the general opinion of most people, vitamins have been known for some hundreds of years, although it is only within the present century that some of them have been isolated from foods such as natural fats and fruits, and their chemical equivalents produced in the laboratory. There are today some thirty-one vitamins and what are known as pro-vitamins, or substances which the body itself converts into vitamins.

The importance of vitamins in nutrition is now fully recognized. Experiments carried out over long periods conclusively show that unless the proper vitamins are present in the diet there is a grave risk of deficiency diseases. Scurvy was a common complaint on the old sailing ships, which were without fresh vegetables and fruit for long periods, although often the sailors were supplied with a plentiful supply of bread, pickled pork, and other foods. This diet was, however, deficient in the necessary vitamin C, found in vegetables and the juice of several fruits, notably the citrus fruits, which was able to give immunity against scurvy. There are many other well-known complaints which can be traced directly to deficiencies of certain vitamins in the diet. In many parts of the world rickets is very prevalent among children and this is caused by a deficiency of vitamin D, found in fish oils, cream, butter and milk. The dreaded disease, beri-beri, is brought on by living on a diet of polished rice which lacks the vitamin B, found in the husks. Another vitamin, vitamin K, is known to play a vital part in the coagulation of the blood and a deficiency of this vitamin is extremely serious, particularly during surgical operations, when wounds are required to heal quickly. Vitamin K is found in several plant sources but the doctor now uses synthetic substitutes made from coal-tar chemicals.

In the modern chemical laboratory no effort is spared to determine the identity of natural vitamins and then to develop methods of producing the vitamin itself or active substitutes from readily available chemicals. The biologist also works closely with the chemist in evolving methods of testing the potency and concentration of vitamins in various preparations.

Some vitamins are single substances, while others are complex mixtures of different compounds, most of which are known to play a part in nutrition.

Vitamin A, which is present in many oils and fats and milk, has been isolated, identified, and prepared synthetically. Chemists have shown it to be closely allied to the substance carotene, which is present in carrots, spinach and broccoli tops, etc. From experiments carried out it is accepted that carotene, sometimes known as the precursor of vitamin A, is converted by the body into this vitamin. Indeed, we obtain more vitamin A from carotene than is present in the vitamin A containing foods we consume. The main contribution made by the chemist to our knowledge of this vitamin has been a more thorough understanding of its chemical constitution, but so far it has not been possible to manufacture large quantities of the synthetic vitamin. The most potent of the natural vitamin A preparations is halibut oil, one drop of which contains 3,200 international units of the vitamin. A deficiency of vitamin A in the diet is responsible for a general lowering of the body's resistance to disease, particularly such ailments as common colds and bronchitis. Vitamin B is frequently referred to as the vitamin B complex, on account of the fact that it is a mixture of at least eight different substances—aneurin, riboflavin, nicotinic acid, pyridoxin, biotin, folic acid, p-amino-benzoic acid, and panthothenic acid. Vitamin B_1, or aneurin, is probably the best known of the B constituents, as its absence from the diet leads to beri-beri. Aneurin, or thiamine, is prepared in the laboratory from derivatives of coal-tar and is the equivalent both chemically and physiologically of the naturally occurring vitamin B_1, which is present in rice husks, as well as in many other forms, including yeast, wheat germ, bacon, whole meal, and egg yolk. Although beri-beri is practically unknown in Great Britain, various forms of vitamin B_1 deficiency are known and identified. They can all be cured by adequate dosage with vitamin B_1 concentrates which are produced as tablets and pills for taking by the mouth. It can also be used for enriching white bread.

COMPOSITION OF VITAMIN B

Vitamin B_2, or riboflavin, is really a yellow pigment found in all plant and animal tissues, but now made synthetically by the chemist. Its absence in diet is known to cause many ill-defined ailments, and an adequate amount of the vitamin is essential to good health. The third constituent of the vitamin B complex is nicotinic acid, which the chemist is able to produce fairly easily and to make available to doctors for the prompt treatment of deficiency diseases, such as pellagra, due to lack of the vitamin in the staple food. Incidentally, pellagra, which is a serious wasting disease, is particularly prevalent where maize is one of the main foods. Knowledge about the other vitamin B compounds is still incomplete, but it is known that they do play a part in nutrition and that their presence in foodstuffs is necessary for continued good health and the building up of resistance to disease.

The anti-scurvy vitamin known as C has been identified as the relatively simple chemical, ascorbic acid. In nature the acid is present in both plant and animal tissues, particularly citrus fruits such as oranges. When prepared in the laboratory the pure acid is a white, odourless, crystalline powder which is freely soluble in water. Doctors have reported that a deficiency of vitamin C in the diet shows itself in many different ways, among the more serious are lowered resistance to the attacks of disease and slowness of healing of wounds.

VITAMINS D, E AND K

Vitamin D is an active health-promoting agent present in fish-liver oils which also contain vitamin A. It is made synthetically by exposing certain natural fatty substances, known as sterols, to ultra-violet light. There are at least two distinct chemical substances with vitamin D activity, and there are probably more. Their chemical constitution is known. The vitamin is commonly known as the anti-rachitic vitamin and is a cure for rickets. Unless adequate quantities of it are present in the diet, many forms of chronic ill-health are liable to become evident.

These substances have been isolated by chemists and found to possess vitamin E activity, and are called tocopherols. This vitamin is known to be widely distributed in nature, particularly in cereal grains, green leaves, and nuts. The richest natural source of the vitamin is wheat germ oil. Man-made equivalents have been prepared with the same activity as the natural tocopherols. Medical opinion is somewhat divided about the value of vitamin E in the treatment of various disorders, but some authorities consider that a deficiency of E has serious effects on the muscular and cardiac vascular systems.

Vitamin K is claimed to be responsible for the clotting of blood, and its presence in food contributes towards the rapid healing of wounds. Chemists have been able to identify and isolate the active constituents of vitamin K, which is present in large quantities in alfalfa. There are several synthetic substitutes which are now being produced in quantity for use by the medical profession.

AMINO ACIDS IN NUTRITION

It has been realized for a number of years that all dietary proteins, such as meat, fish, and eggs, are broken down inside the body to comparatively simple substances known as amino acids. These are used by the body for the building up of tissue proteins. Doctors have shown that the liberation of amino acids from proteins occurs within the intestinal tract and is an important phase of digestion. The products of protein digestion, mainly the simple breakdown substances amino acids, pass through the intestinal wall without change and are absorbed into the blood. From the blood stream the amino acids are removed by all the tissues of the body.

Specialists in nutrition have long considered that the use of pure amino acids would be of considerable value in the treatment of certain diseases. In addition to the natural formation of amino acids from proteins chemists have been able to produce a number in the laboratory, one of the simplest being glycine, which was first made in 1858 by treating bromacetic acid with ammonia.

DISTILLATION EQUIPMENT

ACID-RESISTING STONEWARE VESSELS

FINAL STAGE IN BUILDING UP VITAMIN B₁

The solution is concentrated in an evaporator which, owing to the highly corrosive nature of the substances taking part in the chemical reaction, usually termed reactants, is fitted with pure silver condenser tubes. The solution is then passed to crystallizers where the vitamin B₁ is precipitated with alcohol.

Today some twenty-one amino acids can be prepared synthetically, using a wide variety of raw materials, many of which can be traced back to derivatives of coal-tar.

The modern synthetic drug industry, which now embraces the manufacture of many hundreds of products, some wholly synthetic, others prepared from substances of natural origin, is essentially an off-shoot of the dye industry. Several dyes do, in fact, possess valuable medicinal proportions, for example, the azo dyestuff (prontosil rubrum) was the precursor of the sulpha drug sulphanilamide and other dyestuffs are well known in medicine as antiseptics.

MANUFACTURE OF M. & B. 693

The sulpha drugs are among the most important contributions made by chemistry to medicine and they have played a great part in the treatment of many illnesses. The sulphonamides are particularly powerful in the treatment of coccus infections: those diseases caused by the vicious little round germs which most frequently afflict mankind. Contrary to common belief, sulpha does not actually kill susceptible germs. It merely prevents those germs from multiplying, so that the body can fight infection on equal terms. Sulpha drugs produce exciting and almost miraculous results in many cases of staphylococcic and streptococcic infections, scarlet fever, puerperal fever, pneumonia, gonorrhœa and meningitis. The proper sulpha preparation has been efficiently used in many cases of mastoiditis, tonsillitis, sinusitis, eye infections, peritonitis, blood poisoning, frequently in conjunction with penicillin or other necessary measures.

It was in 1935 that the German chemist Gerhard Domazk found that a new dyestuff, a red azo colour, which he introduced into medicine under the name of prontosil was extremely effective against certain experimental streptococcic infections in mice. Later work by other scientists carried Domazk's researches a good deal farther and revealed the fact that a simple derivative of prontosil, sulphanilamide, was even more effective than the dye in the treatment of pneumonia, osteomyelitis, puerperal fever and meningitis. The explanation for this was that prontosil was itself partially broken down in the body to the more active sulphanilamide.

The introduction of sulphanilamide opened up a vast new field of synthetic life-saving drugs and laid the foundation of a new branch of medical science, chemo-therapy. After sulphanilamide came sulphapyridine, better known as M. & B. 693. This drug, which is easily soluble in water, can be readily crushed and dissolved in water or milk and is easily swallowed and absorbed in the body. It is today the recognized specific for pneumonia. Following in the same series is the drug sulphathiazole. This has some advantages over the other sulpha drugs for certain types of infections. Of the latest sulpha drugs mention should be made of sulphamerazine, sulphamethozine, and sulpha drazine, which, it is claimed, possess special properties and some advantages over the original sulphonamide compounds. Metallic sulphonamide, including silver salts, are being prepared,

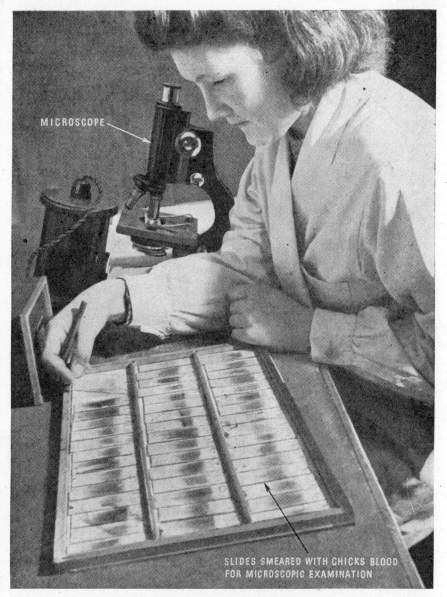

MICROSCOPE

SLIDES SMEARED WITH CHICKS BLOOD
FOR MICROSCOPIC EXAMINATION

FIGHTING THE MALARIA SCOURGE

The new drug Paludrine gives remarkable protection against infection from the malaria-carrying mosquito, and is many more times effective than quinine obtained from cinchona bark, which has for so long been the drug used to combat this scourge. An important fact is that a mosquito is unable to transmit malaria parasites from the blood of the person who has taken the drug. Above is shown an assistant microscopically examining glass slides smeared with chicks blood which has been treated with the drug to determine its effect.

and the sulphonamides are also being used with other chemicals. It is now realized that the efficacy of sulphonamides for dusting wounds and infections is improved by mixing them with urea and other allied chemicals. This technique was developed during the war and proved of great value in army casualty clearing stations and base hospitals. Sulphonamides are also used with penicillin for similar purposes. The sulpha drugs fill a great need in medical science and place at the disposal of the doctor a safe and efficient means of fighting the germs responsible for such infectious diseases as meningitis, gonorrhœa, blood infections, pneumonia, erysipelas, etc.

New methods of making the sulpha drugs are continually being developed and one of the most interesting is their production from aniline made from coal-tar benzene. The aniline is converted into the chemical formanilide, which is then sulphonated with chlorosulphonic acid and the resulting compound treated with ammonia to form sulphanilamide, the original member of the group.

THE CONQUEST OF MALARIA

The discovery of the anti-malarial drug Paludrine in 1945 brought to a triumphant close a chapter in British research which opened in 1856. In that year the great English chemist, William Henry Perkin, then only eighteen years old, began experimenting with coal-tar in an effort to synthesize quinine, at that time the only specific for malaria. It is a matter of history now that Perkin's search ended in failure, but in his experiments he stumbled upon a substance, mauveine, which in turn led to the discovery of the vast range of synthetic dye-stuffs we know today.

To appreciate the full significance of Paludrine it is necessary to realize the position of anti-malarial drugs in pre-war days. Until recent years, the only specific of real value was quinine. This is a natural product extracted from cinchona bark. During the last thirty-five years, however, chemists in many countries have been trying to evolve chemical compounds of their own to combat malaria. Their efforts eventually resulted in the discovery of such drugs as pamaquin (plasmoquin) and mepacrine (atebrin). Neither of these quite achieved their objective.

There are three requirements of the perfect anti-malarial drug. First, a regular small dose taken while in a malarious region must give complete protection against infection; that is, the parasites introduced into the bloodstream by the mosquito's bite must be destroyed before they can develop and produce a fever; secondly, it must control the fever when it has developed in an unprotected person; thirdly, it must prevent relapses by destroying every parasite.

The most dangerous is malignant tertian. The fever it produces is severe and frequently fatal, but there is no recurrence if it is cured. Benign tertian is not so dangerous, but it is persistent. The fever may be cured, but it can recur again and again through the years.

Against malignant tertian, quinine and mepacrine are of little value as pre-

EXAMINATION OF MOSQUITOES

Mosquitoes being sucked into a glass tube prior to being examined for malarial infection. They are bred in an insectarium which is maintained at a high temperature and humidity to simulate tropical conditions.

ventives, but the actual fever can be controlled by a suitable dose of either drug. In the case of benign tertian, quinine and mepacrine prevent the parasites developing, but do not entirely destroy them. In other words, if a person who has once been infected stops taking the drug he is liable to develop a fever as the parasites again multiply. Quinine and mepacrine are, therefore, of limited value as anti-malarial drugs, and pamaquin, though in some respects more powerful, is extremely dangerous to use.

The discoverers of the drug Paludrine broke fresh ground in their quest. Mepacrine and pamaquin are related chemically to quinine, and this class of compound has been examined to the point of exhaustion. They therefore began, in 1943, a painstaking examination of compounds hitherto unexplored for anti-malarial activity. The team consisted of two young chemists, Doctors F. H. S. Curd and F. L. Rose, and Doctor D. G. Davey, a biologist. While the chemists were exploring new fields, the biologist was assessing the worth of the resulting compounds with the aid of novel methods which he had devised for the purpose. It was this close collaboration between chemist and biologist which alone made success possible. Many compounds had to be worked out, tested, and rejected

163

before the goal was reached—in compound No. 4888, now known as Paludrine, and which has been found to give complete protection against malignant tertian malaria, the parasites being destroyed entirely before they can become established in the bloodstream. Volunteers who took as little as o. 1 gramme daily were bitten by as many as two hundred infected mosquitoes without effect. With benign tertian, also, one tablet a day was sufficient to prevent any fever developing. Parasites could not be detected in the blood, and mosquitoes feeding on the blood of the volunteer failed to transmit infection to others.

The Australian experiments also confirmed that the new drug is able to control the actual fever in a malaria sufferer, the dose necessary being extremely small compared with mepacrine or quinine. Paludrine is, in fact, about ten times as powerful as quinine.

Finally, there is the question of relapses. Here no definite answer can yet be given. Relapses have occurred in some cases of benign tertian, but the results suggest that a single tablet of Paludrine taken once weekly will give complete protection, and eventually kill off the parasites in their entirety.

This, then, is the measure of Paludrine's success. In addition, it is non-toxic, has none of the objections associated with mepacrine treatment, and its cost—a point of surpassing importance to millions of impoverished sufferers—will be lower than either mepacrine or quinine. Most important of all is the fact that the mosquito is unable to transmit malaria parasites from the blood of a person taking Paludrine. Thus, the dread cycle of infection has at last been broken.

The formula of Paludrine has now been published in the *Annals of Tropical Medicine and Parasitology*. Paludrine is N_1-p-chlorophenyl-N_5-isopropylbiguanide. To the lay mind, this tends to make it appear as a highly complicated compound. In reality it is very simple—much simpler, in fact, than any antimalarial specific known hitherto.

ISOLATION AND PRODUCTION OF PENICILLIN

The development and production of the famous chemo-therapeutic agents, penicillin and streptomycin, owes a great deal to chemical science, the chemist making an outstanding contribution to the work carried out by the bacteriologist, biologist, and doctor. It was the application of chemical technology to a comparatively simple biological process, the growth of a mould, which made possible the isolation and purification of these precious life-saving drugs.

From 1928, when Professor Fleming of St. Mary's Hospital first noticed the lethal effect of the fungus on bacteria, several years were required to develop processes for the isolation, purification, and concentration of penicillin.

Penicillin is a substance which is produced in minute quantities during the growth of a mould. Moulds are plants which, like ordinary green plants, require food on which to thrive, so that the process of manufacture consists of growing the mould on nutrient liquid, and then extracting the penicillin.

The standard commercial method of making the drug is accomplished in

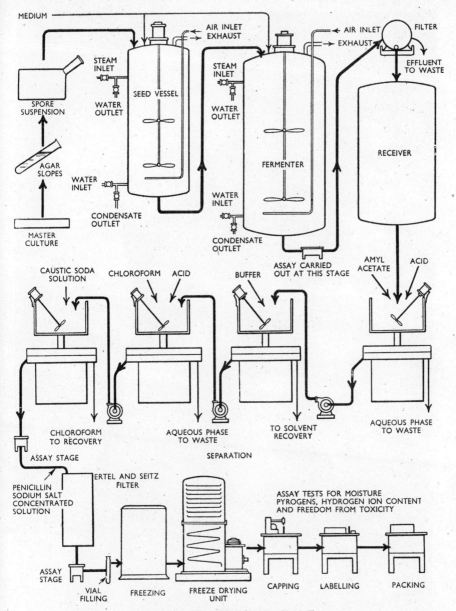

MEDIUM

AIR INLET
EXHAUST

AIR INLET
EXHAUST

FILTER

STEAM
INLET

SEED VESSEL

WATER
OUTLET

SPORE
SUSPENSION

STEAM
INLET

WATER
OUTLET

EFFLUENT
TO WASTE

AGAR
SLOPES

WATER
INLET

FERMENTER

RECEIVER

WATER
INLET

CONDENSATE
OUTLET

MASTER
CULTURE

CONDENSATE
OUTLET

ASSAY CARRIED
OUT AT THIS STAGE

CAUSTIC SODA
SOLUTION

CHLOROFORM   ACID

BUFFER

AMYL
ACETATE   ACID

CHLOROFORM
TO RECOVERY

AQUEOUS PHASE
TO WASTE

TO SOLVENT
RECOVERY

AQUEOUS PHASE
TO WASTE

ASSAY STAGE

SEPARATION

PENICILLIN
SODIUM SALT
CONCENTRATED
SOLUTION

ERTEL AND SEITZ
FILTER

ASSAY TESTS FOR MOISTURE
PYROGENS, HYDROGEN ION CONTENT
AND FREEDOM FROM TOXICITY

ASSAY
STAGE

VIAL
FILLING

FREEZING

FREEZE DRYING
UNIT

CAPPING

LABELLING

PACKING

LAY-OUT OF A PENICILLIN PLANT

After the penicillin has grown throughout the mould it is filtered off and the fluid is acidified and extracted with amyl acetate: the two solvents are well mixed and then separated in a centrifuge. The concentration and purification of the penicillin is further carried out by passing it back and forth between pairs of solvents. The final stage is freeze-drying, after which the vials are sealed off, labelled, packed and ready for immediate use.

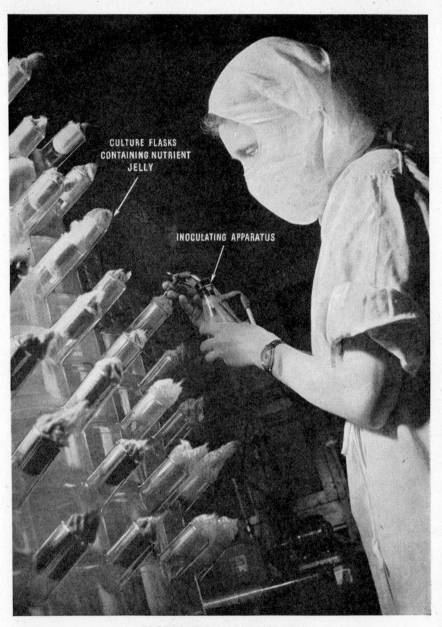

CULTURE FLASKS CONTAINING NUTRIENT JELLY

INOCULATING APPARATUS

PROPAGATION OF PENICILLIN

Wearing a protective face mask, a girl worker inoculates culture flasks containing a nutrient jelly in which penicillin is propagated. The spores germinate quickly, and give rise to still more spores which can be used when larger quantities of spore suspension are needed. The point at which spore suspension is introduced into the manufacturing process is shown in the flow chart on page 165.

several stages. First of all, nutrient or growing medium is prepared by dissolving sugar, mineral salts, and certain other chemicals in water. This liquor is sterilized and when cool sown with the spores of the mould. After a period of nine to ten days, when the temperature of the solution is kept at a steady 23 deg. C., the mould has covered the surface of the liquor and charged the solution with penicillin. Nowadays the same type of process is carried out in vats of 5,000 to

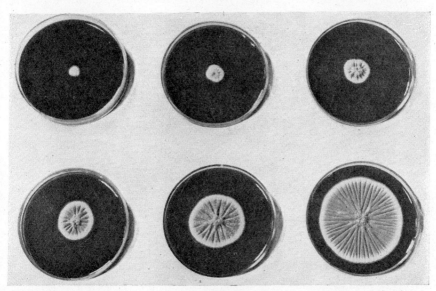

TEN DAYS IN THE LIFE OF A PENICILLIN MOULD

Specimens prepared by Professor Fleming of the mould from which penicillin is extracted, growing in culture dishes on agar-agar jelly, that is the nutrient on which the mould feeds during its growth. From top left to bottom right the rate and form of growth is shown from one to ten days.

10,000 gal., and by keeping the nutrient stirred the inoculuim of growing penicillium grows throughout the liquid. After about five days the mould is filtered off and the penicillin extracted with an organic solvent after acidifying. Then by making this extract alkaline and adding water, the pencillin is transferred again. Each time a reduction in volume and purification results. To recover this the nutrient is treated with a simple solvent which is able to dissolve the penicillin. It is then taken back into a watery solution and recovered by drying at the lowest possible temperature, actually by evaporation of ice from the frozen solution until the block of solid ice is gradually withdrawn to leave penicillin.

Penicillin has, indeed, proved to be a most remarkable drug. It has no toxic action upon the most delicate body tissues and is not weakened in action in the presence of blood, serum, or pus. Since it is powerfully effective against a wide variety of bacteria, including staphylococci, it is, from the doctor's point of view, performing miracles in the cure of infections. Burns which, in spite of treatment with sulpha drugs, became infected and caused death can now be readily healed. Compound fractures and many other types of injury which have become infected heal far more readily by the application of penicillin. The death rate from wounds and the number of amputations have been enormously reduced. Surgeons are now making use of dry penicillin powder mixed with one of the sulpha drugs, such as sulphathiazole. The powder is blown on to the wound with an insufflator. Penicillin in a medium that can be self-administered is being prepared in the form of ointments and creams, lozenges or pastilles, eye-drops and preparations for inhaling.

In the research laboratories of our universities and hospitals work has been going on unceasingly in the attempt to produce penicillin synthetically. This problem has, to a large extent, now been solved and the chemist now knows the chemical formula of the drug; moreover, it is possible to make certain kinds of penicillin synthetically, the process being a long and highly complicated one. It may well be that the future of these complex organic compounds will not be so much with the materials themselves as with their chemical modifications. This is the view of the discoverer of penicillin, Sir Alexander Fleming, who in the Lister Memorial Lecture, 1944, said: "There is still plenty of scope for the chemist to synthesize penicillin and then tinker with the molecule so that the present imperfections of penicillin can be remedied."

ISOLATION AND PRODUCTION OF STREPTOMYCIN

It is realized by scientists that we are only scratching the surface of the drugs produced from moulds of which countless thousands exist. Apart from penicillin, a number of other germ-killing substances have been isolated; the best of these are streptomycin, patulin, gramicidin, streptothricin, actinomycin, etc. The substances known as streptomycin and streptothricin are produced by two related organisms. The former drug offers the most promise and, although it is to some extent dwarfed by penicillin, it is important to recognize that it is valuable against certain disease bacteria which are not sensitive to penicillin. Streptomycin is produced from cultures of the mould *streptomyces griseus*, which grows abundantly in a special liquid consisting of 1 per cent glucose, 0·5 per cent peptone, 0·3 per cent meat extract or 1·2 per cent corn steep, and 0·5 per cent sodium chloride or common salt dissolved in water. The isolation of the streptomycin does not present such serious difficulties as in the case of penicillin. The crude streptomycin is absorbed into activated charcoal and removed from the charcoal by washing with acidified alcohol, which dissolves it. The solution is then neutralized by adding a little caustic soda. The addition of ten volumes of ether gives a highly concentrated aqueous solution of streptomycin, which is further concentrated by evaporation under reduced pressure.

Patulin, derived from yet another mould, is still under test; earlier claims that it was a cure for the common cold have not been fulfilled. The anti-biotic known as chloromycetin promises to be of great value to medicine, as it cures diseases which are immune to penicillin. Already success has been achieved by the use of chloromycetin in the treatment of typhus and typhoid fever, two diseases which hitherto have never responded to any drug. Hureomycin is able to attack some of the more deadly viruses.

Research work carried out by biologists and chemists has shown that not only micro-organisms, but also algæ and many flowery plants and animal products, produce small quantities of substances with inhibitory action on the growth of bacteria. Anti-biotics similar in some ways to penicillin have been produced from Spanish moss, from the petals of certain plants, from tomato plants, soya bean, garlic and many others. One of the most interesting of these is allicin, isolated from garlic, which has long been highly thought of as a medicinal product.

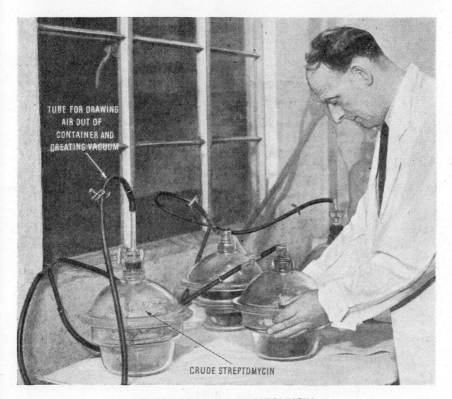

PRODUCTION OF STREPTOMYCIN

Drying off crude streptomycin under vacuum after precipitation of the acidified alcohol. The solution is then neutralized by an alkali, such as caustic soda. After-wards ether is added to form a highly concentrated aqueous solution which can be further concentrated by evaporation under pressure.

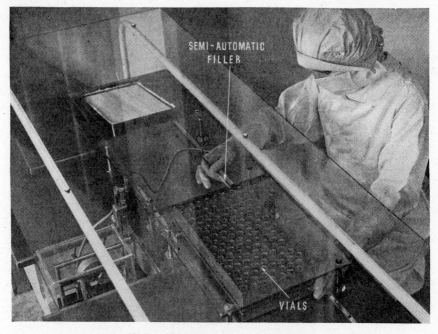

SEMI-AUTOMATIC FILLER

VIALS

SEMI-AUTOMATIC FILLING OF VIALS

After the penicillin solution has passed the assay stage it is filled in vials before passing to the freeze-drying plant, see the illustration on page 175.

In the development of drugs to fight against malaria, important new synthetic insecticides are now being employed to exterminate the disease-bearing mosquito. D.D.T. and Gammexane are the best known and most toxic of all chemicals selected for this purpose. These insecticides are being used for spraying large areas of swamp and bush infected with mosquitoes, and when properly applied, either by hand spraying or from aircraft, do destroy both larvæ and full-grown insects. Both D.D.T. and Gammexane are derivatives of coal-tar, and the latter chemical is made from benzene and chlorine and has the chemical name of benzene hexachloride. It is of interest to note that D.D.T. was first synthesized in 1874, but its insecticidal properties were not discovered until 1936, when the Swiss chemist, Paul Müller, investigated its properties.

The interesting fact about Gammexane, which is an all-British discovery dating back to 1942, is that its insecticidal properties are governed by the position of the chlorine atoms in the molecule. It is only when the chlorine atoms are in one particular position, known as the gamma position, that the chemical is highly toxic to insects, including such dangerous ones to man as mosquitoes and lice.

Important new advances have been made in the use of insecticides. Chemists have found that when D.D.T., Gammexane, and other chemicals, as well as the

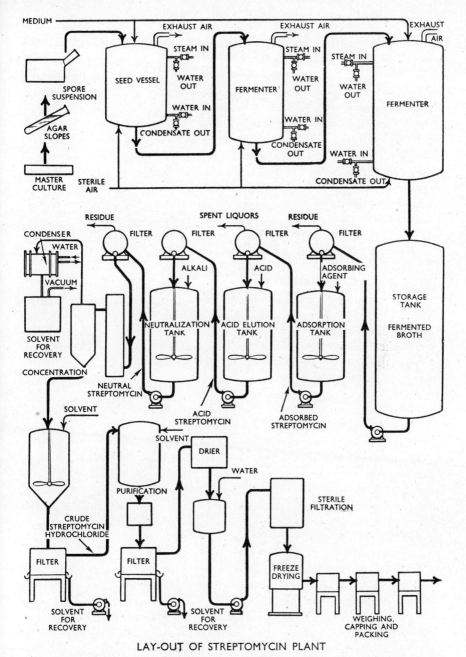

MEDIUM

EXHAUST AIR   EXHAUST AIR   EXHAUST AIR

STEAM IN   STEAM IN   STEAM IN

SEED VESSEL   WATER OUT   FERMENTER   WATER OUT   WATER OUT   FERMENTER

SPORE SUSPENSION   WATER IN   WATER IN   WATER IN

AGAR SLOPES   CONDENSATE OUT   CONDENSATE OUT   CONDENSATE OUT

MASTER CULTURE   STERILE AIR

RESIDUE   SPENT LIQUORS   RESIDUE

CONDENSER   FILTER   FILTER   FILTER   FILTER
WATER

VACUUM   ALKALI   ACID   ADSORBING AGENT   STORAGE TANK

SOLVENT FOR RECOVERY   NEUTRALIZATION TANK   ACID ELUTION TANK   ADSORPTION TANK   FERMENTED BROTH

CONCENTRATION

NEUTRAL STREPTOMYCIN

SOLVENT   ACID STREPTOMYCIN   ADSORBED STREPTOMYCIN

SOLVENT   DRIER

PURIFICATION   WATER   STERILE FILTRATION

CRUDE STREPTOMYCIN HYDROCHLORIDE

FILTER   FILTER   FREEZE DRYING

SOLVENT FOR RECOVERY   SOLVENT FOR RECOVERY   WEIGHING, CAPPING AND PACKING

LAY-OUT OF STREPTOMYCIN PLANT

Flow chart showing the chemical and physical processes in the large-scale manufacture of streptomycin, which is being increasingly used to attack disease bacteria that is immune to penicillin. It will be noted that the process is similar to that employed in the production of penicillin.

171

natural insecticides like pyrethrum and derris, are dissolved in certain liquefied gases, then release of the pressure exerted on the gas will cause the insecticide to be dispersed in the form of an exceedingly fine penetrating mist. Preparations of this kind are known today as ærosols. They are the most effective weapons known to science in the combat with harmful insects, fungi, and even certain disease germs known to be present in the air. Dichlorodifluoromethane, a gas made from fluorine, chlorine, and the simple carbon gas methane, is the most suitable liquefied gas for ærosols to be used against insects. The gas itself is non-toxic, non-inflammable, and non-explosive; moreover, the liquefied gas expands to two hundred and sixty times the volume it occupies in liquid form. It has been shown that a typical formula consisting of 20 per cent pyrethrins extracted from the pyrethrum flowers is several times more effective than the old type of fly spray, one pound of new ærosol is really more fatal to mosquitoes and common house-flies than two gallons of the ordinary fly spray.

GERM-DESTROYING COMPOUNDS

Many new chemicals are now being used as antiseptics in the modern hospital. One of the most interesting series of germ-destroying compounds is derived from ammonia and known as quaternary ammonium salts. Solutions of this type of chemical in water are odourless and colourless; moreover, they are non-poisonous and quite harmless to all metals and materials of construction. A 1–20,000 solution effects a 100 per cent kill on staphyllococcus aureous (bacteria responsible for septic conditions such as boils) in ten minutes.

In one minute this solution will kill 70 per cent of staph. aureous. In the same time, a 1–5,000 solution will kill 99·5 per cent of staph. aureous. This powerful germicide is used at various dilutions to cover the entire range of sterilizing, disinfecting, and deodorizing operations from surgical instruments to dishes and glassware; from inhibition of extreme putrefaction to control of slime and algæ in cooling water and swimming pools. Other important types of chemical antiseptics and disinfectants are based on phenol or carbolic acid and various chlorine-containing compounds such as sodium hypochlorite.

THE NEW ANÆSTHETICS

The older types of anæsthetics, such as ether, chloroform and nitrous oxide (laughing gas), are still widely used, but to them should be added a number of other chemicals capable of inducing anæsthesia. The chemist has so far prepared eight of these: ethyl chloride, vinyl ether, trichloroethylene, cyclopropane, pentothal, kemithan, procaine, and nupercaine. Most of them are fairly simple in composition and several consist of chlorinated compounds; for instance, the new anæsthetic trichloroethylene is made from two simple gases: ethylene, a derivative of petroleum or alcohol, and chlorine, obtained as a by-product in the manufacture of washing soda from common salt. The rapidly extending field of barbituric drugs are made from urea, a simple nitrogen chemical.

DETERMINING THE POWER OF STREPTOMYCIN

Filling cups on the test dishes with drops of streptomycin. The dishes contain jelly in which are planted microbes. These grow except around the cups where they come in contact with the streptomycin. The size of the ring is proportional to the strength of the streptomycin in the cup. One cup in every dish contains strepto-mycin of known strength, which is used to measure the others.

There is now a considerable number of drugs made from minerals and used in modern medicine, for example, arsenic and bismuth. The most famous of the arsenic compounds is the drug salvarsan. Today there is a large number of the so-called arsenicals and most of them are used in the treatment of syphilis, yaws, and relapsing fever. They are all highly toxic substances and have to be used with great care. Some of the bismuth chemicals find somewhat similar applications to the arsenicals and are, in many cases, recommended as an adjunct to the well-known arsphenamine treatment. In connexion with the use of arsenical drugs and also arsenic-containing gases, such as Lewisite, British chemists have found a remarkable antidote or chemical able to reduce its toxicity. This chemical is based on sulphur, which combines with the arsenic and renders it comparatively ineffective. The sulphur antidote was used with great success during the First World War in the treatment of persons attacked by Lewisite.

Mercury is another inorganic or mineral-derived substance which plays an important part in modern medicine, several salts of mercury being used in the treatment of various ailments. The best known is, of course, calomel or mercuric chloride, which is prescribed for certain complaints of the liver. Among the newest drugs made from mercury are those known as mersalyn, Neptal, Mercupurin, Novurit, and Esidrone, all of which are of great value for treating diseases of the heart and lungs. These mercury compounds are very dangerous drugs and need to be taken under the closest medical supervision.

Chemicals known as thiocyanates, which are derived from sulphur and prussic acid, one of the deadliest poisons known, are proving of value to the doctor. For the relaxation of the muscles in certain mental disorders potassium and sodium thiocyanate are of value, but as they are both highly poisonous it is necessary for the doctor to ensure that the thiocyanates are used with the greatest care.

NEW DRUGS FROM THE AIR

From ammonia made from the nitrogen of the air and hydrogen obtained from steam the chemist is able to produce a number of new synthetic drugs. One of these is thiouracil, made from urea, a simple chemical produced in very large quantities from ammonia and carbon dioxide, both of them gases. Thiouracil has proved very valuable for the treatment of diseases of the thyroid, leading to Graves's disease and other serious complications. Although not a cure for these complaints, it is proving of considerable help in reducing the activity of the thyroid gland, and in some cases it helps to overcome the need for serious operations. Apart from the use of thiouracil for treating diseases of the thyroid, it has also been prescribed for angina pectoris, which is an acute form of heart disease characterized by paroxysms of intense pain.

Other drugs based on urea are the life-saving sulphadiazine and the extensive range of barbituric compounds which give relief against pain.

HEPARIN, AN ANTI-COAGULANT

From animal sources many important new drugs are being obtained which are helping the doctor to gain a mastery over certain diseases. Some of these require the development of special techniques which call for the most exacting care and closest control by the biologist and chemist. Of interest is the new medicinal heparin (extracted from the liver) and used as an anti-coagulant in the treatment of coronary and cerebal thrombosis, that is, the coagulation of the blood, forming a true clot.

The isolation and purification of heparin from the liver calls for several chemical processes. First of all the heparin, which is a complex compound, is combined with barium and the barium salt is then treated with excess of ammonium carbonate to remove the barium. The heparin is then thrown out of solution by adding acetic acid, concentrated, washed with ether, and dried. Heparin is used as a sterile solution which is injected into a vein. Surgeons now

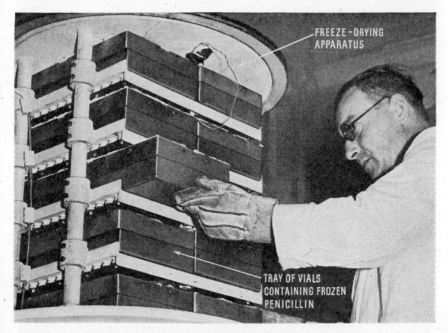

FREEZE-DRYING APPARATUS

The vials containing frozen penicillin solution are packed in racks over which the top half of the camber closes. The plant is then evacuated and the moisture is removed without raising the temperature above freezing point.

make use of this new drug for the prevention of blood clotting or thrombosis after serious operations. In those cases where hæmorrhage sets in during the heparin treatment, the original coagulation of the blood may be restored by injection of the drug protamine.

The hormones are excretions of certain glands, such as the thyroid or pituitary glands, which stimulate or retard certain natural functions of the body. New synthetic hormones, known as the synthetic œstrogens, have been produced by chemists for use by the medical profession for the treatment of certain types of cancer, particularly cancer of the prostate gland, which is fairly common complaint in men. It was in January, 1939, that the first reports were published about the synthetic hormone stilbœstrol, and during later years doctors throughout the world used it in the treatment of various diseases common to women as well as men. It is expected that the research work on hormones now proceeding in the laboratories of our great hospitals will add new synthetic hormones to the present restricted range, and it is certain that knowledge gained of the action of stilbœstrol will be of considerable value to scientists studying the cause and curative treatment of that most dreaded of all malignant diseases, cancer.

CONTROLLING THE GRID SYSTEM

The switching control room for south-east England, where instructions are issued for the operation of all the switches in the grid system in the area. The grid system, which is one of the finest distribution systems in the world, consists of over 3,600 miles of 132,000-volt lines and more than 1,500 miles of lower-voltage lines which span the areas the country is divided into for the purpose of control. The grid system is run by the Central Authority (and its fourteen local Divisions) of the British Electricity Authority. This Central Authority owns all the generating stations, and carries out the function of "wholesaler." The fourteen Area Boards buy the electric current from the Central Authority and then, acting in the capacity of "retailers," sell it to the consumers.

CHAPTER ⑥ Power in the modern age

___

WHEN we flick the knob of an electric-light switch in our homes we expect the electric bulb to respond immediately. Our hand torch, which brings us all the virtues of electric light in a form no bigger than a matchbox; the telephone, which enables us to communicate with any part of the world; radio and television providing a constant background to our lives, giving information and entertainment; all these have become absolute essentials. Yet only in 1889 was the first municipal supply of electricity installed at Bradford. The telephone was perfected by Graham Bell in 1876, but it only came into universal use at the turn of the century. Broadcasting began on a regular basis no earlier than 1922.

Although most of the principles underlying these daily essentials were known at least a hundred years ago, it is only quite recently that they have been brought into everyday use. Most of the electric current now generated is used for industrial purposes. The lighting load, once almost the sole outlet for the sale of electricity, has become a relatively small fraction of the total current generated.

HOW INDUSTRY RELIES ON ELECTRICITY

Consider a modern factory, concerned, for instance, with the manufacture of furniture, illustrated overleaf. It may have a number of lathes, automatic planing machines, circular saws and bandsaws, all driven by separate electric motors varying from 1 to 20 h.p. There may be electrically-heated gluepots, and suction pipes to collect sawdust, also depending on electric power to drive them. For lifting large baulks of timber there may be an electrically operated crane. For spraying woodwork, compressed air is needed, and electric motors drive the compressors. To facilitate drying, the furniture may pass through tunnels in which infra-red rays, electrically produced, dry the finishing coats like magic; and the moving platforms will also need electrical energy. The workshop must be heated for the comfort of the workers, and these days good electric lighting is essential. Apart from general lighting in the roof, individual lights may be required in various positions. We have not finished yet. Air-conditioning is also electrically operated. There may be "Music While You Work" from loud-speakers and, obviously, electrical energy is needed for the radio set and the large

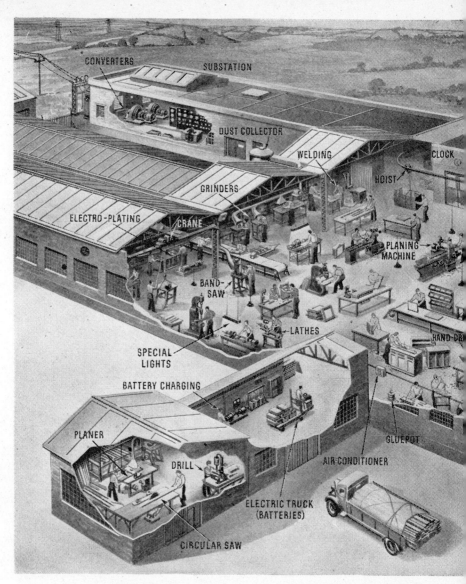

Labels on the illustration: CONVERTERS, SUBSTATION, DUST COLLECTOR, WELDING, CLOCK, HOIST, GRINDERS, ELECTRO-PLATING, CRANE, PLANING MACHINE, BAND-SAW, LATHES, HAND-DR—, SPECIAL LIGHTS, BATTERY CHARGING, PLANER, GLUEPOT, DRILL, AIR-CONDITIONER, ELECTRIC TRUCK (BATTERIES), CIRCULAR SAW

THE APPLICATIONS OF ELECTRIC

This sectional drawing of a modern furniture factory serves to illustrate the multitudinous uses of electric power in industry. All the machines, that is, wood-turning lathes, planing machines, circular saws and bandsaws, etc., are driven by independent electric motors varying from 1 to 20 h.p. Lifting tackle for handling baulks of timber is electrically operated. To facilitate drying, the furniture is passed through infra-red rays. For the comfort of the workers, the workshops are heated electrically, and lighted with normal bulb and fluorescent lighting. Air-conditioning apparatus, so necessary in a factory where wood dust is present, is

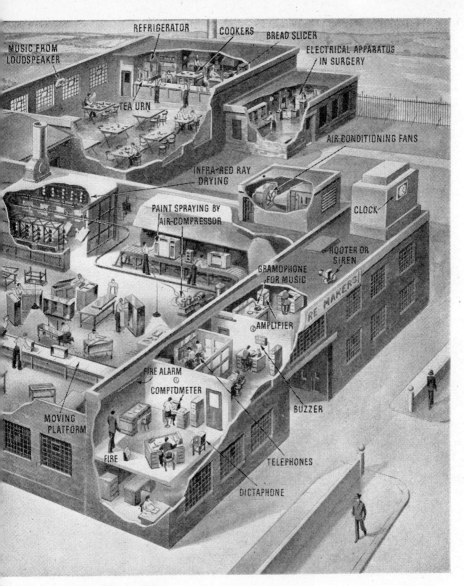

Labels on illustration: MUSIC FROM LOUDSPEAKER — REFRIGERATOR — COOKERS — BREAD SLICER — ELECTRICAL APPARATUS IN SURGERY — TEA URN — AIR-CONDITIONING FANS — INFRA-RED RAY DRYING — PAINT SPRAYING BY AIR-COMPRESSOR — CLOCK — GRAMOPHONE FOR MUSIC — HOOTER OR SIREN — AMPLIFIER — FIRE ALARM — COMPTOMETER — BUZZER — MOVING PLATFORM — FIRE — TELEPHONES — DICTAPHONE

POWER IN A MODERN FACTORY

electrically operated. Electrical energy is required to operate the radio sets and amplifiers with which modern factories are equipped. In the offices such equipment as comptometers, duplicators, dictaphones, telephones, etc., require minute quantities of electrical energy. Even this is not the end of the story, for in the kitchens which supply the workers' canteen, electricity is used for heating water, for cooking, and for a variety of electrical labour-saving machines which are familiar items of equipment in the modern kitchen. In this factory the power is tapped from the grid mains and not generated in an independent power station.

central amplifier. The internal telephone exchange which provides communication all round the works depends on the mains for its power supply; electric clocks, fire or burglar alarms will add to power consumption.

In the offices, electric power drives the comptometers and duplicators. A dictaphone needs a tiny motor, and even the bells which summon secretaries require minute quantities of electrical energy.

A canteen will impose a considerable demand on the mains, with its large cooking range, water-heaters, potato-peelers, refrigerators, and bread slicers.

Industry depends at every turn on electrical energy, just as the ordinary citizen needs electricity day and night. In the home; in places of entertainment (as an example, the cinema today is entirely dependent on electrical energy); for travelling; indeed for every purpose, electrical energy has, directly or indirectly, become indispensable in a modern civilized community.

FIRST PRINCIPLES OF ELECTRICITY

While there are several methods of generating electrical energy for domestic and industrial uses, the dynamo driven by steam, oil, gas, or water-power is by far the most commonly used.

The dynamo was made possible by the research of Michael Faraday (1791-1867), who discovered the principles of the relation between electricity and magnetism. The existence of the magnet and many of its properties had been known for centuries before Faraday's time. In the electrical field, however, little was known of what was called the "electric fluid," other than its manifestations in the form of "static." An example of the electrical experiments which had been made up to that time was the "electrifying" of glass rod by rubbing it on silk, so that it would pick up small particles of paper and fluff.

Faraday discovered that between the poles of a magnet, the familiar horseshoe type makes a good example, there are "lines of magnetic force." By holding a magnet beneath a piece of paper covered with finely divided iron filings, and tapping the paper gently, anyone can see that the "lines of force" take shape among the particles of iron.

He then experimented with inserting other materials into the magnetic field (the area covered by the lines of force). He found that if any conductor of electricity, for instance, a copper wire, is inserted, and then moved about so as to cut the invisible lines, an electric voltage is induced in it. For an electric current to flow it must have a closed circuit. Faraday made his first dynamo by using a simple loop of wire on a spindle, which he revolved between the poles of a magnet. By means of metal rings, on an insulated bush, the voltage generated was carried away to complete the circuit and to perform such work as lighting a lamp.

Faraday, however, progressed far beyond this stage. He discovered the laws governing the relationship between electricity and magnetism. He found, among other things, that the faster the conductor was moved, the higher the voltage produced. He also followed up the discoveries of Oersted and others, who had

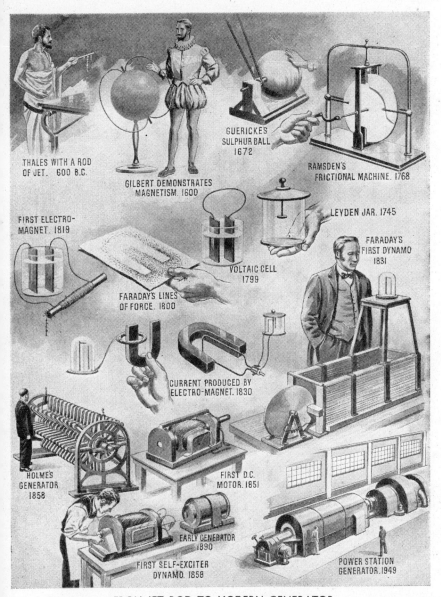

THALES WITH A ROD OF JET. 600 B.C.

GILBERT DEMONSTRATES MAGNETISM. 1600

GUERICKE'S SULPHUR BALL 1672

RAMSDEN'S FRICTIONAL MACHINE. 1768

FIRST ELECTRO-MAGNET. 1819

LEYDEN JAR. 1745

FARADAY'S FIRST DYNAMO 1831

VOLTAIC CELL 1799

FARADAY'S LINES OF FORCE. 1800

CURRENT PRODUCED BY ELECTRO-MAGNET. 1830

HOLMES GENERATOR 1858

FIRST D.C. MOTOR. 1851

EARLY GENERATOR 1890

FIRST SELF-EXCITER DYNAMO. 1858

POWER STATION GENERATOR.1949

FROM JET ROD TO MODERN GENERATOR

The main stages in the development of man's knowledge of the fundamental principles of electricity and magnetism and how they have been applied to generate electric power. Although the phenomenon of magnetism was observed in ancient times, very little attention was given to it and no material advance of knowledge was made until the end of the sixteenth century. From that time onwards steady progress attended the efforts of those who experimented in the fields of electricity and magnetism to discover its nature and uses.

already found that when a coil of wire carried an electric current it became a magnet. In the same year that Oersted (1820) made his discoveries, Arago and Davy observed a similar phenomenon on a piece of unmagnetized iron. The following year Schweizzer found that the magnetic effect was increased by passing the current through a number of turns of wire. It should be noted that Ampère conducted experiments to demonstrate some of the laws of electromagnetism, as did Sturgeon in 1825, and Henry in 1828. All this paved the way for the machine which is the complement to the dynamo, the electric motor.

MEANS OF GENERATING ELECTRICITY

Although all commercial supplies of electrical energy come from dynamos (or, as the modern large sizes are called, *alternators*, since they generate alternating current), there are other means available, and each has its special use.

At the end of the eighteenth century, Volta, an Italian philosopher, had discovered that when plates of dissimilar metals were placed in a solution of salt a slight electric current was generated. This was the foundation of the primary battery, which is now used for such applications as the hand torch and for radio high-tension batteries. Electricity generated in this fashion is expensive. For example, to light a house by primary batteries would cost about four shillings a unit, and they would need constant renewal.

If the junction of two dissimilar metals is heated, a minute voltage is generated, provided the remote ends of the metal bars are kept cool. This method of generating electricity, called the thermo-couple, is used mainly in the field of electric measurement.

Certain materials have the property of causing minute currents to flow when light is thrown upon them. This phenomenon is the basis of the photo-electric cell and is described in detail in Chapter 8.

In short, there are electro-chemical means (the battery), electro-thermal means, and photo-electric methods of generating electricity; but none of these is of commercial significance as a large-scale power source. The electromagnetic method remains supreme so far as industry is concerned.

COMMERCIAL PRODUCTION OF ELECTRICITY

As a consequence of the demands of industry, the dynamo began to develop from the rudimentary machine constructed by Faraday. First of all, devices were found to produce direct current, that is, current which flows steadily from one pole, through the circuit, and back to the other pole. A loop of wire, revolving in a magnetic field, does not produce a current of this sort, because, as Faraday set out in his laws of the relation between electricity and magnetism, when a wire cuts the magnetic "flux" *downwards*, a voltage is generated in one direction; but when it cuts the lines of force *upwards*, the voltage is reversed. Thus there are two reversals for every revolution. By means of a device called a commutator, these reversals can be again reversed as they happen. Thus, it will be seen that

ALTERNATOR
GOVERNOR
EXCITER WHICH MAGNETIZES ROTATING PART, PERMITTING IT TO GENERATE CURRENT IN THE STATOR
OIL PRESSURE RECEIVER FOR THE OIL-OPERATED VALVES WHICH GOVERN THE TURBINE
WATER TURBINE BELOW THIS LEVEL

INTERIOR OF HYDRO-ELECTRIC POWER PLANT

The alternators shown above are driven by reaction turbines, which are a highly developed form of primitive water-wheel; see the sectional drawing of this design of turbine on page 198. This type of turbine is used for heads of water of low or medium height; for a higher head an impulse turbine is employed. It has been calculated that the world's potential water-power is 667,000,000 h.p. In Great Britain and Northern Ireland there already exists plant generating about 550,000 h.p. and it has been estimated that an additional 700,000 h.p. might be brought into service. These figures do not include tidal forces, although plans for tapping this huge source of energy have been under active consideration for some years.

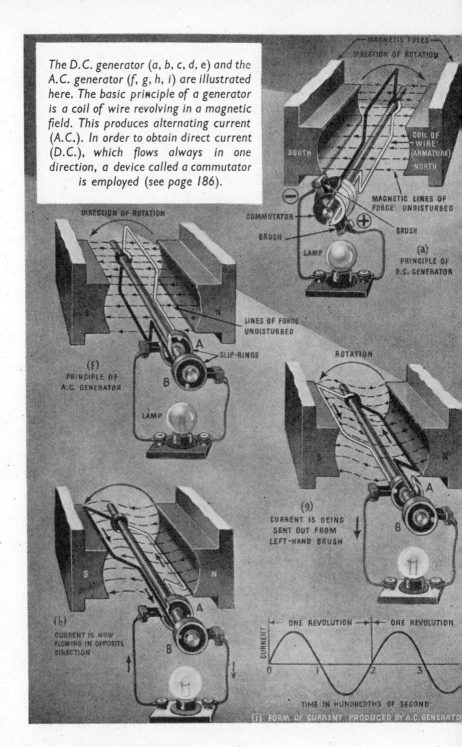

The D.C. generator (a, b, c, d, e) and the A.C. generator (f, g, h, i) are illustrated here. The basic principle of a generator is a coil of wire revolving in a magnetic field. This produces alternating current (A.C.). In order to obtain direct current (D.C.), which flows always in one direction, a device called a commutator is employed (see page 186).

MAGNETIC POLES
DIRECTION OF ROTATION

COIL OF WIRE (ARMATURE)

SOUTH

NORTH

MAGNETIC LINES OF FORCE UNDISTURBED

COMMUTATOR

BRUSH

BRUSH

LAMP

(a)
PRINCIPLE OF D.C. GENERATOR

DIRECTION OF ROTATION

S

N

LINES OF FORCE UNDISTURBED

A

SLIP-RINGS

(f)
PRINCIPLE OF A.C. GENERATOR

B

LAMP

ROTATION

S

N

A

(g)
CURRENT IS BEING SENT OUT FROM LEFT-HAND BRUSH

B

S

N

A

(h)
CURRENT IS NOW FLOWING IN OPPOSITE DIRECTION

B

ONE REVOLUTION | ONE REVOLUTION

CURRENT

0   1   2   3

TIME IN HUNDREDTHS OF SECOND

(i) FORM OF CURRENT PRODUCED BY A.C. GENERATOR

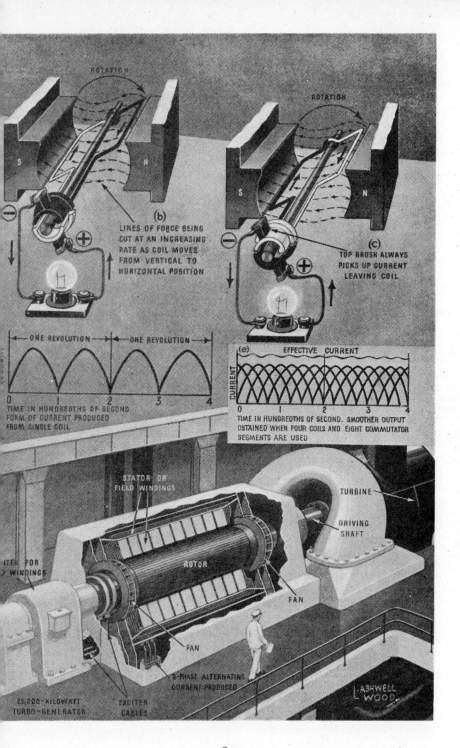

ROTATION

(b)
LINES OF FORCE BEING
CUT AT AN INCREASING
RATE AS COIL MOVES
FROM VERTICAL TO
HORIZONTAL POSITION

S   N

ROTATION

(c)
TOP BRUSH ALWAYS
PICKS UP CURRENT
LEAVING COIL

S   N

← ONE REVOLUTION → ← ONE REVOLUTION →

0   1   2   3   4
TIME IN HUNDREDTHS OF SECOND
FORM OF CURRENT PRODUCED
FROM SINGLE COIL

(e)   EFFECTIVE CURRENT

CURRENT

0   1   2   3   4
TIME IN HUNDREDTHS OF SECOND. SMOOTHER OUTPUT
OBTAINED WHEN FOUR COILS AND EIGHT COMMUTATOR
SEGMENTS ARE USED

STATOR OR
FIELD WINDINGS

TURBINE

DRIVING
SHAFT

ITER FOR
) WINDINGS

ROTOR

FAN

FAN

3-PHASE ALTERNATING
CURRENT PRODUCED

25,000-KILOWATT
TURBO-GENERATOR

EXCITER
CABLES

L. ASHWELL
WOOD.

185

a current is produced at the terminals which is always in the same direction. Developments which followed enormously increased the power output of the dynamo. The first was to increase the strength of the magnet by making it in the form of an electro-magnet. This consists primarily of a coil of wire wound round an iron core. The strength of the flux, or magnetic field, could thus be increased, and the field varied at will in order to control the output. With this development came the winding of the armature, or rotating part, with many coils, to increase the number of times the flux-lines were cut in one revolution.

THE ELECTRIC POWER GENERATOR

The principle of the generator is illustrated on pages 184-5. In the A.C. (alternating current) generator (f, g, h) the induced current is collected by the slip-rings *A*, *B*, and this current changes direction, or alternates, according to the speed of the wire coil. The form of current produced is shown at (i). The D.C. (direct current) generator (a, b, c) has a device called a commutator instead of slip-rings, and this produces a current which flows always in the same direction. The result of smoothing D.C. current by using four coils and eight commutator segments is shown at (d) and (e).

For the large-scale generation and distribution of power for industrial and domestic uses it is usual to produce alternating current. The reason for this is that alternating current can easily be transformed up or down in voltage, which greatly facilitates transmitting power over long distances. The modern large-scale dynamo can, therefore, dispense with the commutator, and deliver its current in the alternating form in which it is generated. Owing to the difficulties of connecting to the armature, however, when the voltage is high, the roles of the moving part (the rotor) and the stationary portion (the stator) are reversed. This means that the magnetic field is the revolving part, and its lines of force are swept round to cut the stationary conductors.

Imagine three simple alternators, each with a simple loop, disposed one behind the other on a long shaft, and driven by an engine at one end. It will be appreciated that all three will generate exactly the same voltage alternations. If the second loop is moved round by 120 deg., and the third by 240 deg., it will be realized that the alternations of voltages will follow one another in sequence, equally spaced at 120 deg. round a circle.

If all three simple alternators were combined in one machine, three separate voltage waves in each revolution would be produced. This is now common practice, since in this way the greatest output can be obtained from one size of generator, and the greatest amount of power can be transmitted across the three wires which carry three-phase current.

The alternators in our great power stations will generate a voltage varying from 6,600 volts to 33,000 volts on the three-phase system. The frequency of alternation is standardized in Britain at 50 cycles per second. In America it is 60 cycles. The largest alternators in Great Britain are of 100,000-kW capacity, which need about 134,000 h.p. to drive them, but 60,000-kW installations are more usual and there are very many 30,000-kW sets in operation. To appreciate the enormity of the figures, it may be a useful comparison to realize that a one-bar electric radiator consumes 1 kW; thus a set of the largest size would supply 100,000 such radiators.

The alternators used in modern power stations are usually driven by a steam turbine. Early dynamos were driven by reciprocating steam engines of the type now seen mainly on railway locomotives, but the limits of power, and more especially speed, were soon reached with reciprocating machinery. Present-day alternators revolve at 3,000 r.p.m. If alternators must be driven by relatively slow-speed devices, such as Diesel engines and water-wheels, they can be specially designed to do so with great efficiency, but the cost and space occupied are considerably greater than in the case of the high-speed sets.

SOURCES OF POWER

We have seen that to generate electrical energy in the modern large-scale sense a prime mover or motive power is needed which will rotate a shaft, and to rotate this shaft power must be applied. What are the sources from which this power is derived? In the main they are three in number, coal, water and oil. Placed in that order, they represent the main sources used in generating the world's electric power.

In Great Britain, coal is by far the most important fuel used for the generation of electric power. Plant generating no less than 11,540,190 kW derives its energy from the combustion of coal.

It takes approximately 1·42 lb. of coal to produce one unit of electricity. Each pound of coal has a calorific value of about 11,000 B.Th.U. It would, therefore, if burnt under theoretically perfect conditions, raise the temperature of 11,000 lb. of water by 1 deg. The average thermal efficiency, the amount of electrical energy produced in a power station for the consumption of a given amount of fuel as compared with the amount theoretically possible by using all the heat in the coal, is now about 30 per cent for the most efficient stations. Thus there is still a great challenge to power-station engineers; the challenge to find means to utilize the amount, roughly two-thirds, of the heat from the coal now wasted up the chimney and in the cooling water.

Experts consider that the limit of efficiency of the present method of coal burning in power stations is about 40 per cent. There are researches in progress, in Britain and in America, to use coal, in a very finely powdered form, directly in a gas turbine, without the intervention of steam and its associated boilers and condensers.

Coal, of course, has to be burnt, and its heat cannot be directly applied to the creation of the rotating form of power needed for electrical energy. An intermediary has to be used, something which will expand or contract with the application of heat, and this, in practically all cases, is water vapour or steam.

GOVERNOR AND CONTROL VALVES

LOW-PRESSURE TURBINE

HIGH-PRESSURE TURBINE

CONDENSER

COOLING TUBES

UTILIZING THE POWER

This cut-away drawing shows how steam generated in a high-pressure boiler impinges on the rotor blades fitted round the circumference of the high-pressure and low-pressure turbine wheels and drives the rotor. The steam is generated in boilers, and often a temperature as high as 850 deg. F. at 1,000 lb. per sq. in. is

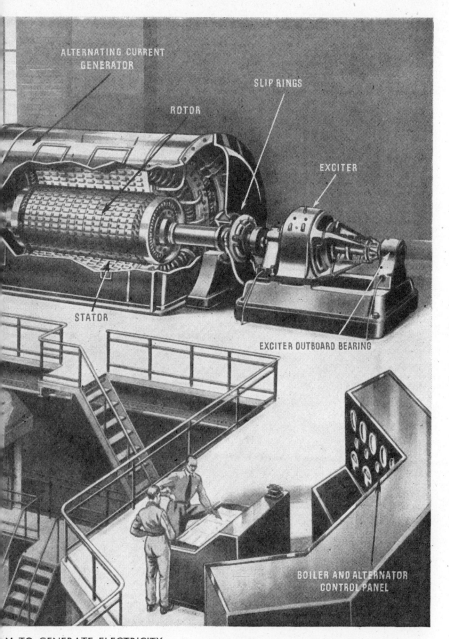

ALTERNATING CURRENT
GENERATOR

SLIP RINGS

ROTOR

EXCITER

STATOR

EXCITER OUTBOARD BEARING

BOILER AND ALTERNATOR
CONTROL PANEL

...M TO GENERATE ELECTRICITY

*uilt up before it is released to the turbine jets. The steam from the boilers is
...d first into the high-pressure turbine and from there, at a considerably reduced
...ressure, it is directed into the low-pressure turbine. It then passes into the
...ondenser, where it is cooled and, eventually, returned to the boilers as water.*

Rare installations have been put into service in which mercury vapour has been used to take the place of the high-pressure steam. After passing through the turbine, it gives up its heat to water which, on becoming steam, does further useful work on the low-pressure stages of the turbine.

As boilers grew larger, hand firing soon became impracticable, and the first type of mechanical stoker consisted of a chain grate. Modern developments of these grates are still used. Large numbers of links, known as fire-bars, are assembled to form an endless belt driven slowly by a drum at the front and a drum at the back. There are air spaces between the fire-bars. The coal descends from hoppers above the boiler house through long downcoming pipes, which are flexibly mounted at the upper ends so that the lower portion can move slowly along the width of the grate and deposit the coal evenly across the moving belt.

Once the boiler fire has been started (by the humble means available to the housewife in the home, i.e., first paper and sticks, and then a little coal), the whole area of the coal on the grate catches fire and forms a blazing mass many inches deep. The thickness of the coal layer, and the speed of the chain grate as it moves endlessly into the boiler, form the means by which the output is regu-

MILLS FOR PULVERIZING COAL

Mills in which huge steel balls are slowly rotating and pulverizing the raw coal. These, situated adjacent to the boiler, reduce the fuel to a fine powder.

INTERIOR OF A MODERN BOILER HOUSE

Firing aisle in the North Tees B Power Station, showing the pulverizing fuel delivery tubes to the boiler, and the burner controls.

lated: if more steam is required, more heat is needed to generate it, and consequently more coal.

In order to ensure the utmost efficiency of combustion, the boiler engineer often adopts the same means as the housewife unconsciously employs when she wishes to make the fire blaze up: he breaks the lumps into small pieces. The reason for this is to expose many sides of the lumps of coal to the heat of the fire and thus cause it to catch more easily. The modern boiler engineer goes farther than that: he pulverizes the coal, i.e., reduces it to a fine powder. Each pound of coal is thus reduced to tiny particles, presenting an enormously increased surface to the flame and ensuring complete combustion. This type of boiler utilizes what is known as pulverized fuel, or P.F. To burn coal in this way large mills, adjacent to the boiler, are provided, in which huge steel balls are slowly rotating under enormous pressure. These pulverize the coal, and the powder-like coal is removed from the mill by an air blast. The resulting mixture of finely-powdered coal and air is then fired by using nozzles, almost as if one were spraying a liquid fuel into the furnace.

There is no grate in this type of boiler, and the ash, which forms a very small

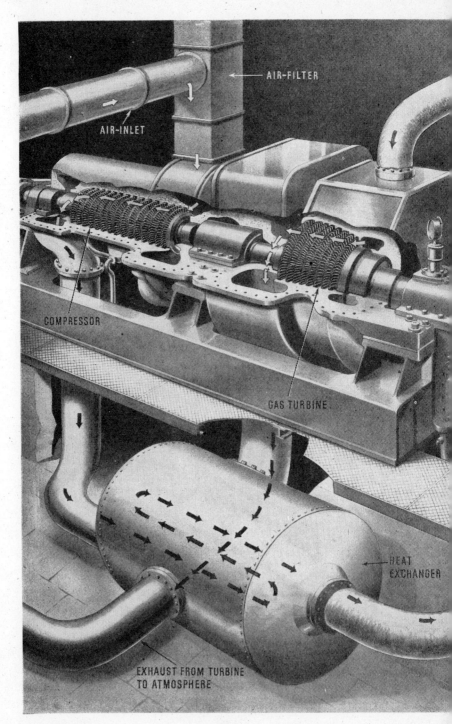

AIR-FILTER

AIR-INLET

COMPRESSOR

GAS TURBINE

HEAT EXCHANGER

EXHAUST FROM TURBINE TO ATMOSPHERE

COMBUSTION CHAMBER IN
WHICH FUEL AND HOT AIR IS
BURNT AND SENT TO TURBINE

OIL FUEL
SUPPLY PIPE

HOT COMPRESSED AIR
TO COMBUSTION CHAMBER

The gas-turbine engine consists primarily of a turbine wheel fitted with blades similar to the steam turbine, but the motive force is provided by the burning of fuel oil. The hot gases generated in the combustion chamber are allowed to expand against the blades of the turbine, and drive the mainshaft round.

proportion of the amount of coal burnt, takes the form of a fine grey sand.

The fierce flame produced by the combustion of coal, either on a chain grate or by P.F. devices, meets a series of steel tubes in which the water is contained. There are drums of high-quality forged steel at the top and bottom of the boiler, and the steel tubes run between them. The path of the water, from the bottom of the boiler to the top, is thus subdivided in order to expose the greatest amount of surface to the heat. From the top drum, where the steam is formed, pipes lead to a further set of tubes placed in the hottest part of the furnace. These serve the purpose of superheating the steam to give it even more energy than it had before.

From the boiler the steam is led off to the steam range, and so to the turbines; but the flue gases are sucked out by fans and driven to the chimney where, in many cases, devices are installed to remove grit and consequential annoyance to those who live near power stations.

As well as the elementary boiler details which have been briefly described above, there are, of course, large numbers of other devices which form part of the highly complicated lay-out of the boiler house of a modern power station. There are feed pumps to keep the water level exactly right, and devices to measure the carbon dioxide and carbon monoxide in the flue gases, to ensure that complete combustion is taking place. There is also a control desk at which the modern equivalent of the stoker can sit, if he wishes, in a light lounge suit, and control the boiler without ever coming in contact with dirt. Without leaving his chair he can start, speed up, slow down, or stop the many fans which blow air into the boiler, and which extract flue gases; the motors which control either the pulverizing mills or the chain grates; the feed pumps, and the other auxiliary appliances. He has meters giving exact records, not only of the temperature and pressure of the steam, but also of the temperature of vital parts of the boiler, so that he can detect at once if any part is getting too hot and is liable to cause trouble. Sometimes an "electric eye" is installed outside the building so that he can see, by remote control, whether the chimney is emitting black smoke. If it is, he knows that combustion conditions are not correct, and he can take steps to remedy the defect.

Occasionally boilers are built in which oil forms the fuel. The general design is the same as that employed for a pulverized-fuel installation, except that there are special nozzles. Having seen how steam is generated we next come to methods of using its expansive power to rotate the shaft of the dynamo.

SPEED OF MODERN GENERATORS

In the early days, the reciprocating steam-engine, that is, the type of engine in which a piston moves up and down in a cylinder and is forced away from the end of the cylinder by the pressure of the steam, was used almost exclusively, not only, of course, for power generation, but for all motive-power purposes. Indeed, there remains to this day examples of reciprocating steam-engines, having many cylinders and large flywheels, which although not primarily used on a commercial scale for this purpose, do drive electric dynamos. The limitations of such machines, however, for electricity generation arose in respect of their speed of rotation. In order to manufacture a generator of reasonable size it was necessary to increase the speed as much as possible. When, as in the present day, alternating-current generators are dealt with, they must run at a fixed number of revolutions per minute in relation to the number of alternations or frequency of the supply system. For the commonly-used frequency of 50 cycles, a two-pole generator, which is the most compact device from a manufacturing point of view, must revolve at 3,000 revolutions per minute. A steam-engine could not achieve this speed, since the inertia of the heavy pistons is so great that the force required to stop and start them at 6,000 times a minute would be far too great.

Thus the development of large-scale electricity generation, such as we now find, depended on the ability of the steam engineer to find a new form of prime mover; and in 1884 Charles Parsons made the first practical steam turbine. In the turbine there are, of course, no reciprocating parts, and the whole of the movement is purely rotatory. Although turbine design presents its own problems owing to the severe stresses set up in the rotating parts, patient research overcame this hindrance to the development of high-speed turbines, and a new era in electrical generation commenced. It was soon realized that the turbine could be made in the largest sizes, and was, moreover, found to be extremely efficient.

THE STEAM TURBINE

The basic principle of the steam-operated turbine is very similar to that of the jet of water on the blades of a mill-wheel, and was used in China many thousands of years before Christ. The turbine uses a jet of high-pressure steam which serves the same purpose, but there are, of course, so many improvements that it would be difficult to realize the similarity between the primitive Chinese water-wheels and a modern 100,000-h.p. turbine.

The steam from the boiler carries with it an enormous expansive force by reason of its high temperature and pressure. It is led to a row of nozzles, in the form of fixed curved blades in the stationary part of the turbine. Here it impinges against a similar row of blades mounted on the rotor, or rotating part. It passes through these, and some of its force is expended in driving the rotor round. It then meets a further row of fixed blades or nozzles, which direct it against a fresh set of moving blades on the rotor. Again it loses some of its force. As the pressure gradually drops in the successive stages, the blades are made larger and larger, so that they present greater areas to the lower-pressure steam. In many designs the turbine is made in two separate sections, called the high- and low-pressure cylinders. The two large connecting pipes, which form such a feature of photographs of large turbo-alternators, carry the steam from the high-pressure cylinder to the lower-pressure side. They are frequently paralleled by two other pipes, below the floor level, which perform the same function.

FUNCTION OF THE TURBINE BLADES

When a given volume of steam is suddenly cooled it becomes water: the water obviously occupies less volume than steam. Thus a vacuum is caused, and in the steam turbo-alternator this natural phenomenon is used to considerable advantage. As is shown on pages 188–9, the steam passes first through the high-pressure (small blade) stages, and then through the low-pressure (large blade) nozzles, and it is finally sucked out by the vacuum caused when the steam is suddenly cooled in the condenser. Thus the rotor is, so to speak, pushed round by the live steam, and pulled round by the vacuum. The condenser takes the form of a large cast-iron vessel, usually divided into two halves. The steam passes vertically downwards as it is sucked between a large number of small tubes containing cold water.

The problem of finding a suitable site for a power station is often complicated by the large amount of cooling water needed. In a 120,000-kW station, for

BURRINJUCIC DAM, NEW SOUTH WALES

When the water from the dam is not needed to generate power by passing through the turbines it is harmlessly discharged to a by-pass race. As will be seen, the discharge water is diffused in a cone. This is accomplished by what is termed a diffusing discharge regulator which disperses the water in a hollow cone, the water thereby losing its energy and causing no harm to the tail race, its foundations or other surrounding structures. The discharge regulator is so designed that it can be operated by hand or, alternatively, by remote control.

example, as much as one million gallons an hour will be required. The gigantic power stations situated on the Thames, such as Battersea, Barking, and Fulham, can solve the problem by using the river water and pumping it by huge pumps. The water used for this purpose becomes quite hot before it is discharged back to the river. The plant is provided with revolving screens to prevent fish and other foreign bodies entering the condenser. Sometimes the large concrete cooling towers often seen near power stations are needed to cool the water after it has left the condenser. Water is pumped to the top of these towers, which may be 150 ft. high, and then trickles down over a veritable forest of open-air wooden slats down into a pool below. It is finally pumped back into the condenser and fed back to the boilers.

The second great source of energy for generating power (after coal, by the use of steam) is water. In water-power plants, the primary source of energy is the sun. It lifts the water from the seas and rivers and lakes and drops it again on the high ground, thus giving it potential energy. Every year the rivers of the world carry down to the seas and oceans some 6,524 cubic miles of water. The

INSTALLING A ROTOR AT THE BOULDER DAM POWER PLANT

In this type of generator the rotor consists of a number of pole-pieces fitted vertically around the rotor, as shown above. The stator contains the armature windings, which can also be seen. The reasons for preferring a rotating magnetic-field generator are: (1) it is easier to make a sound mechanical construction of the field poles and.windings, since the end connexions of the armature windings, if rotated, would tend to be displaced by centrifugal forces, and (2) it is preferable to have the high-voltage windings stationary.

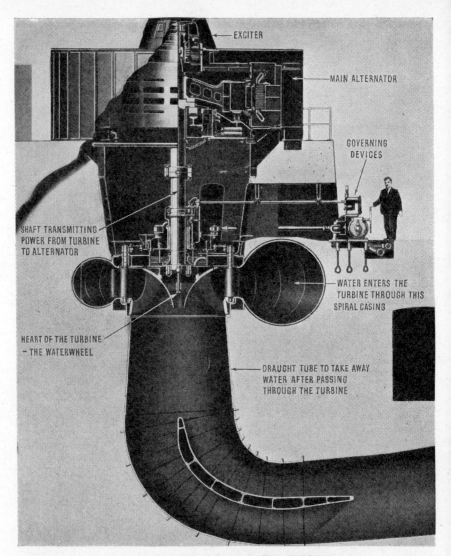

EXCITER

MAIN ALTERNATOR

GOVERNING
DEVICES

SHAFT TRANSMITTING
POWER FROM TURBINE
TO ALTERNATOR

WATER ENTERS THE
TURBINE THROUGH THIS
SPIRAL CASING

HEART OF THE TURBINE
- THE WATERWHEEL

DRAUGHT TUBE TO TAKE AWAY
WATER AFTER PASSING
THROUGH THE TURBINE

CONSTRUCTION OF A WATER TURBINE

The design of turbine shown above is the reaction type used with low or medium heads of water, and, in principle, is similar to the primitive water-mill. Water from the head race is directed by means of penstocks to a spiral casing surrounding the turbine. The turbine wheel that drives the alternator is provided with two sets of vanes. The fixed or guide vanes are stationary, and direct the water on to the vanes fitted to the rotating part of the turbine. After passing through the turbine the water is directed to the tail race and thence to the river. Governing devices are installed to enable the speed of the shaft driving the alternator to be adjusted. One of the advantages of hydro-electric plant is that it can be operated by remote control and does not need operators in constant attendance.

energy existing in that enormous quantity of water, if it could all be harnessed to generate electric power, would solve our power problems for all time. The world's potential water-power which has been surveyed, and could possibly be developed, is 667 million h.p.; of this figure, some 77,800,000 h.p. has been already put to use in generating electrical energy. In Great Britain and Northern Ireland about 550,000 h.p. of water-power plant already exists, and the latest surveys put the minimum figure of additional horse-power which might be brought into service at 700,000 h.p. Even if all this were developed, the total amount of power so produced would amount to only about 20 per cent of our total requirements.

These figures exclude the possibility of using the tides to generate power. In this connexion there is the vast project for building a barrage across the River Severn, and there has also been a number of references of late years to a scheme associated with the straits between the Isle of Anglesey and the mainland. These and other tidal projects have not yet been passed by all the experts as practicable on economic grounds, but there may be extremely interesting future developments in this field: it may be that Great Britain will be the first nation in the world to harness this inexhaustible store of energy for generating purposes.

HYDRO-ELECTRIC POWER GENERATION

Water-power is, unlike coal, a non-wasting asset. It is not, however, free power. The layman, seeing a waterfall or a river, thinks that the erection of a dam, a pipe-line, and a power station is the simplest thing in the world—and the cheapest. In practice, the hydro-scheme engineers will know that the real problem is to find a stream where the output can be maintained at all times of the year, and where the civil engineering costs will not be higher than is economic. In many cases, even with high cost of coal at the present time in Great Britain, a steam station can be shown to be a cheaper alternative to the erection of a hydro-electric power generating station.

The engineers who survey the terrain must study the sunspot cycle of eleven years: if a scheme is based on rainfall estimates over a lesser period, they may find that the first season after the power station is ready provides a drought which reduces the powerful jets of water to a trickle. Hydro-electric men say that the driest season ever remembered by the oldest inhabitant will be the one following the starting of the plant. They must also estimate the amount of water held back by vegetation and underground pools: they must beware of designing stations which are themselves submerged at unpredictable flood-times. The scheme must function all the year round, or else a steam station will have to be built as well to safeguard the supplies in the off-season. Navigation and fishing rights, as well as the preservation of amenities, have to be regarded. They must guard against floating ice blocking the water inlets. The capital cost of the huge dams, pipe lines, and civil work generally, far exceeds that of a steam plant. Moreover, the sources of water-power are often remote from the centres of population where

Aerial view of the Karapiro Power Station, New Zealand. Power is generated by three hydro-electric alternators, each of which generates 33,000 kilovolt-amperes.

the power is to be used, and expensive transmission lines are, therefore, necessary to transmit the current.

Inherent in some of the possible difficulties mentioned above lie the reasons why there are not more hydro-electric power schemes in Great Britain.

Water-wheels can be operated by a fall of water as low as 6 ft., and as high as 5,000 ft. They all owe their origin to the simple water-mill used by the ancients for the irrigation of their land.

There are two main types, the reaction and the impulse. In the reaction type, a highly developed form of the primitive water-wheel is used. The wheels may be used either horizontally or vertically, but vertical construction with the alternator mounted above is more often employed in larger installations; a sectional view of the latter type is illustrated on page 198.

These wheels are used for heads of water of the low and medium varieties. For a higher head, as when obtaining power from the water in a gorge between high mountains, the impulse wheel is frequently employed. In this type the water is directed into one or more jets, being carefully controlled by special needle valves which exert their force on a wheel on which a series of cups are mounted.

Apart from the actual hydraulic and electrical plant, every hydro-power scheme requires a vast array of civil engineering features, such as dams, tail races, surge tanks, and the like. The surge tank is a concrete structure, outside the power

station, into which the water is instantly diverted if it is necessary to shut down the plant in an emergency. The enormous pressure of the water in the pipe-lines, if diverted from its normal outlet in the turbine, would cause bursting to take place if surge tanks were not installed.

Delicate and ingenious electrical apparatus has made it possible to start up and shut down huge hydro-electric stations entirely by remote control from great distances, without a single operator being present at the hydro-electric station itself. This demonstrates one of the advantages of this form of prime mover over the steam station. The intricacies and complexities of high-pressure boiler plant are such as need the constant attendance of highly-skilled operators.

TESTING A VERTICAL OIL ENGINE

Considerable research and testing is carried out on all types of engines in order to increase their efficiency and output of useful work. In the view above a large vertical oil engine is seen undergoing exhaustive tests. In this test the output of energy from the engine, as measured at the flywheel, is determined from the amount of current which is generated in the alternator.

The third source of electric power comes from the energy produced by the combustion of oil fuel in a reciprocating internal-combustion engine, usually of the Diesel type. This Diesel-power generation has certain specialized applications. There are good technical reasons why very large oil-engine-driven plants are not likely to be developed, but nevertheless where a small station has to be built to feed a limited community the Diesel reigns supreme. It also has important application as a prime mover for emergency generation in such places as broadcasting stations, water pumping, sewage disposal, and many other installations.

Where oil is used in a Diesel engine roughly two-thirds of a pound of oil is needed to generate one unit. There is an installed capacity of 80,735 kW of Diesel-driven plant in the United Kingdom compared with 11,540,190 kW of generating plant installed in steam stations and 346,389 kW of water-turbine-driven plant.

The speed of an oil-engine set, since the engine is of the reciprocating type, must again be subject to the limitations mentioned earlier under the heading of reciprocating steam engines, and generators for the oil-engine stations are designed differently from those used by steam turbines. Sets of about 1,800 h.p. form, in general, the largest which can be practically employed.

As we have seen, the three main sources of power spring from coal, water and oil. There are several other possible means of generating electricity and we might first consider the use of the wind. Power for pumping water and grinding corn has been obtained from the wind for centuries, as can be seen by the use of windmills in Holland and elsewhere, and occasionally in this country. Unreliability of the wind source is its chief difficulty and also the fact that the average wind-speed in this country is only $7\frac{1}{2}$ m.p.h. There may be gales of as much as 100 m.p.h., occurring perhaps not more than once in two or three years. Thus the towers on which the power windmills have to be mounted have to be immensely strong, and so capital costs are high, while the need to turn the blades of windmills into the wind renders necessary a complicated and expensive rotatory mechanism at the top of the tower.

The size of windmill blades to secure a given horse-power may be somewhat surprising to those who are not familiar with such problems. For instance, the old-fashioned windmill with its large blades only develops an average of 14 h.p. when the wind is blowing at 15 m.p.h. A 45-kW generator in Australia needed

CONTROL PANEL FOR ADJUSTING TESTS ON CIRCUIT BREAKERS

OSCILLOGRAPH, FOR RECORDING AND PHOTOGRAPHING TRANSIENT CURRENTS AND VOLTAGES

FINAL CONTROL OF EXTRA HIGH-POWER TESTS

HIGH-TENSION RESEARCH LABORATORY

The increasing use of higher voltages necessitates considerable research into the properties of insulators, etc. The view above shows the control room in a high-tension laboratory in which such research is carried out; the interior of a high-tension laboratory is illustrated on page 205.

28-ft.-diameter sails mounted on a 100-ft.-high tower, while the largest windmill generator in the world is at Grandpa's Knob, Vermont, U.S.A., where a 1,000-kW windmill is erected. It has blades of 65-ft. diameter on a 110-ft.-high tower.

Research is in progress, in Britain, into the possibility of scientifically designing a standard windmill for use in the Highlands of Scotland in connexion with the Hydro-Electric Board's schemes, for use in isolated communities.

In the Sahara Desert a generator was installed in which the heat of the sun was used directly to boil water and produce steam. Large copper reflectors were installed, which focused the sun's rays on to heating elements. The plant, however, has not been a practical success. In one or two parts of the world natural gases arising from the earth's surface have been used to produce steam-power.

It is not likely that the miscellaneous power sources mentioned above will ever add greatly to the world's power needs. The two new developments of the future are, first, the use of atomic energy and, secondly, the gas turbine.

ATOMIC ENERGY AND ELECTRIC POWER

The use of atomic energy, although widely publicised as the result of atom-bomb developments, is not likely, in the opinion of the leading scientists, to play an active part in power generation for perhaps fifteen to twenty years. The method employed would be to use the atomic pile as a means of generating heat. Just as in the case of burning coal, one could not use the flame of the coal directly to drive the prime mover, so also a transferring medium must be found for the atomic pile. Briefly, fission of atoms of material such as uranium 235 takes place when blocks of such material are placed close together, separated by a retarding medium, such as carbon in the form of graphite. The control of the nuclear fission which then takes place enables great heat to be generated. The carrying away of this heat to perform useful work is not the greatest of the problems, since there is also generated an amount of radio-activity which would be harmful not only to the person operating the plant but also to the actual material of which the rest of the equipment was constructed.

Thus the atomic pile itself must be protected by thick walls of concrete of a special kind, and no human being can possibly exist within these walls when the pile is operating. Control, therefore, must be by remote means. Assuming that water is the medium used to transfer the heat from the pile to a turbine in which the heat energy is converted to electricity energy, it must be realized that the resultant steam will also be highly charged with radio-activity: and this brings further problems in the way of protecting both personnel and materials against its effects. Finally, the actual cooling water used to condense the steam and return it to the atomic boiler will also be charged with radio-active substances, and before it can be discharged into a river or a lake it must either be kept for a considerable time in a closely-guarded reservoir to lose its radio-activity or other equally cumbersome and expensive means must be adopted to prevent damage

Labels in image:
GUARD RING (EARTHED)
LOW-VOLTAGE ELECTRODE
HIGH-VOLTAGE ELECTRODE
VOLTAGE-MEASURING SPHERE-GAP
500-kV TRANSFORMERS THESE FORM A MILLION-VOLT, 1,000-kVA TEST CIRCUIT
TANK FOR TESTING HIGH-VOLTAGE APPARATUS
BAKELITE SUPPORTS INSULATING TRANSFORMERS

HIGH-VOLTAGE TESTING LABORATORY

The control of the staggeringly high voltages used in the transmission of power over long land-lines brings new problems which the engineer must solve to ensure a constant and reliable supply of electric power for industry and the domestic consumer. For example, insulators must be designed not to break down under very high voltages, also switchgear must withstand similar pressure without burning out. These and many other problems are investigated in high-voltage laboratories similar to that shown above. Note in the lower right-hand corner of the picture, the tank for testing apparatus such as switchgear.

to human and animal life from the dangerous emanations in the water. There is another possible method of using the heat generated in the atomic pile. This method dispenses with water, and uses hot air to drive a gas turbine; but again the large quantities of air which emerge from the turbine, having performed their useful function, would be charged with radio-active substances, and very special precautions would have to be taken to protect the operators.

THE GAS TURBINE

The second challenge to the established electric power-producing prime movers is the gas turbine. The use of the jet engine during the war was a great step forward in the design of prime movers in which no reciprocating parts were used. The gas turbine for commercial and industrial use has been developed directly from the jet engine. It consists primarily of a turbine wheel having blades more or less similar to the steam turbine, but where the motive force is provided by the burning of oil fuel. The resultant hot gases expand, through nozzles, against the blades of the turbine, thus driving it round. In order to provide large quantities of air to make up the high-pressure jets, a compressor is

EXPERIMENTAL 500-H.P. GAS TURBINE PLANT

This view shows the first British industrial gas turbine station (5,000 kilowatts). This type of turbine allows the use of an axial flow compressor which gives a higher efficiency than the commonly used centrifugal type.

needed, and this is mounted on the same shaft as the turbine itself. It consists of another turbine wheel, this time with differently shaped blades which suck in the air by fan action, and drive it into combustion chambers situated all round the circumference of the turbine, where it joins the burning oil.

A considerable part of the energy of the gas turbine is taken up in driving its own compressor. What is left of the energy is available at the shaft end, and this can be coupled to an alternator for electrical power purposes. There are two systems employed, the open and closed cycles. The open-cycle system has been simply described above. In the closed-cycle system there is a second turbine, solely employed to drive the air compressor for the main turbine.

EFFICIENCY OF GAS TURBINES

The efficiency of the gas turbine does not exceed 30 per cent and, therefore, its advantages must be found in other fields than that of power efficiency. These advantages lie mainly in the fact that the actual first cost may be considerably less than that of an equivalent steam station, since the amount of civil work required is naturally less, as no boiler house is needed, and no vast cooling water system has to be constructed. Thus the station can be situated away from all natural water sources, an advantage over a steam station which in certain localities may be extremely valuable. The gas turbine can be started up immediately and its high speeds mean that the alternators can be designed for maximum efficiency.

On the other hand, the limiting factor in gas-turbine designs is the temperature of the gases as they reach the turbine blades. Temperatures of the order of 1,500 deg. F. are used, and this enormous temperature means that the blades are subject not only to the great heat, but to severe mechanical stresses.

It is only by very intensive research that steel manufacturers have been able to find a metal which will stand up to the extremely vigorous duty which the gas turbine imposes, since the majority of metals when heated to this temperature become soft and lose all their mechanical strength. Continual progress, however, is being made in this direction and gas-turbine stations have been working in several parts of the world. In Great Britain, a 15,000-kW set, and other machines of comparable size, are now being built for the public electricity supply system.

NATIONAL SCHEME

The British National Grid System certainly earns a place among the marvels of modern science. It is unique in many respects. In the first place Great Britain is the only country in the world to have a complete national scheme for electricity generation. The densely populated areas of Lancashire and Yorkshire, and those around London, give rise to the greatest sudden increases in electrical load in the world. The number of power stations controlled from a few central control points is greater than anywhere else, and this feature alone constitutes a technical marvel which even responsible engineers, at the time of the inception of the scheme, thought to be a completely impracticable undertaking.

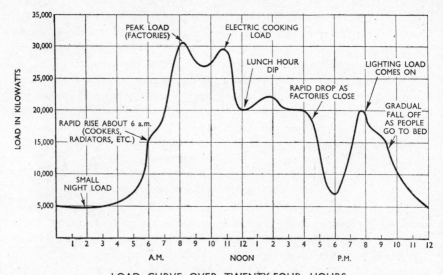

LOAD CURVE OVER TWENTY-FOUR HOURS

Graph showing the fluctuations in load (measured in kilowatts) that power stations have to accommodate during twenty-four hours.

The principles behind the grid scheme are threefold:

(*a*) Economical operation; (*b*) partial elimination of stand-by plant; and (*c*) safety of supply. To elucidate them we shall have to get clear one or two fundamental facts about electricity supply.

In earlier pages of this chapter we have seen that the only practical method of large-scale electricity generation is by steam turbo-alternator or by water-power. It should be clearly understood that it is impossible to store electrical energy except in small, uneconomical quantities, in storage batteries or accumulators.

Thus the load, that is, your electric cooker, the factory's large motors, the

Diagram showing the advantages of the interlinked system as opposed to the independent system. In the former arrangement one generating set can be used to supply power when the load is increased.

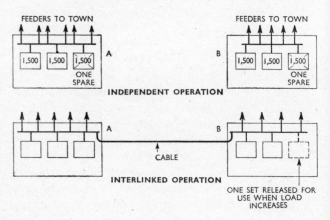

television transmitter, etc., must be met as it arises. For example, directly you switch on a 60-watt lamp over your bed a little more coal must be added to the boiler, to generate a little more steam, to drive the turbine a little more powerfully, and thus supply the energy required by your lamp.

It follows then that the amounts of electricity generated must follow the load, minute by minute. Thus the power station must have plant available for the maximum load likely during the twenty-four hours; but this plant is not being used to its full capacity for most of the time.

A manufacturer making and selling, say, soap can make a steady amount during working hours all the year round, and can store the surplus in the off

STEPPING DOWN THE VOLTAGE

The type of transformer illustrated here is used to step down the pressure of 132,000 volts to 33,000 volts before passing to a substation.

season to meet the heavy demand when it comes. This is impossible in electricity supply and, therefore, in the case of one power station working on its own, as was the universal case prior to the grid, the whole scheme was uneconomic in this respect. Consider the load curve illustrated on page 208, which shows the variations in load requirements during twenty-four hours.

It is obvious from consideration that there must be at least enough plant to cover the peak load of 30,000 kW. Suppose there were just one turbo-alternator, of 30,000-kW capacity. It would have to run all the time and would only use its full capacity at about 8 a.m. each day, then only for a short time. For the rest of the twenty-four hours it would be running at much less than full load. This is uneconomic, for the technical reason that a turbo-alternator is most efficient at full load or thereabouts, and, from another point of view, a capital outlay has been made equivalent to the cost of a 30,000-kW plant. This capital is not being fully utilized for the greater part of its available working life.

Allied to this consideration is the fact that it is obvious that one set would not be sufficient. It might break down, also it needs maintenance and overhaul. If a power station has only one set, the district it was supplying would be without electricity while the necessary maintenance and repair were carried out. Therefore, at least two sets are necessary.

In practice, with an independent station of this kind, the engineers would usually use three sets, say 15,000 kW each, making a total of 45,000 kW. For full-load periods, two sets would provide the 30,000 kW needed. During the night

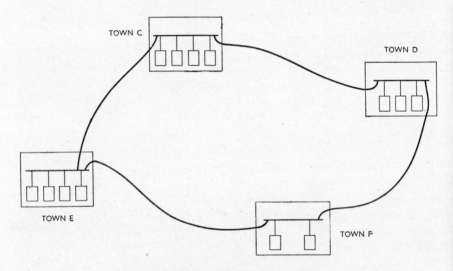

INTERLINKED GENERATING STATIONS

Four towns each linked by cables form a ring. Town D, for instance, can receive electric power from C or F, or, through the ring connexions, from town E. This system of interlinking ensures a reliable supply of power to each town.

hours, and for part of the evening load, one set would suffice. The third set, together with its boiler and other apparatus, would be under overhaul, or else act as stand-by in case of breakdown.

Consider, now, a second town, more or less the same as the first, with the same sort of load curve as shown, and situated some twenty miles away. Let us suppose it has a similar power station with three 15,000-kW sets installed.

At any given moment there will be one set in each station lying idle, that is, standing by. Moreover, at all periods, other than the peak times, the plant which is actually running is not operating at its full efficiency.

It does not take long for the enterprising engineer to see that there is a way out of this apparently unavoidable state of inefficiency. If a cable were laid between the two stations, the stand-by set in one station could act as spare for both. Of the total of six sets in the two stations, one at least could be scrapped or kept available so that full load could be met without installing new plant.

INTERLINKING POWER STATIONS

Thus a great saving is effected, but an even greater benefit can also be obtained by the installation and use of an interlinking cable. The best way to operate any set is to run it at full load. During the night hours there is a load of about 5,000 kW at the first station, and a load of about the same at the other, making a total of 10,000 kW. Under independent operation there would be a 15,000-kW set working at one-third load in each station—an inefficient state of affairs.

Now, suppose that an agreement was reached between station A and station B whereby one of them shut down altogether when the light-load period was reached. Not only would one set be released for scrapping (if old and inefficient) or for future extension of total load, but by suitable arrangements between the operators, one set, say in station A, could carry the total load of both towns during the night hours, that is, 10,000 kW. Here is the basis of two of the three fundamental principles of grid operation stated at the outset: economic operation, and partial elimination of stand-by plant.

The third principle, safety of supply, is seen more clearly when an extension of our simple interconnexion scheme is made, to include, say, four towns. The four towns shown opposite have each been linked by cables, to form a ring. Town D, for instance, can receive supply from town C or town F; or, through the ring connexions, also from town E.

The third advantage of interlinked operation comes to light. Before the interlinking cables were laid, if a complete failure occurred at town D, such as a major fire, affecting the whole boiler house, then town D would be completely out of action for a long time, perhaps for weeks. But now, with the interconnectors, such a major failure would inconvenience no one. Towns C, E, and F would have to make up the total loss of town D's plant, by running their sets for longer hours and at greater output: and the total stand-by of the four towns' plant would be decreased, for the time being. Even if one of the cables failed, town D would still receive supply from the other. A ring of this kind can always be broken in one place, but not, of course, in two places.

A committee, under Lord Weir, was appointed to consider the whole question of electricity supply, and as a result of its deliberations it was decided to set up, in 1927, the Central Electricity Board, in order to give effect to a scheme which embodied the principles which have been outlined in the foregoing pages.

UNDERGROUND POWER LINES

View of the subterranean cables which carry the electric power generated at the Battersea Power Station to the grid for distribution.

The first problem facing this Board was the practical construction of the grid to interlink all the country's power stations. In order to transmit power for any distance, one can work in two ways. An analogy which makes this clear is to consider the conveying of water. To get the same amount of water to a given place, in a given time, one could use a large pipe and a low pressure, or one could employ a small pipe and a high pressure. For pipe read conductor, and the case is the same with electrical energy. To carry large, thick conductors across hundreds of miles of countryside would be an expensive and impracticable matter. Therefore, the highest voltage that could be conveniently handled at the terminating points, 132,000 volts, was chosen. This enables the conductors to be of reasonably small diameter, and the wires one sees strung between the

PYLON

INSULATORS

ALUMINIUM CABLE

OIL-FILLED SWITCHES

BUS-BARS

OVERHEAD POWER LINES AND SUBSTATION

The tall pylons to the left support the cables which carry the 132,000-volt power from point to point throughout the grid. In this view the power is being fed into a substation. Here the various lines linking the town with the other neighbouring electricity undertakings are brought to bus-bars or common linking bars, each with a switch to enable it to be cut off. There will also be two, three, or sometimes more feeders to the town itself. These will have transformers, see page 209, to convert the pressure down from 132,000 volts to whatever is the local voltage, usually 6,600 volts, 11,000 volts, or 33,000 volts. Substations are usually located on the outskirts of the town, and distribution to the consumer is by underground cables.

80-ft.-high pylons of the grid are, in fact, about as thick as a man's forefinger, and are composed of outer strands of aluminium wire, twisted over a core of stranded steel. The aluminium carries the current, being almost as good a conductor as copper, and the steel strands sustain the tension.

At each town when connexion is made between the grid and the local power station there is a grid substation, of the type seen on page 213. Here, the various lines linking this town with the other neighbouring electricity undertakings are brought to bus-bars or common linking bars, each with a switch to enable it to be cut off. There will also be two, three, or sometimes more feeders to the town itself. These will have huge transformers, to convert the pressure down from the 132,000 volts of the grid to whatever is the local voltage, usually 6,600 volts, 11,000 volts, or sometimes 33,000 volts. There will also be one or more bus-coupler switches, perhaps a bus section, and there may also be reactors or enormous iron-cored choke coils, to limit the current in the event of a fault.

<h2 style="text-align:center">BRITISH ELECTRICITY AUTHORITY</h2>

A further step in making Britain's electricity supply more efficient, not to say unique among the world's systems, was taken on 1 April, 1948. The whole of the electricity supply of Great Britain was nationalized and placed under the control of the British Electricity Authority. This authority has the enormous task of supplying 11 million consumers with 42 thousand million units of electric power a year. Its organization provides for the central authority, that is, the British Electricity Authority itself, running all the power stations and the main transmission lines linking them together on the grid system described above; while the duties of distributing and selling electricity in the towns and countryside is delegated to fourteen Area Boards, which are largely autonomous and are composed of eminent authorities who understand the consumers' conditions in the areas over which they preside. There is one exception to this general framework, and that is the North of Scotland Hydro-Electric Board, which combines the functions of the central authority, as regards generation and transmission, with those of an Area Board for its own locality.

The number of power stations in Great Britain at the time of nationalization of electricity was 142, with a total installed capacity of 11,588,306 kW. The grid system linking them together comprises 5,172 miles of transmission lines, of which 3,685 miles operate at 132,000 volts, and the remainder at 66,000 volts or lower voltages. The grid substations, where connexion is made between the central authority's main transmission network and the area boards' distributing points, number 349. The central authority, faced with the problem of transmitting larger and larger loads, are building an experimental line operating at 264,000 volts between Neepsend, in Sheffield, and Staythorpe, in Lincolnshire. There are many miles of cable now operating at 132,000 volts, a technical feat of the highest magnitude, since while there is no definite limiting feature to the voltage which can be used on air-insulated conductors strung on high pylons, the problems of confining 132,000 volts in a cable can easily be pictured.

The total demand on the grid system reached, in 1947, the enormous figure of 9,060,000 kW, which expressed in horse-power reaches the colossal figure of 12,100,000. To get some conception of the power needed to meet this demand, the average express locomotive travelling at 60 m.p.h. develops about 2,000 h.p. We have to imagine, then, that 6,050 express locomotives are operating at one and the same time to equal the power needed to meet the highest demands made by domestic and industrial consumers on the grid system of Great Britain.

HIGH-TENSION SWITCHES

The control of this vast amount of power brings enormous problems to the designers of switches and transformers, and each year sees new designs brought forward to meet the problem.

Imagine a tumbler switch in an ordinary dwelling house. Those who have seen the switch operating without the cover will have noticed that when the switch is slightly defective, and does not snap as quickly as it should, a spark is seen, which may reach sufficient proportions to burn minute holes in the blades every time the switch is operated. Even on a switch used for a single 100-watt lamp, that is, one-tenth of a kilowatt, this pitting and burning can become quite serious in a short time. Imagine now what happens when a 10,000-kW load is switched off. The switch would draw an arc which could cause not only a fire, but an explosion, were it not properly designed.

The earliest type of switch relied on large quantities of mineral oil, in which the switch contacts were immersed, to quench the arc, while very powerful springs were fitted to the blades so that the opening of the switch took the shortest possible time. Although this method was partly successful, the early designs did, in fact, cause many fires and explosions, mainly because the designers had no real knowledge of the exact theory of the arc, and of the conditions which caused the arc intensity and duration to be large or small.

ELECTRONICS AND SWITCHGEAR

A great step forward was taken when manufacturers developed short-circuit testing stations, in which very large alternators were specially built purely for the purpose of testing switches of every description to destruction, i.e., blowing them up. Allied to these advances, the science of electronics came to the aid of the switchgear designers by providing the cathode-ray oscillograph, a means of recording the transient circuit conditions at the exact moment of breaking the circuit. As a result of these researches, the oil-filled switch was greatly improved, mainly by the addition of an arc-control device in which, broadly speaking, the pressure developed by the gases formed in the oil at the instant of the arc was itself used to drive fresh oil across the arc's path, and so quench it. The oil needed for each of the three phases of a 132,000-volt switch was, as a result of these experiments, reduced by this means from 1,300 gallons to 30 gallons.

The newest development in switchgear for high power and high voltages is the use of compressed air to blow out the arc. Air-blast circuit-breakers, as they are called, are rapidly coming into increasing use for controlling the circuits of the British grid system. Here, no oil is used, but compressed air at about 200 lb. to the square inch is released in large volume across the contacts. These are forced apart by the air pressure, against a strong spring. Air is normally a good insulator, but directly an arc is drawn, the air in the immediate vicinity becomes ionized, or made conducting, and this condition enables an uncontrolled arc to spread to dangerous proportions. The compressed-air supply, however, blows away this ionized air very rapidly and thus the arc is completely controlled and extinguished almost instantaneously. Even the enormous arc which would be formed when a circuit is interrupted into which many large power stations are feeding can be completely extinguished in less than 0·4 of a second.

CONTROLLING THE GRID SYSTEM

The problem of controlling a large network really hinges on cutting out a defective portion in the quickest possible time, but the greatest difficulty is to ensure that the sound portions are not interrupted at the same time. In other words, to discriminate exactly between the section of the transmission network on which there is a fault and the adjacent sound sections. For instance, in a ring-main layout as shown earlier in this chapter, any one link in the chain can be interrupted without loss of supply, but if two links are interrupted one or more of the towns will be without electricity. Imagine an aeroplane crashing into one of the grid lines. The wires are brought to earth, and enormous currents flow at once. These currents flow to the fault through the adjacent sound portions as well as from the two ends of the feeder where the accident has happened.

In a highly complicated network like the British grid, relays and measuring devices of the utmost exactitude are needed to ensure a reliable protective gear layout and to prevent unwarranted loss of supply, and one of the requirements of such devices is a channel of communication between the two ends of a feeder. To lay a cable specially for this purpose when only an overhead line exists would be expensive, and one of the solutions has been to use radio-frequency or carrier current superimposed on the actual grid lines themselves, thus giving one more example of the march of electronic science assisting the power engineer.

Having provided a channel of communication in this fashion, the electronic engineer does not stop at giving assistance only in the matter of fault control. He provides telephonic communication along the grid lines, and in some cases highly complicated apparatus, similar to that used in the automatic telephone exchanges, enables the power station engineer situated many miles away to have complete control of one of the gigantic grid substations, which are thus operated entirely unattended. He can read the currents on all the feeders, alter the voltage ratios of the transformers, and learn instantly of any unusual conditions such as the opening of switches through faults of the network, all by this means.

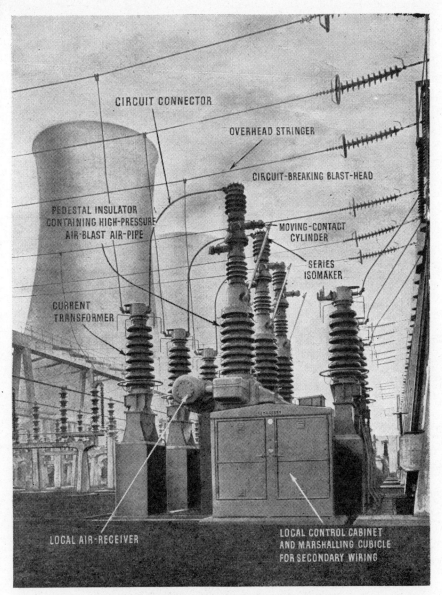

CIRCUIT CONNECTOR

OVERHEAD STRINGER

CIRCUIT-BREAKING BLAST-HEAD

PEDESTAL INSULATOR
CONTAINING HIGH-PRESSURE
AIR-BLAST AIR-PIPE

MOVING-CONTACT
CYLINDER

SERIES
ISOMAKER

CURRENT
TRANSFORMER

LOCAL AIR-RECEIVER

LOCAL CONTROL CABINET
AND MARSHALLING CUBICLE
FOR SECONDARY WIRING

COMPRESSED-AIR AND MODERN SWITCHGEAR

Circuit-breakers in high-tension transmission lines must be provided with a means of extinguishing the arcs which are formed when switches are operated. Sometimes this is done by immersing the circuit-breakers in oil. A recent development is the air-blast circuit-breaker. A typical installation is shown above, which uses compressed air to extinguish the arc. The enormous arc which would be formed when a circuit, being fed by many power stations, is interrupted can be completely extinguished in a fraction of a second.

BUN CONTAINING HYDROGEN DISCHARGE TUBE. SOURCE OF PROTONS

VOLTAGE MEASURING RESISTANCE

HIGH VACUUM PUMPS

INSULATING SUPPORT COLUMN

VOLTAGE GENERATING STACK

POWER INPUT FROM 200,000 VOLT TRANSFORMER

MILLION-VOLT ATOM SMASHER

The high-tension laboratory attached to the Cavendish Laboratory, Cambridge. The apparatus provides a tremendous current of particles for disintegrating atoms, and is materially contributing to our knowledge of atomic structure.

CHAPTER 7 The atomic age

FOR many years it has been realized that great quantities of energy could be released if some method could be devised of splitting up the very heavy atoms of which certain elements are composed. Over forty years ago, in fact, a scientist predicted that when a means of tapping this vast store of energy was discovered, its first application would be the invention of a bomb infinitely more destructive than any yet known; afterwards, however, the principle would be adapted to reducing the hardships of life and bringing about a better standard of living.

Today that prophecy is coming true. The tremendous explosive power and searing heat of the atomic bomb are being tamed to provide atomic power for industrial use: one pound of ordinary uranium is the equivalent, as a fuel, of some nine tons of coal. Working on different lines a scientist has already succeeded in transmuting a thin film of mercury into gold by bombarding it with atomic missiles, while in great cyclotrons precious radio-active materials are today produced in quantity to replace scarce natural radium for medical uses.

What is the secret of this vast reservoir of power which will give us a super-explosive, or the modern equivalent of the philosopher's stone, capable of transforming base metals into gold, and altering the structure of various materials so that they are changed into something quite different?

The answer lies in the discovery of how to subdivide or shuffle the individual atoms of various elements. For a long time scientists believed that the atom was the smallest indivisible particle from which an element was made. They likened atoms to building bricks, which could be arranged in different ways to form a variety of different materials. Two thousand years ago, in fact, the Greek philosopher Democritus put forward this theory, but it had little effect on science until Dalton developed it in the early years of the last century.

This explanation, however, turned out to be far too simple, for the individual atom is now known to be a very complex affair. Microscopically small as it is, an atom is not visible even under the most powerful microscope that science can devise, and one thousand million atoms will just span a penny. Each atom can be likened to a miniature solar system in which planets circle around a central "sun" or nucleus in well-defined orbits and at immensely high speeds.

To understand the structure of this tiny universe we can consider the simplest example, the hydrogen atom. The nucleus is formed by one particle called a proton. This is positively charged. Around this circulates another type of particle, called an electron, which is negatively charged. More complicated atoms have a greater number· of electrons circulating around at immense speeds, while the nucleus may contain a number of protons, and, in addition, some particles which have no electrical charge, and are accordingly called neutrons.

It will be seen, then, that our comparison with a miniature universe is not exaggerated. Although the nucleus measures only from one-third to one-half of a billionth (millionth of a millionth) part of an inch across, and the total diameter of the atom is little more than a hundredth of a millionth part of an inch, vast relative distances separate the nucleus from the electrons. If the nucleus were magnified to the size of the sun in our solar system, the nearest electron would be as far away from it as the planet Pluto is from the sun: roughly 3,600,000,000 miles. Theoretically this means that it should be possible to compress a ton of steel so that it would occupy little more than a cubic inch of space. It is thought today that some of the coldest stars, particularly those termed dwarf stars, consist of highly concentrated matter compressed to this extent.

ELEMENTS AND ISOTOPES

We have seen that the nucleus may contain one ·or more protons, as well as some neutrons, while the number of electrons circling round it also varies. There may be only one, or as many as ninety-two, as in the case of the element uranium. The number of electrons circulating round the nucleus is termed the "atomic number," and determines the element which an atom will form, such as lead, iron, gold, and so on. The number of protons in the nucleus determines the weight of the atom, since two or more varieties of the same element may have the same atomic number, but different weights. These atoms of the same chemical element and with the same chemical characteristics, but having different atomic weights, are called isotopes.

The usual atomic weight of uranium, for instance, is 238; but the special variety, or isotope, of uranium which is used in the production of atomic energy is uranium 235. Yet another isotope, made from thorium, which is now used, is. uranium 233. A further isotope of the same element has an atomic weight of 234. All four have the same number of electrons, but the structure of the nucleus is different in each ·case.

With this general idea of the structure· of the atom in.mind, it will be easier to understand how the operation of splitting the atom is carried out. It should be realized, however, that this. is rather a loose term. For many years it has been possible to dislodge one· or more electrons from the solar system· of the atom. A great deal of energy is not required to do. this, and many laboratory processes involve disarranging the structure of the electrons in an atom. The crucial test came when an attempt was made to disintegrate the nucleus itself.

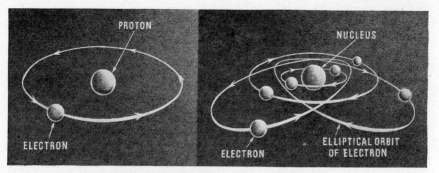

PLANETARY STRUCTURE OF THE ATOM

An atom consists of a nucleus which carries a positive electrical charge around which one or more negatively charged electrons circle, behaving in very much the same way as the planets revolve round the sun. Above is shown the structure of a hydrogen atom (left) and a carbon atom (right).

It is now generally accepted that the nucleus consists of one or more protons and a number of neutrons. Now the protons have positive electrical charges, and consequently repel one another strongly; at the same time, however, short-range forces of attraction, about which very little is known at present, tend to hold them together. These forces of attraction also hold the uncharged neutrons in place within the structure of the nucleus.

To simplify our conception of the nucleus, therefore, we can imagine the protons and neutrons as a number of billiard balls or marbles, some of which, the protons, are strongly repelling one another, but all linked together in a pattern by lengths of elastic; the whole structure is in a state of tension, but the opposing forces balance each other out, and a state of quilibrium is maintained.

The alpha particle which carries a positive charge and identified as the nucleus of a helium atom, can penetrate between the electrons, but is repelled by the positively charged electrical field surrounding the nucleus. It was upon this phenomenon, known as alpha-particle scattering, that Lord Rutherford based his theory of the nuclear structure of the atom which laid the foundation for the modern conception of the atom.

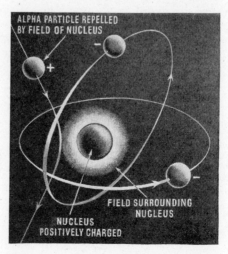

At the *top* of the *diagram* is shown a uranium 238 atom. This, like other radio-active elements, is unstable, continually throwing out alpha or beta particles, as shown by the arrows. When a particle is flung out the atom becomes an atom of a different element. A succession of such changes will take place until a stable state is reached, after millions of years, as an isotope of lead.

URANIUM I
238
β PARTICLE   α PARTICLE
UX₁ 234   UX₂ 234   U II 234
IONIUM 230
RADIUM 226
Ra Em 222
Ra A 218
Ra B 214   Ra C 214   Ra C' 214
Ra D 210   Ra E 210   Ra F 210
LEAD 206

Suppose that the equilibrium of this delicately adjusted structure is upset by suddenly introducing another proton or a neutron: what happens? The most likely occurrence is that the unbalanced forces will cause one or more of the elastic strips to break, allowing a particle to fly out from the nucleus. The alteration in tension as the particles rearrange themselves may now cause other strips to break, so that further particles are thrown out, until eventually the whole system becomes balanced and stability is restored.

Scientists had good reason to believe that something on these lines takes place, since the atoms of some of the heavier elements are constantly rearranging themselves, and throwing off particles and rays in the process. The chief of these radiations are termed alpha particles, which are really high-speed helium nuclei, and electro-magnetic radiations, such as X-rays and gamma rays, caused by disturbances of the electrons close to the nucleus.

This spontaneous breaking up of atoms is termed radio-activity, and there are three families of radio-active substances, uranium, actinium and thorium. Radium is produced during the gradual disintegration of uranium, and in the case of each family of elements the disintegration of one produces yet another radio-active material, until finally, after millions of years, stability is achieved in the form of an isotope of lead.

It has been calculated that thirty-five billion atoms are disintegrating every second in a gramme of radium. This means that over a period of two thousand years radium loses half its strength. By similar calculations it has been determined that uranium disintegrates far more slowly: it loses half its radio-active power over a period of six billion years. Other intermediate elements, such as radio-active tracers produced in atomic piles, have much shorter lives, some losing half their strength in the course of weeks, others lasting only days, and some having a radio-active life measured in minutes.

Research workers, among whom were Madame Curie and Lord Rutherford, quickly realized that the alpha particle would repay intensive study, and that it might prove a useful projectile with which to bombard the nuclei of atoms.

This tiny projectile, consisting of two protons and two neutrons, is shot out of the atom at a speed twenty thousand times as great as that of a rifle bullet. At about 12,000 miles per second its energy is tremendous and it is capable of penetrating deeply into the structure of the atom. The radium atom has an orderly life history of many million years; then rearranges itself, emitting an alpha particle which, after a short time, clothes itself with electrons and becomes an atom of helium.

During the past fifty years scientists have been working with minute quantities of matter, too small to be seen under the most powerful microscope, yet means of counting the individual particles and of tracing and recording their flight have been devised. Unless this could have been done, in fact, progress in atomic research would have come to a standstill.

The nearest approach to seeing an atomic particle at present possible is to observe the tiny flash of light which occurs when an alpha particle or a high-speed proton strikes a screen coated with zinc sulphide, which becomes bril-

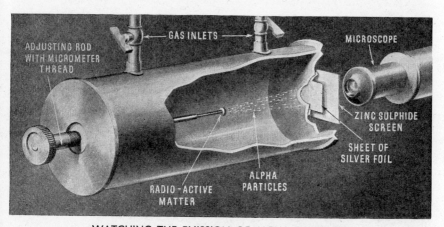

WATCHING THE EMISSION OF ALPHA PARTICLES

The nearest approach to getting a glimpse of the internal structure of the atom is by observing the bright flashes or scintillations of light which occur when a stream of alpha particles emitted by radio-active matter, such as radium, strikes a screen coated with zinc sulphide. This simple but very effective instrument is called a spinthariscope and has played an important role in atomic research.

liantly luminous under atomic bombardment. Most of the early experiments involved the use of such a screen, which forms the essential part of a simple but effective instrument called a spinthariscope, see page 223.

At one end of a small metal tube is a glass screen covered with zinc sulphide, while at the opposite end is a lens. In the centre of the tube is a minute speck of radium on a pin's head. On looking through the lens brilliant scintillating flashes on the screen can be seen, each caused by an alpha particle from the radium striking the screen. It was by counting these flashes caused by a known quantity of radium that Rutherford was able to calculate the rate at which radium disintegrates, arriving at the figure, mentioned earlier, of 35 billion atoms disintegrating every second in a gramme of this precious element, throwing out 35 billion alpha particles per second.

The scintillation method, however, has given place to less tedious methods of detection. The new means of detection depend on the fact that when a high-speed charged particle, such as an alpha particle or an electron, passes through air or a gas, it disrupts the molecules of the air or gas and produces small, charged fragments called "ions." These ions render the air or gas a conductor of electricity, and extremely sensitive electrical measuring devices have been developed to measure the electrical charge imparted by the ions. This in turn indicates the number of atomic particles which have caused the ionization.

To go any further into this aspect would call for considerable scientific

EARLY ATOM-SMASHING PLANT

Model of the apparatus used by J. D. Cockcroft and E. T. S. Walton in their researches into atomic structure at the Cavendish Laboratory, Cambridge. The experiments proved that the nucleus could be disrupted by atomic projectiles and, more important still, that Rutherford's theory of atomic structure was correct in its essentials.

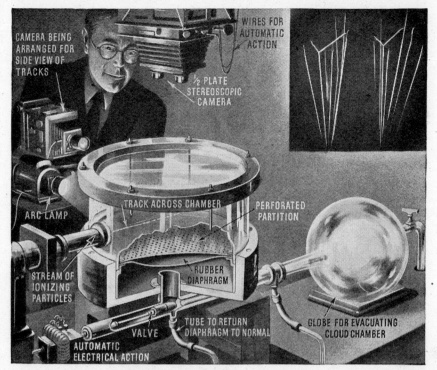

PHOTOGRAPHING ALPHA PARTICLES IN A WILSON CLOUD CHAMBER
The alpha particles streaming across the chamber cause tiny drops of water-vapour to condense on the ions formed in the wake. These tracks are clearly visible when illuminated by a powerful light, and are photographed by the stereo-scopic camera situated above the chamber; inset shows typical alpha tracks. A vacuum is created to allow condensation to form round the ions.

knowledge, besides leading us too far astray from the main path of atomic discovery. One method of detecting the ions must be mentioned, however, since it has contributed immeasurably to the progress of atomic research. This is the Wilson cloud chamber, which actually renders it possible to see and photograph the flight of a large variety of nuclear particles.

The principle is shown diagrammatically above. Imagine a glass-walled chamber filled with water vapour. The base of the chamber is formed by a rubber diaphragm. If it is drawn suddenly downwards a partial vacuum will be caused in the chamber, and this renders the tiny water droplets very liable to condense on any object inside the chamber. Now suppose that a shower of alpha particles is released in the chamber. The drops will not condense on such minute particles, but they will condense on the ions formed in the track of each particle. Thus, when illuminated by a powerful light, the tiny dewdrops reveal

INTERIOR OF ATOM-SMASHING MACHINE

This machine is used in modern atomic research to bombard specimens of material with electrically-charged particles travelling at the incredible speed of 30 million to 100 million miles per hour. Small charges of electricity are sprayed on belt conveyors and deposited on a big metal hemisphere (see picture opposite). The accumulation of these small charges builds up a tremendous voltage which propels the particles through the discharge tube. The whole apparatus is contained in a steel tank into which air is pumped to about 100 lb. sq. in.

the track of each atomic particle, including any sudden diversions caused by collisions with other atoms. The value of such an apparatus should not need stressing.

As was expected, the alpha particle proved a useful weapon in penetrating the defences of the atom, and as early as 1919 Rutherford succeeded in changing a few atoms of nitrogen gas into oxygen by bombarding the nitrogen atoms with alpha particles, while by 1924 Rutherford and Chadwick had disintegrated most elements in a similar manner.

Nevertheless, the research workers quickly appreciated that the alpha particle had serious shortcomings as a missile for bombarding the nucleus of the atom. Because it consists of four protons, which are positively charged, and two neutrons without any charge, it has, in effect, two positive charges. Consequently, whenever it comes into the vicinity of a nucleus, with its own strong positive charge, there is a violent repulsion between the two, and the alpha particle is apt to be deflected in spite of its speed.

Obviously one method of obtaining a particle of improved penetrating power was to use a proton, which had only a single positive charge. What is required, moreover, is an intense stream of particles which can be directed on to a small target so that the chances of striking nuclei are multiplied, as compared with bombardment by alpha particles from radio-active substances, which give an efficiency, at the best, of one in a million, the majority of the

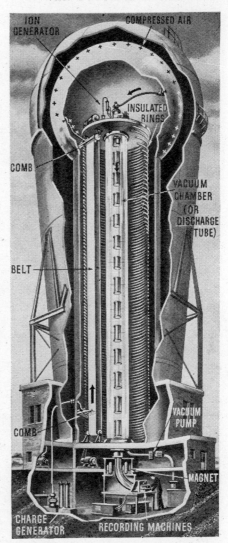

The principle of the Van de Graaff generator illustrated above is that electric charges can be conveyed from point to point by means of insulated rotating disks. In this generator the disks are replaced by a belt, which is charged from a generator and fed by means of combs. In principle and operation it is similar to an escalator, but instead of people electric charges are conveyed.

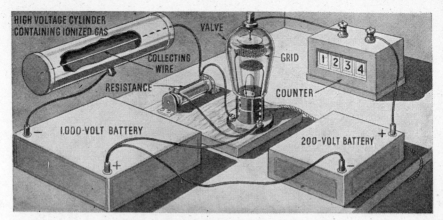

HOW THE GEIGER-MULLER COUNTER WORKS

A single alpha or beta particle passing through a cylinder filled with gas will cause a discharge of current. In the Geiger-Muller counter this current is amplified by the valve and operates an electrical counting device. This instrument is used for checking the intensity of radiation given off by radio-active substances.

particles becoming hopelessly entangled in the protecting layers of electrons and never reaching their targets.

At Cambridge, Cockcroft and Walton experimented with the production of a copious stream of protons by passing an electric current through hydrogen gas. The next step was to accelerate these particles to the required speed. This was done by using very high electrical voltages, in the neighbourhood of half a million volts. Nowadays energies equivalent to the fantastic figure of one hundred million volts can be applied to atomic particles, but this is not done by using actual voltages of this magnitude. Instead, an apparatus known as the cyclotron is used for this purpose.

To understand the principle of this machine it must be appreciated that the atomic missile, whether it be a powerfully charged proton, an alpha particle or a negatively charged electron, will be strongly attracted by any surface or body which possesses the opposite electrical charge.

Electrons, for instance, will fly rapidly to a positively-charged plate, while protons will travel towards a negatively-charged one. The higher the voltage on the plate, the greater the speed at which the particles fly towards it.

When the plate is maintained at a very high voltage, the particles can be likened to drops of water in a waterfall rushing over a precipice of tremendous height, and gaining a correspondingly high energy as they fall. Just as a gallon of water, weighing roughly ten pounds, would be said to gain 10,000 foot-pounds of energy as it falls down a precipice 1,000 feet high, so an electron attracted by a plate maintained at a potential of 10,000 volts is said to gain an energy of 10,000 electron-volts.

Very high voltages, in the neighbourhood of a million volts or more, are very difficult to produce, and dangerous to control, hence the cyclotron was developed, in which an electric "precipice" of 150,000 volts may be all that is required.

The construction of the cyclotron is clearly depicted on page 230. It will be seen that it resembles a flat, circular metal box, cut into two halves. The halves are usually referred to as the "dees." Across these two halves is maintained a high voltage, so that the gap between them forms the electrical precipice over which the atomic particles fall headlong.

Next it will be noticed that the two halves of the box, or "dees," are placed between the poles of a powerful electro-magnet. This is to take advantage of the fact that if a charged atomic particle is placed in the field between the poles of a magnet it will begin to circle around between the poles.

The source of atomic particles is in the form of an electric arc inside the dees, and a vacuum, or as nearly as possible a vacuum, surrounding them, so that the particles can move freely without being slowed down by striking the molecules of gases present in the atmosphere.

Now suppose that the current in the electro-magnet is switched on, and an electron is produced by an electric arc inside the dees. Under the influence of the

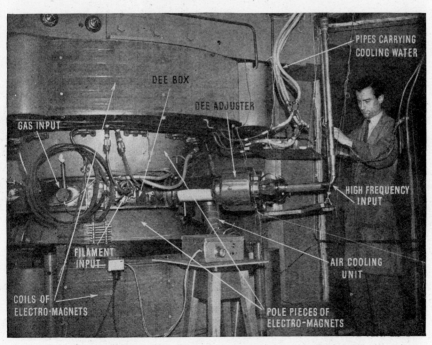

CYCLOTRON IN THE MOND LABORATORY, CAMBRIDGE
Adjustment being made to an atom-smashing machine. The principles of operation of this machine are diagrammatically shown overleaf.

electro-magnetic field the electron will begin to travel round and round in a circle inside the dees. Next, the dees are connected to the positive and negative poles of a source of electricity generating, say 100,000 volts, so that the right-hand dee becomes positive and the left-hand one negative.

It will be evident that as the circling electron, or other particle approaches the gap between the dees, as shown below, it will be faced with a "precipice" of 100,000 volts, and, as it jumps the gap, the attraction of the positive dee will greatly accelerate it. The electron then continues its circular path, but because it is now travelling much faster it will swing farther away from the centre of the dees, just as a stone flies out when swung round on the end of a string.

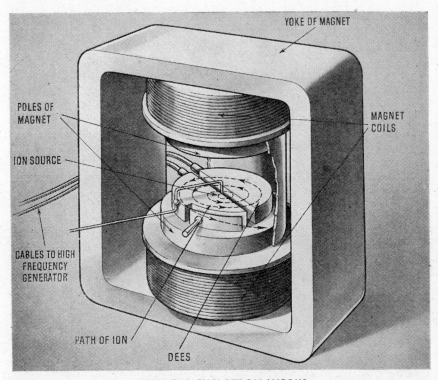

YOKE OF MAGNET

POLES OF MAGNET

MAGNET COILS

ION SOURCE

CABLES TO HIGH FREQUENCY GENERATOR

PATH OF ION

DEES

HOW THE CYCLOTRON WORKS

Electrons or other atomic particles are produced by an electric arc at the centre of the dees between the poles of an electromagnet. Forced by the magnetic field to follow a spiral path, they are accelerated and attracted across the gap between the dees by a high-voltage alternating current, and are finally flung out at immense speed on to a target. Under the bombardment the target element becomes unstable, that is, it will shoot out further radiations and particles, thus behaving in every respect like a radio-active element, such as radium. The value of this machine in medical research will be readily appreciated.

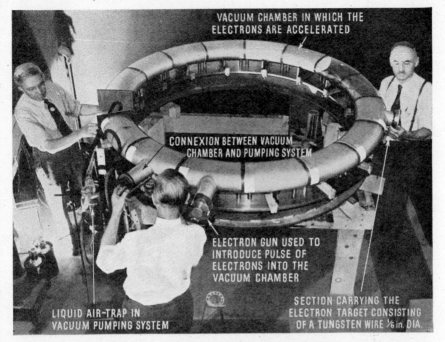

ASSEMBLING VACUUM CHAMBER IN A BETATRON

The betatron is in principle and construction similar to the cyclotron illustrated opposite, and has been developed to generate beams of higher voltages.

The electron is now rapidly approaching the gap between the dees again, and if the current remains unchanged the negatively-charged surface which faces it will repel it and slow it down, or bring it to a standstill. At the critical moment, therefore, the current applied to the dees is reversed, so that the electron is again faced by a positively-charged surface on the other side of a 100,000-volt precipice. It is again accelerated, and, having now acquired 200,000 electron-volts of energy in two steps, will swing wider than before.

Thus, as the particle whirls round and round in the cyclotron, accelerated in successive steps of 100,000 electron-volts by the alternating current, it travels through a wider and wider circle, following, in fact, a spiral path, until eventually it flies out of the opening of the dee on to the target. An electrode, maintained at a high voltage, helps to deflect the particle into the exit or target chamber which is situated on the side of the machine.

Since a succession of particles is being produced in the arc at the centre of the dees, the effect is that of an incredibly intense machine-gun fire of particles, each endowed with an energy of from fifteen to one hundred million electron-volts, concentrated on to a small target. The effect, as can be imagined, is overwhelming as far as the atoms of the target are concerned. The high-speed

231

particles, whether they be electrons, protons or a special heavy type of particle produced from heavy hydrogen and known as a deuteron, embed themselves in the nuclei of the atoms of the target, or dislodge one or more of the existing particles from it.

In either case the effect is the same. A different element is created, and, because this has been done by artificially upsetting the balance of the nucleus, the element is generally unstable, i.e. will shoot out further particles until equilibrium is restored. A radio-active substance has, in fact, been artificially created, with a life depending on the particular element. Delivered without delay to hospitals and research laboratories, it will enable life-saving treatment or essential research to be carried out with the minimum of expense, as compared with the use of rare and costly natural radio-active substances such as radium, the price of which is about one hundred thousand times that of gold.

ARTIFICIAL RADIO-ACTIVE ELEMENTS

Most readers will be familiar with the curative effects of the rays emitted by radium or by X-ray apparatus, as described in Chapter 8. The artificial radio-active elements can be used in a similar manner, but have added advantages. Since almost any element can be made radio-active, a substance can be chosen which can be administered to a patient without having any ordinary medical effect on the body. A substance, moreover, which is absorbed by certain tissues only, such as phosphorus, which is taken up by the bones, spleen and liver, as well as by certain cancerous growths. Substitute radio-phosphorus for the ordinary element, and we have a means of applying X-ray or radium treatment to a localized spot from inside the body, in precisely controlled amounts. With normal external irradiation, the rays must pass through healthy tissues to reach a deep-seated growth, and cause so-called radiation sickness in doing so.

Another use is to administer minute doses of radio-active elements to human beings, animals and plants in quantities which are not sufficient to cause any physical effects; yet the radiations can be traced by instruments or photographed, so that the course of the element as it passes through the blood stream, tissues or the cells of growing plants can be accurately determined. This has proved an inestimable boon to the doctor, biologist and research chemist.

In describing the cyclotron and its benefits, however, we must not overlook the fact that it was by using more orthodox high-voltage equipment in a laboratory at Cambridge that Cockcroft and Walton succeeded, in 1932, in doing something which had hitherto baffled scientists: they bombarded lithium with high-speed particles accelerated by a voltage of 700,000 volts, and disintegrated it into two roughly equal halves.

Until then experimenters had only succeeded in upsetting the balance of the nucleus and causing disintegration and artificial radio-activity. Now, for the first time, a nucleus had been instantaneously split into two parts, with the release of a considerable amount of energy, totalling 17 million electron-volts. It should

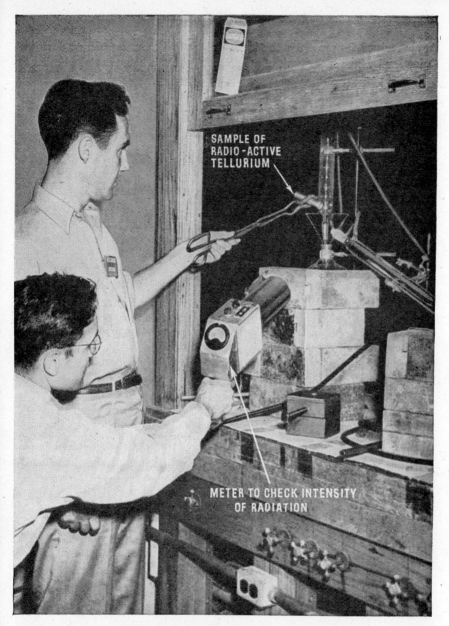

SAMPLE OF
RADIO-ACTIVE
TELLURIUM

METER TO CHECK INTENSITY
OF RADIATION

ATOMIC ENERGY FOR MEDICAL RESEARCH

One of the most important developments since the discovery of atomic fission is the production of artificially radio-active elements, known as tracer elements, for medical research. The view above shows a stage in the extraction of radio-active iodine from bombarded or radio-active tellurium. The operator in the foreground is using a special meter to measure the intensity of radiation.

be appreciated, however, that this is not truly related to nuclear fission described below, and which is the basis of atomic energy that is being exploited as a new source of power.

Even more interesting to scientists, although less spectacular, was the fact that the combined masses of the two particles into which the nucleus was divided did not add up to the original mass of the nucleus. In other words, matter had been destroyed, or, more precisely, had been converted into energy, thus proving one of the aspects of Einstein's Theory of Relativity, that matter can be converted into energy.

It was even possible to verify this particular aspect of Einstein's theory of the equivalence of mass and energy, made as early as 1905, that one pound of matter is equal to eleven thousand, four hundred million kilowatt hours.

NUCLEUS AS A SOURCE OF POWER

Naturally scientists were fully aware of this vast potential store of power locked up in the nucleus of the atom. Unfortunately, it seemed possible to release only relatively small quantities of it at a time, because the quantities of material used in the experiments were infinitesimally small, being measured in fractions of a millionth part of a gramme. The electrical energy needed to bombard the atomic nuclei, in fact, was greater than that obtained when a nucleus was split.

Obviously what was required was a self-sustaining series of splittings, or "fissions," to use the scientific term. If the splitting or fission of one atom could be made to start a chain of fissions in the surrounding atoms, a rapid release of power in great quantities could be obtained.

A spontaneous series of nuclear fissions of this type is called a chain reaction, and can be compared to the manner in which an ordinary fire quickly spreads through any inflammable material. Igniting a small quantity of a fuel, such as paper, wood, coal, paraffin or petrol, causes sufficient heat to ignite the surrounding fuel, which in turn releases more heat and ignites a still greater quantity of fuel; combustion in an engine cylinder is a particularly good example.

COMBUSTION AND ATOMIC ENERGY

Now combustion as we know it is due to the rearrangement of the outer electrons in the atoms of the fuel; although the fuel is changed outwardly, no matter is actually destroyed. There is, it should be appreciated, an infinitesimal change in mass due to chemical change. The heat liberated may be used to warm our homes, boil water, or cook food, or indirectly in the form of steam to drive steam engines and turbines; it also provides power by causing the expansion of gases in the cylinders of a petrol or oil engine. Steam, gas, petrol, and oil engines are, therefore, termed heat engines by the scientist and engineer.

Fission results in the destruction of a minute percentage of the atomic fuel, and, in the case of the atomic bomb it is this tiny proportion which is changed into a tremendous amount of energy in the form of heat.

234

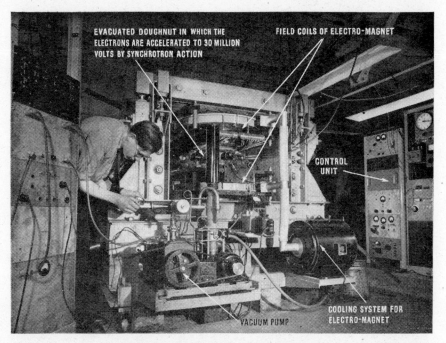

ATOM-SMASHING PLANT AT HARWELL
Newly developed high-voltage synchrotron being used to study synchrotron techniques and to guide the design of the monster machines now being built.

If the fission of the atoms takes place at a moderate rate, this heat can be used to provide power, just as in the case of an ordinary fuel. If the fission is allowed to proceed at a runaway speed, on the other hand, the vast amount of heat suddenly radiated will so expand the surrounding air that enormous pressure is developed, resulting in a blast wave which is capable of completely destroying everything within its effective range.

To liberate this tremendous energy, then, a chain reaction must take place. But for the discovery of the neutron, it is unlikely that this source of power could have been effectively tapped. In 1932, while Cockcroft and Walton were concentrating on splitting the nucleus of the lithium atom, another British scientist, Chadwick, confirmed the presence of a high-speed, uncharged particle which was emitted by the nucleus when bombarded by atomic missiles. Research in Germany, and by Irene Curie and Joliot in Paris, had suggested the existence of this particle, which was to prove the key to atomic fission.

Since the neutron has no electrical charge, it cannot be directly detected by any of the methods mentioned earlier. The only way of counting and observing neutrons, in fact, is by their effect on other atomic particles, and this explains why their existence was confirmed only at a comparatively late stage in atomic research. A swiftly moving neutron occasionally collides with the nucleus of an atom, thus imparting to it some of its momentum and causing the nucleus itself to become a high-speed particle; since the nucleus is electrically charged, it will cause ionization which will affect the various detectors already described, and its path can thus be traced.

The progress of a neutron was once compared by Lord Rutherford to the passage of an invisible man through a dense crowd: his path could only be traced by the movement of the people he had collided with or elbowed aside. The comparison is not altogether true, however, for the neutron, unlike the invisible man, may be captured or absorbed by the nucleus it strikes. This causes a nuclear reaction which liberates sufficient electricity to cause ionization, so that the capture of the neutron can be detected.

Consider the advantages now offered to the scientist. He had at his disposal a high-speed projectile which, being free from any electrical charge, would neither be attracted nor repelled by the network of electrons circling round the nucleus of an atom, nor by the nucleus itself. Consequently once a neutron had been liberated it would continue to travel forward at high speed until it collided with a nucleus, when it might bounce off or be absorbed.

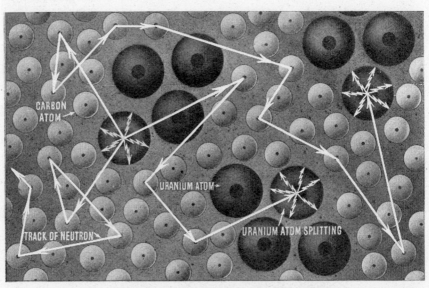

ACTION OF A CARBON MODERATOR

The function of a carbon moderator is to slow down the speed of the neutrons which are emitted after fission of the uranium. The uranium atom towards the left of the illustration has split, releasing neutrons, the tracks of three being shown. One will escape from the pile (left). The two others have been deflected by carbon atoms, and eventually strike other uranium atoms, which split and produce fresh neutrons to continue the chain reaction.

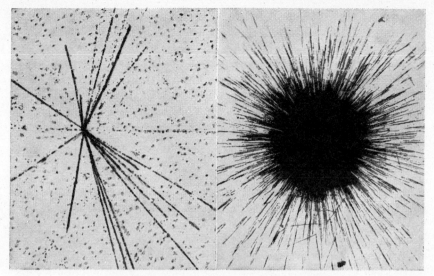

PHOTOGRAPHING ATOMIC EXPLOSIONS
*When a disintegrating atom, that is, any of the family of radio-active elements, is
embedded in the emulsion of a photographic plate, the tracks made by the particles
emanating from it are recorded by their direct action on the silver salts contained
in the emulsion; two examples are shown above. The features of these particles,
such as energy and momentum, can be determined by measuring the tracks.*

There was still the drawback that, since the nucleus offers only one hundred
millionth part of the target area of the atom, a neutron is only likely to hit a
nucleus after travelling through one hundred million atoms; to produce neutrons,
too, involves the use of high voltages, as in the case of other atomic particles, so
that the process was still relatively inefficient.

The position was improved in 1939, however, by the discovery that, when the
nucleus of a uranium atom is split, not only is an exceptionally large quantity of
energy released, but from one to three neutrons are also thrown off. Supposing
that these neutrons in turn strike other uranium nuclei and cause them to split,
releasing still more neutrons to carry on the fission, we shall have a chain
reaction similar to the burning of a normal fuel: the process will become self-
supporting, and because of the energy developed will cause terrific pressure
and, consequently, an explosion; alternatively it can be controlled by some
external means, such as the control rods used in an atomic pile.

Nevertheless, there were still difficulties to be overcome before this could be
realized in practice. Uranium 238, the isotope which forms 99·3 per cent of natural
uranium, contains impurities which tend to absorb the neutrons and thus bring
the chain reaction to a standstill. Even when almost pure uranium 235 is used,
many of the neutrons escape from the surface of the metal before encountering

nuclei, so that there is obviously a critical size for the block of metal, below which the reaction will cease, due to the loss of neutrons exceeding their production in the metal.

A third difficulty is the fact that the speed at which the neutron is travelling largely determines whether the nucleus will be split, or whether it will absorb the neutron without fission, forming a new element, plutonium 239. It was, therefore, necessary to use a material which would act as a "moderator" and slow down the speed of the neutrons, since the low-speed particles were found, strangely enough, to be the most efficient in causing fission.

FUNCTION OF A MODERATOR

An efficient moderator is so-called "heavy water." This is water which contains hydrogen atoms of twice the normal weight. Normally one atom of heavy hydrogen is present only in some 6,500 atoms of ordinary hydrogen. If a heavy electrical current is passed through water for a very long period, however, the ordinary hydrogen is given off as gas and eventually a concentrated amount of heavy water is obtained. It takes over seven hundred gallons of ordinary water to produce one pint of heavy water, so that the process is slow and extremely expensive.

Where large quantities of cheap electric power are not available, heavy water is prepared by a special distillation process, or by causing hydrogen and steam to react in large towers; the latter an intricate process which is, nevertheless, the most economical of those in use at present.

Owing to the high cost of preparing heavy water, its use is confined at present to small atomic power units mainly intended for laboratory use, and as a source of heavy hydrogen particles or deuterons, for use as atomic missiles. For commercial purposes very pure carbon in the form of graphite is used as a moderator, its comparative cheapness and ready availability largely offsetting the fact that a very much larger atomic pile is required.

CONTROLLING ATOMIC POWER

By arranging rods of uranium in a lattice structure in a block of carbon, the neutrons can not only be slowed down, but given a better chance of striking nuclei before escaping from the lattice. This structure is called an atomic "pile."

Assuming that a steady flow of power is required, control over the reaction is essential. This is done by inserting in the pile rods or strips of a metal which readily capture neutrons, such as boron or cadmium steel. Sufficient strips are inserted to prevent any chain reaction taking place, and the strips are then withdrawn, allowing the free neutrons to begin to cause fission and multiply. The degree to which the control strips are withdrawn determines the power given off by the pile; sensitive instruments in the pile measure the radio-activity and operate automatic controls which move the rods into or out of the pile.

It has already been stressed that the energy given off by atomic fission is largely in the form of heat. Since the pile would quickly be destroyed by the very high temperature generated, the uranium rods must be cooled. Various methods are available, among them air cooling, water cooling, and cooling by means of a liquefied chemical.

In the first large piles built in America, water cooling was used, and since these piles were only intended to produce plutonium for atomic bombs by burning uranium 238, the heat was allowed to go to waste by directing the cooling water to flow into the Columbia River after allowing it to stand in open-air basins until the radio-activity acquired during its passage through the pile had died down.

This cooling water was well below boiling point on leaving the pile, and before the atomic pile can be used as a boiler to generate steam for use in a power station the engineer and the scientist will have many problems to overcome, both from

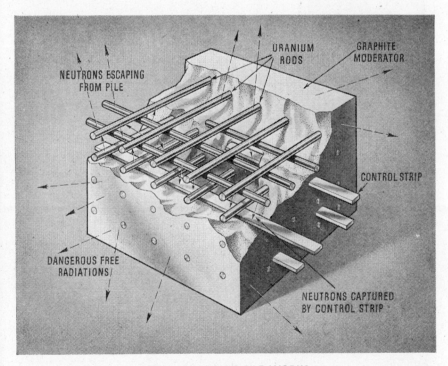

HOW AN ATOMIC PILE WORKS

In this drawing the rods of uranium are shown embedded in a block of graphite. Neutrons escaping from the rods cause the atoms in the rods to split, thus setting up a chain reaction. The graphite slows down and deflects most of the neutrons, but some escape from the pile, which must be surrounded by a protective shield to trap the dangerous stray radiations and protect the operators. The reaction is controlled by sliding into the pile strips of metal which capture the neutrons.

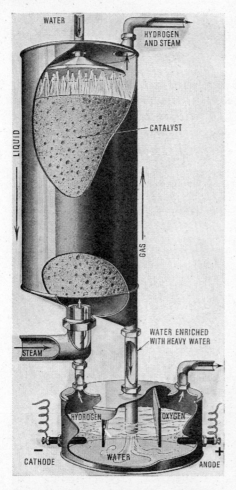

Water is converted into hydrogen and oxygen by passing an electric current through it. The hydrogen is mixed with steam and bubbles up through water flowing down through the catalyst. Heavy hydrogen atoms in the gas combine with the water, which thus contains an increasingly large proportion of heavy water.

the mechanical and the atomic points of view. The material from which the steam pipes are made, for instance, must be strong enough to withstand high steam pressures, yet must not absorb neutrons and so stop the reaction. Possibly a solution may be found in circulating a chemical with a high melting-point, such as bismuth, which melts at 672 deg. C., through the pile, and then employing the high-temperature liquid to heat a boiler.

Other engineering difficulties are introduced by the necessity for surrounding the pile with massive concrete walls to absorb the radiations given off, which are so powerful as to render it quite impossible for anyone to approach the pile when it is working. The shields must not only be radiation-proof, but also airtight, since the air surrounding the pile becomes radio-active.

The uranium rods must be loaded into the pile and unloaded by remote control, and, since the by-products of the fission are also highly radio-active, the spent rods must be handled by remote control during transport to the processing plants in which the plutonium and other products are separated, each stage also taking place in heavily shielded, remotely controlled tanks.

Mention of the separation of plutonium from the used rods brings us to the next important stage in the development of atomic power. We have seen that the isotope, uranium 238, is not an altogether ideal atomic fuel. A rare isotope, uranium 235, which forms 0·7 per cent of natural uranium, is a much better fuel; it more readily maintains a chain reaction, and enables a much smaller pile to be used for a given amount of power. Plutonium, too, is a more efficient fuel.

Uranium 235 and plutonium 239, in fact, were the only nuclear fuels originally available in which a chain reaction would develop quickly enough to enable them to be used as explosives. In an atomic bomb the reaction must build up so quickly as to be complete in the instant of time before the bomb is shattered by the explosion.

Obviously, once the component parts of the bomb become separated neutrons will escape, and the chain reaction will stop. We have also seen that when a piece of concentrated nuclear fuel exceeds a certain critical size an uncontrollable chain reaction will start. To produce an efficient atomic bomb, therefore, the radio-active fuel must be divided into two or more pieces, each piece being below the critical size, and these must be brought rapidly together when it is desired to explode the bomb.

As the pieces approach one another and neutrons cross the gap between them a chain reaction is likely to start in each piece. This would, of course, result in a premature disintegration of the bomb as just described, giving an ineffective explosion. Speed in bringing them together is, therefore, the essence of the operation. The best method of rapidly bringing two parts together immediately suggests itself: to fire one part at the other, like a bullet from a gun.

TESTING THE ATOMIC BOMB IN THE BIKINI ATOLL
Gigantic mushroom of smoke and water rising after the release of the first underwater atom bomb. The test ships can be seen in the foreground.

The detailed arrangements of the atomic bomb are, of course, of the utmost secrecy, but it has been revealed that this is, in broad principle, the method adopted. The problem is complicated by the necessity for incorporating a suitable moderator to prevent escape of neutrons. Graphite, besides acting as a moderator, also reflects neutrons back into the fuel if it surrounds the bomb, and also has the advantage of acting in a similar manner to the damper used with a normal explosive. The role of a damper is to restrain the initial expansion of the explosive until the reaction has built up to the maximum, thus providing a more violent explosion.

Patiently these problems were solved one by one until, shortly after eight o'clock on the morning of 6 August, 1945, an American Superfortress, flying at 30,000 ft., dropped the first atomic bomb over the Japanese city of Hiroshima.

HEAT OF ATOMIC EXPLOSION

As the equivalent of 20,000 tons of T.N.T. exploded high in the air above the town there was a blinding flash, a roaring sound, and a tremendous blast wave swept the town, accompanied by a hurricane of wind which for a moment reached a speed of 500 miles per hour. The blast wave created enormous destruction; what was left by the blast wave was rapidly destroyed by the innumerable fires, simultaneously kindled by the searing heat of the atomic explosion.

Since the early research work on nuclear fuels was of necessity directed towards the production of an atomic bomb of this type, efforts were mainly concerned with producing sufficient quantities of the concentrated isotopes uranium 235 and plutonium 239 from the natural uranium. The successful production of these fuels in useful quantities, however, gives promise of lighter, more compact atomic power plants for peaceful uses in the future.

SEPARATING URANIUM 235

The uranium 235 isotope can be separated from uranium 238 by chemical or by electro-magnetic means. In the first case the natural uranium may be changed into a gas, which is forced through fine filters. The uranium 235 atoms, being lighter, pass through the filter a little more quickly than do the uranium 238 atoms; by repeating the process a very large number of times, concentrated uranium 235 is obtained. A somewhat similar scheme is to dissolve the natural uranium in a liquid, and to take advantage of the rates at which the two isotopes move through this liquid in a tank, one wall of which is heated and the other cooled, see lower drawing on opposite page.

Both these processes are too complicated to describe in detail, and give only a very gradual increase in the proportion of uranium 235 in the basic uranium. The electro-magnetic method, on the other hand, enables the two isotopes to be virtually separated, although the rate of production is slower.

In this apparatus gases from uranium salts are bombarded by electrons. Some of the charged atoms which result pass through a slit in a plate, which

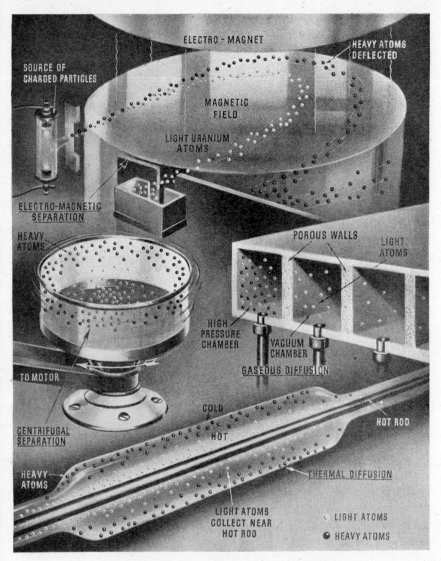

ELECTRO - MAGNET

HEAVY ATOMS DEFLECTED

SOURCE OF CHARGED PARTICLES

MAGNETIC FIELD

LIGHT URANIUM ATOMS

ELECTRO-MAGNETIC SEPARATION

HEAVY ATOMS

POROUS WALLS

LIGHT ATOMS

HIGH PRESSURE CHAMBER

VACUUM CHAMBER

GASEOUS DIFFUSION

TO MOTOR

CENTRIFUGAL SEPARATION

HEAVY ATOMS

COLD

HOT

HOT ROD

THERMAL DIFFUSION

LIGHT ATOMS COLLECT NEAR HOT ROD

LIGHT ATOMS

HEAVY ATOMS

METHODS OF SEPARATING URANIUM ISOTOPES

The isotope U235 is the part of uranium used as an atomic fuel, and must be separated from the heavier and more abundant isotope U238. In the electro-magnetic method (top) electrically-charged particles are deflected by an electro-magnet, only the lighter U235 atoms passing into the collector box. The centrifugal method (left) is similar, the lighter atoms collecting at the centre. In the gaseous diffusion system (right) only the lighter atoms pass through the successive filters. In the thermal diffusion method (bottom) the U235 atoms congregate around the heated rod, while the heavier U238 atoms collect near the outer wall of the tube. The electro-magnetic and thermal diffusion methods are the more widely used for the separation of U235 from U238.

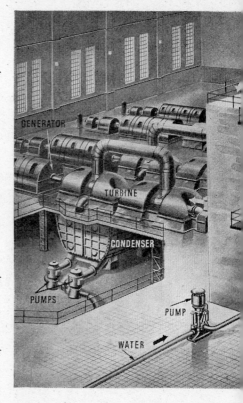

In this imaginative drawing of an atomic pile in an electricity generating station, the probable features of the atomic power plant of the future are shown diagrammatically. The heat of the atomic reaction transforms water, fed into the power cylinders by a pump, into superheated steam which is used to drive turbines coupled · to the electrical generators. After passing through the high- and low-pressure turbines the steam is condensed and the water fed back to the atomic pile. The pile is surrounded by concrete to trap stray neutrons, while special precautions are also taken to remove all traces of radio-activity from the steam before it passes to the turbine. The pile is controlled from the desk in the foreground, and detectors are installed in the building ·to give warning of dangerous radiations.

focuses them into a beam. They are then accelerated by an electric field which gives both the lighter uranium 235 and the heavier uranium 238 atoms the same speed. After passing through a second slit, the beam of atoms is deflected through a semicircle by another magnetic field.

Since the heavier atoms of uranium 238 possess greater momentum, however, they turn through a slightly wider curve than the uranium 235 atoms; the beam will thus split into two, and the heavier and lighter atoms will strike a third plate a slight distance apart. By arranging slits in the plate at the appropriate points the two types of atoms can be collected; a simplified diagram of this apparatus is shown on page 243.

Some idea of the magnitude of the task that confronted both scientists and engineers in separating uranium 235 from uranium 238 can be gained from the fact that the first gas diffusion plant built in America consisted of a four-storey building which covered sixty acres and cost over £100 million. The electromagnetic plant consisted of 175 separate buildings costing about £90 million, and was the first large-scale plant to produce useful quantities of uranium 235, the key element in atomic energy development.

What are the prospects of the atomic power plant as a substitute for conventional power units in the near future? At present it seems that nuclear fuels can

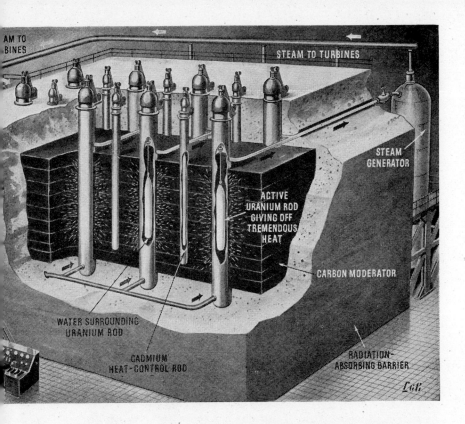

STEAM TO TURBINES

STEAM
GENERATOR

ACTIVE
URANIUM ROD
GIVING OFF
TREMENDOUS
HEAT

CARBON MODERATOR

WATER SURROUNDING
URANIUM ROD

CADMIUM
HEAT-CONTROL ROD

RADIATION-
ABSORBING BARRIER

only be used in large-scale power stations for the generation of electricity or the production of steam power and heating for very large factories or factory estates. The main difficulty in producing smaller power units suitable for driving ships, railway locomotives, aircraft or road transport lies in the great weight of the shielding necessary to absorb the dangerous radiations emanating from the atomic fuel in order to protect the operators.

Even a comparatively small atomic power unit, developing the equivalent of, say, two or three thousand horse-power, would require shielding which would weigh upwards of a hundred tons. Compare this with the high-powered aero-engine of today, developing 3,500 horse-power or more, and weighing less than a ton and a half, or the gas turbine or jet propulsion engine of half this weight for an equivalent power.

It can be argued, of course, that the modern four-engined air-liner may carry as much as fifteen or twenty tons of fuel for a long flight, whereas the weight of atomic fuel required to produce a similar power output for the same period would be measured in pounds instead of tons. Even this saving, however, cannot offset the tremendous weight of the shielding necessary for the atomic power units; nor is the shielding, like the aircraft's fuel, steadily consumed by the engine during the flight, thus gradually reducing the load the aircraft has to carry.

It would seem, therefore, that the most likely application of the smaller atomic power units will be in large ships; possibly other means of utilizing nuclear fuels or improved methods of shielding may eventually revolutionize our present ideas, and open up fresh scope for compact, economical power units for military and civil aircraft and cars.

Any large-scale use of atomic power, however, will immediately raise the question of adequate supplies of nuclear fuel. Uranium is found principally in deposits of pitchblende occurring in Canada, the Belgian Congo and Czecho-slovakia; it is also obtained from carnotite and autunite in the western states of America. Although other uranium-bearing deposits are found elsewhere in the world, some authorities doubt whether the natural resources could last for many years if mined on the scale necessitated by extensive use of atomic power. Other nuclear fuels may, and probably will, be produced. Thorium, for instance, can be used to produce uranium 233 in reactors in which uranium 235 or pluto-nium supplies the necessary inflammable agent, as a chain reaction cannot be started in thorium alone.

Again, the wider production and use of nuclear fuels for peaceful purposes

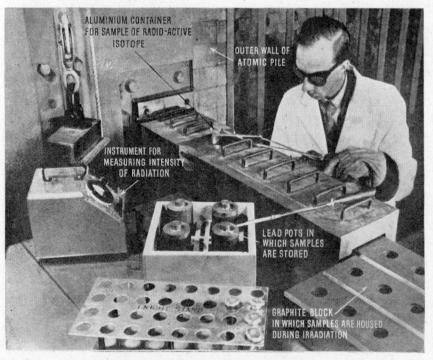

PRODUCING RADIO-ACTIVE ISOTOPES

Radio-active isotopes being removed from the atomic pile. This view shows a section of the Atomic Energy Research Establishment, Harwell.

CONTROLLING ATOMIC POWER
*Control room for the graphite low-energy experimental pile (known as Gleep)
at the Atomic Energy Research Establishment, Harwell.*

brings in its train the risk that they may be diverted to the production of atomic bombs and other weapons. The international control of atomic weapons, in fact, presents an extremely serious problem for those seeking the establishment of world peace, since nuclear fuels could be diverted to weapon production at many stages, from the mine to the final reactor.

The scientists concerned with the development of the atomic bomb have confessed that during the early stages of their work they hoped that some insurmountable difficulty would be encountered to prove that atomic fission could not be employed on a large scale. The bombs dropped on Hiroshima and Nagasaki have shown that that hope was unfounded. It remains to ensure that this weapon, capable of unimaginable destruction, does not fall into irresponsible hands, and destroy the civilization to which it can give so much wealth.

Even more significant is the fact that uranium is a comparatively rare element, of which only a small proportion can be converted into a nuclear fuel. Of the concentrated fuel, only one part in one thousand is in turn converted into energy. If a chain reaction could be produced in a common element, and an efficiency of only five per cent obtained, mankind would either have the power to destroy the world and possibly the universe at will, or the key to a new era of undreamed-of power and speed, and the comfort and happiness of a world of plenty.

247

CONDENSER TO TUNE ONE
ELEMENT OF THE TUNING COILS

TWO ELEMENTS OF A TUNING COIL WHICH
SETS THE FREQUENCY OF THE TRANSMITTER

SETTING THE AMPLIFIER IN A BROADCAST TRANSMITTER

A general view of the rear of a 100-kilowatt broadcast transmitter, showing a circuit truck for the final modulated amplifier. Each truck is set up for the transmission of a different frequency. Note the rail system installed for guiding the trucks accurately to their proper places in the cabinet.

CHAPTER 8 The radio age

IT is a commonplace of this century that energy can be transferred from place to place. Our lives are full of instances; we press a switch and electrical energy comes along wires from a distant power station to warm us; we press another, and more energy of the same sort goes into our radio set, there to be controlled by radiant energy from some far-off broadcasting station. Also, we may hopefully expose ourselves to the fleeting sunshine of an English summer, thinking thereby to acquire a little healthful tan from the sun's ultra-violet radiation.

Radiant energy plays an ever-growing part in our lives and engrosses the attention of more and more men of science. Yet if we ask them what radiant energy really is, the answer is apt to be highly seasoned with Quantum Theory and Relativity. A generation ago we had it all neatly tied up and labelled. Radiant energy was a wave-motion in a hypothetical medium called the ether. This was postulated as something non-material of perfect elasticity, all-pervading, and with the property of passing freely through the substance of all material things. We went so far as to visualize the ether filling the open spaces between the atoms and molecules of a solid substance, and so being able to transmit wave-motions right through it. Atoms and electrons were thought of as tiny patches of strain in the ether, energy in static or locked-up form. This conception is not unlike the modern doctrine of matter as something that can be converted into energy. Of late, this tidy edifice of thought has developed some grievous cracks under the assault of the Einstein school and others, who deny the existence of an ether. However, the familiar forms of radiant energy, heat, light and radio waves, do undoubtedly exhibit features similar to things which we know to be wave-motions, such as the air waves we call sound.

If we are to think in terms of waves, the obvious starting point is to gain some idea of their wavelengths. Our knowledge of sound waves teaches us to expect that this will be a fundamental property; the character of a sound depends on the wavelengths or frequencies composing it. The expectation is justified. Waves of radiant energy have properties which are closely related to their wavelengths. Starting from a wavelength of the order of forty kilometres and extending downward to two or three millimetres, there is the range of radiations in use as

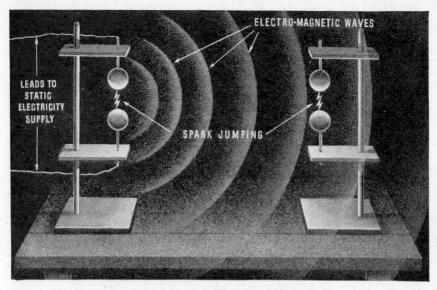

GENERATION OF ELECTRO-MAGNETIC WAVES

When a spark jumps across two charged spheres electro-magnetic waves are generated. These can be detected by placing in their path two uncharged spheres which will spark owing to a charge induced by the waves.

radio or wireless waves. From about a few millimetres down to a small fraction of a millimetre there is a gap in our knowledge; if there are radiations of such wavelengths we know nothing of them as yet.

The next shorter wavelength that we know is that of radiant heat, and from this we pass without a jump into that of the infra-red radiations, and so through the visible spectrum of red, orange, yellow, green and blue light to the invisible ultra-violet. Then come X-rays, gamma rays, and finally cosmic rays.

Among the radio waves themselves there are notable differences in properties according to their actual wavelength. All are alike in being created by electro-magnetic processes, and in their power to generate electric currents in suitable apparatus at a distance, but their behaviour when propagated through space varies widely. The long wavelengths show considerable power to bend round obstacles, and when travelling to far-distant places seem to follow smoothly round the earth's curved surface. As the wavelength is reduced this property weakens, and another becomes more and more noticeable. Upward slanting waves begin to be reflected down obliquely from some region in the upper atmosphere, see diagram on page 252.

Much research has been devoted to this strange phenomenon, and it is now known that there are several atmospheric layers, high above the earth's surface, which can bend radio waves back towards the ground. These layers, associated with the names of Heaviside and Appleton, are the means whereby the shorter waves travel great distances. With such radiations it is found that the waves which travel direct along the surface, called the "ground waves," soon die out, and can be heard only for short distances. The "sky waves," on the other hand, may be reflected back to earth many hundreds of miles farther on. Striking the ground, they may again be reflected, glancing off obliquely upwards, and once more returned to earth by yet another reflection from the upper layers of the atmosphere. In this manner the waves may cover great distances in a series of hops.

These reflection effects begin to be important by the time one comes down to the ordinary broadcast waveband, and become progressively more so towards the lower end of the band. They are the prime cause of that irritating phenomenon, fading. Imagine that the receiving aerial is at such a distance from the sender that it picks up energy which has travelled by two different routes, one the direct path over the earth's surface and the other a sky path, involving reflection from the Heaviside layer. Since the energy is of a vibratory kind, it is evident that if two packets thereof come by routes of different lengths they may or may not happen to be vibrating in step with each other when they arrive. If they do chance to be in step, the receiver will pick up an extra strong signal; if they are exactly out of step, it will receive little or nothing. Clearly, if the degree of reinforcement or opposition varies, so will the strength of the received signal, and

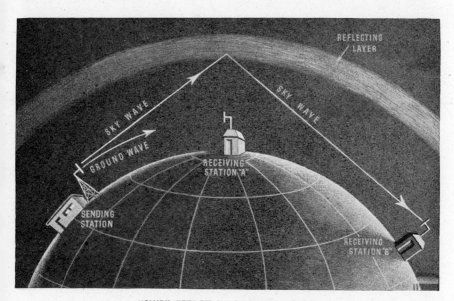

"SKIP" EFFECT IN BROADCASTING

The ground waves from the sending station do not reach station "A," and the reflected sky waves can be received only at a much greater distance—as, for example, at station "B." This phenomen is known as the "skip" effect.

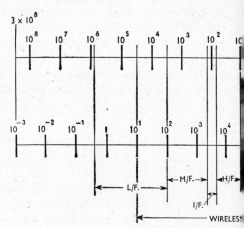

Vibrations which travel in a vacuum with a speed of 186,000 miles per second are electro-magnetic in origin and obey similar laws, such as reflection and refraction. The difference between the various groups of waves can be attributed entirely to the differences in wavelength.

that is how fading most often comes about, for the reflecting layers in the upper atmosphere are far from stable, and constantly alter in height, surface configuration, and reflective quality. Consequently, the signal from a distant broadcasting station is apt to vary in strength all the time. For this reason automatic volume control is fitted to so many receivers.

Sky reflections explain another peculiarity of radio waves, especially of the medium and short ones; they account for the greater range of a station after dark. During the day the reflecting atmospheric layers are exposed to the bom-

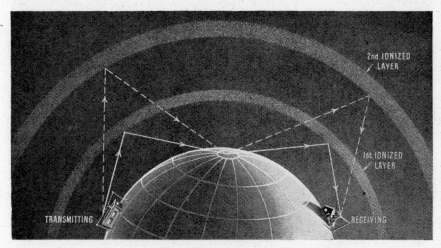

REFLECTING RADIO WAVES BY IONIZED LAYERS

This diagram shows in simplified fashion the effect of the ionized layers of the upper atmosphere on the distance short waves can be transmitted. The lower layer is known as the Heaviside Layer and the upper the Appleton Layer.

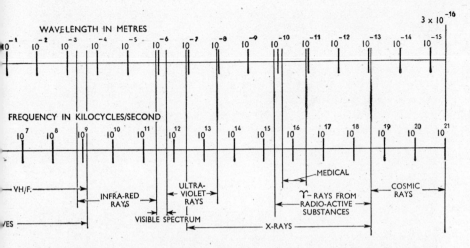

bardment of a variety of radiations from the sun, and are rendered turbulent and irregular thereby. They also ascend to a greater height, and become generally less effective as reflectors of these wavelengths as a result. By day, therefore, the range of a medium-wave broadcasting station is little if any more than the distance at which the ground wave can be heard. After dark the sky wave begins to extend the range enormously, often travelling strongly to distances which the ground wave cannot reach at all.

The relative carrying power of the sky and ground waves is a function of wavelength. At the lower extreme of the broadcast waveband, the ground wave is already becoming less and less effective, while the sky wave is capable of great ranges at night. Still lower down the scale this effect is accentuated. Early in the exploration of short waves it was discovered that a wavelength of sixty metres was capable of providing strong reception in Britain of a station at Pittsburg, U.S.A., by night, yet the daylight range of this station was quite short.

An odd phenomenon often observed on the shorter waves is the "skip" effect, which causes a zone of silence round the station at certain distances. Travelling away from the sender, one hears it at first by the ground wave, then this dies out and nothing is heard until, much farther away, the first sky wave returns to earth (see illustration on page 251).

Even the relative night and day range is to some extent a matter of wavelength, for well down the scale, somewhere below twenty metres, there are waves which appear to reverse the usual rule. In these regions, too, the ability to follow round the curvature of the earth gradually disappears, waves of, say, five to fifteen metres showing only a trace of it. The range of their ground wave is thus normally limited to little more than the optical horizon of the sending station. This is characteristic of the waves used for television, radar, and navigational aids such as Gee, most of which are of this order of length.

Much patient research, in which amateur radio men have played a notable

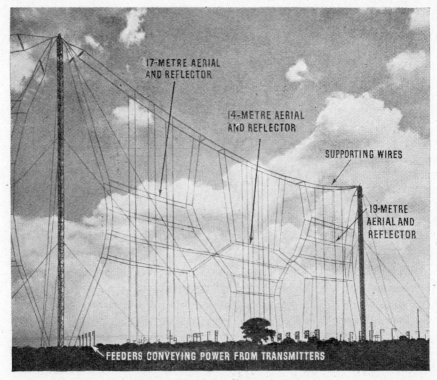

17-METRE AERIAL AND REFLECTOR

14-METRE AERIAL AND REFLECTOR

SUPPORTING WIRES

19-METRE AERIAL AND REFLECTOR

FEEDERS CONVEYING POWER FROM TRANSMITTERS

SHORT-WAVE TRANSMITTING AERIALS

B.B.C. transmitting aerials and reflectors for the 14-, 17- and 19-metre wavebands. This apparatus is used for transmitting programmes to such countries as India, Western Australia, West Indies, and Central America.

part, have been devoted to the detailed study of the different short wavelengths and their power to cover great distances. It is now possible to select a wavelength to reach a particular place at almost any time of the day and year, for there are seasonal complications.

Research still goes on upon one of the most interesting aspects of short-wave propagation, namely, the effect of sunspots. These phenomena are evidently accompanied by substantial changes in the normal solar radiations, and produce corresponding effects in the earth's upper atmosphere; electric storms and great displays of the aurora commonly follow big solar eruptions.

The effect on radio wave propagation is again largely a function of wavelength, notable consequences being mostly confined to the shorter waves, as might be expected from their dependence on the state of the reflecting layers for their ability to cover great distances. There is, therefore, a general correspondence between short-wave conditions and the eleven-year cycle of variation in sunspot intensity. It would be rash to dogmatize until more wavelengths have been in use for a complete sunspot cycle, but it seems likely that the general rule will hold good for all, and it will be found that conditions are best when sunspots are plentiful and poorest at the times of minimum. It does not follow, however, that periods of exceptionally intense solar activity necessarily imply specially good radio conditions; at such times freak effects are common, and at times a complete black-out may extend to the longer waves as well.

FOCUSING ULTRA-SHORT WAVES

It is chiefly on the very shortest waves, of the order of centimetres or millimetres, that information is still lacking, for these wavelengths only began to be used widely during the past ten years, chiefly for special military purposes. They have, incidentally, many interesting features, particularly their adaptability to radiation in a focused beam. It is indeed the almost universal practice to use them in this fashion, emitting them either from a horn not unlike a big version of an open-air loudspeaker, or from the focal point of a parabolic electrical mirror.

A focused beam of these extremely short waves tends to maintain a straight line, and has little power to bend round obstacles, or to follow round the earth's curvature under normal atmospheric conditions. There are, however, certain abnormal conditions which produce what is called anomalous propagation, "anoprop" for short, and when these occur a beam of centimetric wavelength radiation can follow the curvature for extraordinary distances. A similar effect has been observed on wavelengths of one to two metres, not often in British latitudes, but quite commonly in the tropics. It can occur, too, on the television wavelengths of some six to seven metres, where it accounts for many of the freak ranges sometimes reported, but here it is decidedly a rarity.

All these diverse phenomena can be explained on the assumption that we are dealing with a wave-motion, although the explanation at times involves mathematical concepts out of place in a general work. Indeed, some of the most remarkable peculiarities of radio waves could well be predicted from previous knowledge of the behaviour of light, always working on the assumption, of course, that both forms of radiant energy are, in fact, wave motions.

WAVE-GUIDES

It has been mentioned that focused beams are the rule for waves of centimetre and millimetre lengths. In this connexion, too, it is common to use a curious technique for leading the waves up to the horn or aerial from which they are to be radiated; they are carried thereto along a "wave-guide," which is, in effect, just a metal pipe of suitable diameter. Waves of 10 cm. length have been conveyed from the sending apparatus on the ground to a high aerial, suffering but slight loss of power in the process.

Perhaps an idea of the working of a wave-guide can best be obtained by realizing that although waves injected into it may generate electrical energy in the metal walls, that energy is so related to the energy of the waves within that the power it represents remains linked to that of the waves, travels with it, and can at the far end again become available for radiation.

With a broad idea of the properties of radio waves in mind, some more precise conceptions of their actual nature can be deduced from the methods used in sending and receiving them. There is much of interest in these processes, but before going on some necessary preliminaries must be cleared up.

WAVELENGTH AND FREQUENCY

It has already been remarked that radio waves represent a vibratory form of energy. Of this we may be sure, since the electric currents which generate them can be shown experimentally to be vibratory, or oscillatory, in nature. Moreover, it is not difficult to find out how rapidly they vibrate, that is, how many times they oscillate in a second. The speed of vibration turns out to be very great: the currents corresponding to a wavelength of 300 metres, for instance, oscillate a million times a second, and on the short waves the figure becomes enormous. To avoid writing long rows of noughts, radio people employ larger units, the kilocycle for 1,000 cycles or oscillations a second, and the megacycle for 1,000,000 cycles.

These frequencies can be determined by direct and fundamental measurements of which we need have no doubt. Wavelength, on the other hand, is a more abstract conception, its numerical reckoning being done indirectly from a knowledge of the frequency of vibration and the speed of travel of radio waves. Both these things we know (the latter is 186,000 miles per second, the same as for light and other electro-magnetic waves), and we argue that the wavelength is the measure of the distance that a wave travels in the interval between its own emission from the source and the emission of the next one.

TRANSMISSION OF RADIO WAVES

Now to examine the actual process of transmitting radio waves. We will take the simple case of an aerial consisting of a single vertical wire, hung at the top from an insulator and connected at the bottom to a radio transmitter. The latter can be imagined as pumping jets of electrons into the aerial wire at the particular frequency to which the apparatus has been adjusted. If, for instance, the transmission is to go out on a wavelength of 300 metres, the apparatus will send a jet of electrons up the aerial wire a million times a second. Each jet can be thought of as rushing up the aerial, coming to the insulator at the top, and then retreating to the bottom again. The constant repetition of this rush and return sets up a vibratory disturbance in the surrounding space and this disturbance spreads outwards from the aerial in the form of waves travelling at the velocity characteristic of all electro-magnetic radiations.

Making their way by one or another of the modes of propagation already described, suppose the waves presently come across a distant receiving aerial.

In this they will set little jets of electrons rushing up and down exactly as did those in the sending aerial. These jets, and the energy they represent, will be minute in quantity by comparison with those at the sending point, but modern radio receivers are capable of amplifying and making audible exceedingly small signals. Their power to do so depends entirely on that invention which is the foundation of all modern radio, the thermionic valve.

In its elements the device is simple to understand. As the name thermionic implies, the starting point is something which is heated. This may be a little piece of tungsten wire, like the filament of an electric bulb, or a small metal cylinder with a tungsten or molybdenum heater element inside which warms it indirectly. In either case the heating is done by passing an electric current through the wire or special element. The function of this current is to produce heat in the filament for the emission of electrons as described below.

EJECTION OF ELECTRONS FROM HEATED METAL

Heated metals tend to eject electrons from their surfaces. Normally the emission is blanketed by the surrounding air, and the electrons cannot escape. Let the process occur in a vacuum, however, and the result is otherwise; the electrons now meet no opposition and they escape in clouds, to wander about in the evacuated space.

Next suppose that somewhere in the evacuated bulb there is placed a metal plate, electrically charged to a positive voltage. If it is suitably near the heated source of the emission it will strongly attract the (negative) electrons, and draw them into itself. If a complete circuit is provided so that the electrons can pass round through the source of positive voltage, and make their way back into the heated metal, a continuous circulation will be set up. Here, then, is the apparent paradox of an electric current flowing through an empty space without any form of conductor, such as a wire or cable, to carry it.

PURPOSE OF A GRID

This effect has the practical value of providing a one-way device, quite useful at times, but not capable of giving the amplifying effect needed to make audible the minute signals of a far-distant station. That property was added to the original valve when methods were discovered of controlling the steady stream of electrons flowing from the heated source to the charged plate. It was found that, if a wire grid or mesh is placed so that the electron stream must pass through it to reach the plate, then extremely small electrical voltages applied to the grid cause relatively large variations in the volume of the stream.

In this way the minute amounts of energy picked up by the receiving aerial can be induced to control bigger quantities supplied by the local source of positive charge on the valve's plate. This is the working principle of all amplifying valves. Modern types, it is true, contain more than just the three essential elements of electron source, grid and plate, but the additional electrodes are

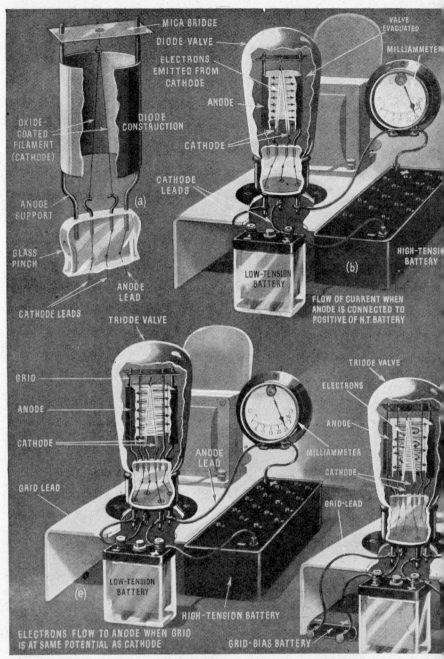

MICA BRIDGE

DIODE VALVE

ELECTRONS
EMITTED FROM
CATHODE

ANODE

VALVE
EVACUATED

MILLIAMMETER

OXIDE-
COATED
FILAMENT
(CATHODE)

DIODE
CONSTRUCTION

CATHODE

ANODE
SUPPORT

(a)

CATHODE
LEADS

GLASS
PINCH

HIGH-TENSION
BATTERY

(b)

LOW-TENSION
BATTERY

ANODE
LEAD

CATHODE LEADS

TRIODE VALVE

FLOW OF CURRENT WHEN
ANODE IS CONNECTED TO
POSITIVE OF H.T.BATTERY

GRID

ANODE

CATHODE

GRID LEAD

TRIODE VALVE

ELECTRONS

ANODE

ANODE
LEAD

MILLIAMMETER

CATHODE

GRID-LEAD

(e)

LOW-TENSION
BATTERY

HIGH-TENSION BATTERY

ELECTRONS FLOW TO ANODE WHEN GRID
IS AT SAME POTENTIAL AS CATHODE

GRID-BIAS BATTERY

PRINCIPLES OF THE DIC

Drawings (a), (b) and (c) show the construction and operation of a simple diode
valve, that is, a valve consisting of a cathode and an anode, while (d), (e) and (f)

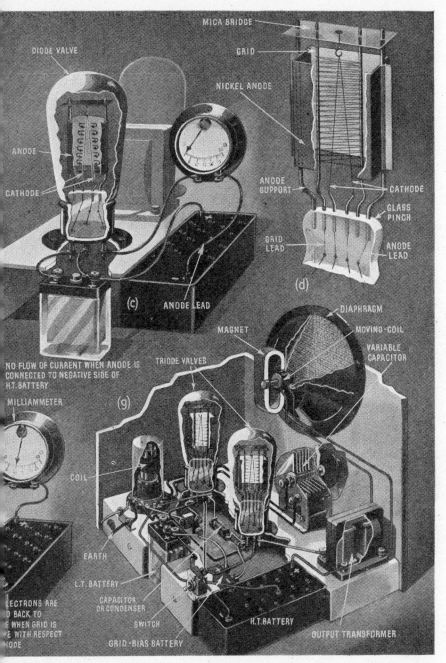

MICA BRIDGE

GRID

DIODE VALVE

NICKEL ANODE

ANODE

CATHODE

ANODE
SUPPORT

CATHODE

GLASS
PINCH

GRID
LEAD

ANODE
LEAD

(c) ANODE LEAD

(d)

NO FLOW OF CURRENT WHEN ANODE IS
CONNECTED TO NEGATIVE SIDE OF
H.T. BATTERY

DIAPHRAGM

MAGNET

MOVING-COIL

TRIODE VALVES

VARIABLE
CAPACITOR

MILLIAMMETER

(g)

COIL

EARTH

LECTRONS ARE
BACK TO
WHEN GRID IS
E WITH RESPECT
ODE

L.T. BATTERY

CAPACITOR
OR CONDENSER

SWITCH

GRID-BIAS BATTERY

H.T. BATTERY

OUTPUT TRANSFORMER

TRIODE RADIO VALVES

*similarly illustrate a triode valve. The cutaway drawing (g) shows the arrangement
of the principal components that are used to make up a simple wireless receiver.*

inserted to secure improved detail functioning and in no way affect the basic principle; the construction and operation of diode and triode valves are illustrated on pages 258-259.

A radio receiver, properly regarded, consists of valves and their adjuncts. The valves, in fact, do all the essential tasks except one, that one being the selection of the particular station. This is the business of the tuning devices. A technical discussion of tuning would probably be out of place here, but a broad view of the phenomenon of resonance involves no difficulty, and certainly adds to the interest of even the most general survey.

A logical starting point is the receiving aerial. Suppose that this consists of a vertical wire, stretched between insulating supports at top and bottom. Passing radio waves send little packets of electrons flowing up and down the wire, and if all the waves sent out by all the stations within range did this with equal effectiveness the result would be chaos, not a system of communication. In fact they do not, for the wire will respond best to a particular wavelength, selecting it from the rest. This is a matter of length; strictly speaking it is the so-called electrical length that counts, but for a straight wire suspended well clear of other objects this and the physical length are the same thing for most practical purposes.

BROADCASTING CONTROL

A programme engineer in a listening cubicle controlling the programme in the studio that can be seen in the background. From the cubicle the programme passes to the main control room to be co-ordinated with other programmes.

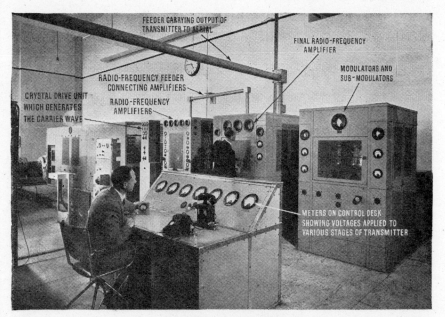

SOUND TRANSMITTER

In this control room the sound component of a television broadcast is transmitted. The unit which generates the carrier wave on which the sound is superimposed is indicated on the left-hand side of the illustration.

Consider the case of a wire of just the right length to suit a particular wavelength. The first wave on striking the aerial will send a bunch of electrons rushing up it, and this bunch will just get to the top and down again in time to be sent up once more by the next wave. In this way successive waves build up a more and more energetic rushing up and down of electrons, just as by giving a swing a series of well-timed pushes you can send it higher and higher.

This building up of energy does not take place in a wire of the wrong length. What happens then is closely analogous to the effect on a swing of giving it irregular pushes with the wrong timing: there is a certain amount of to-and-fro, but it never achieves the magnitude of the oscillations built up by properly timed impulses.

In practice, the arrangements which perform the selection of the desired wavelength are contained inside the receiver, where it is easy to make them adjustable and so give the operator control of the process of tuning. The resonating aerial is rarely used for reception on the broadcast waveband, though it is common enough on short waves.

Tuning with the compact circuits inside a receiver depends on the same basic principle as the resonating aerial. The tuning is fixed by the time taken for a packet of electrons to run from one end of the circuit to the other and back again.

When this is adjusted to the time interval between the waves, the circuit reson-
ates. The necessary length of path for the oscillating current is provided by
coiling up some wire in a compact form, and the time period is further lengthened
by placing at the ends a device which acts as a reservoir. This the electrons fill
each time they reach the end of the circuit, and empty again as they reverse and
leave it. The storage capacity of this device is usually adjustable, and provides
the tuning control; it is called a variable capacitor.

The reader has now a picture of the two fundamental principles of radio
reception. These, to sum up, are the selection of the desired signals by means
of resonating devices, and their amplification to the necessary extent with
thermionic valves.

So far it has been assumed that the object has been simply to pick up radio
waves as such. If the aim is to establish telegraphic communication this is almost
all that is required, since what communication engineers call the "intelligence"
is conveyed by starting and stopping the sender's radiation with a Morse key.
The case is less simple when the waves are to carry speech and music. For this
the sender usually radiates waves continuously, and merely varies the strength
of its output in accordance with the nature of the sounds to be carried. This
system is called amplitude modulation. A rival method of which more is likely
to be heard in future is the frequency modulation system, in which the sending
wavelength is varied to convey the sounds, the variation being done at the
frequency of the musical note, or whatever the sound may be.

PRINCIPLES OF AMPLITUDE MODULATION

The amplitude method is the one in most general use. Waves thus modulated
produce at the receiver a continuous flow of oscillating currents that rise and fall
in strength to represent the sounds which are being transmitted. If, for instance,
a musical note of the pitch of middle C is being transmitted, the waves (and the
currents they set up in the receiver) will rise and fall in strength 256 times per
second, this being the frequency of middle C.

The rise and fall effects are extracted from the oscillating currents by the
valve called the detector. It is here that the one-way property of the original
two-electrode valve is often used. It works somewhat as follows. If an oscillating
voltage is applied to the plate of such a valve it will attract electrons only when
it is positive. Hence, although the applied voltage is alternating, the resulting
current will flow one way only. This current, moreover, will rise and fall as the
strength of the radio wave waxes and wanes in accordance with the modulation
at the sender.

At this stage the receiver has produced currents of the right sort for reproduc-
ing the original sounds by means of some suitable electro-acoustic device, but
they are usually still too weak to operate a loudspeaker. Some further amplification is therefore given by one or two valves of suitable type for handling the
currents in their new form. This part of the receiver is known as the audio-or

low-frequency section. The radio- or high-frequency amplifying portion is that which deals with the signals before they reach the detector.

After sufficient audio-frequency amplification the signal currents are passed into the loudspeaker. In principle, this is a simple device. Of the many types developed during the last thirty years, only the moving coil remains in general use. Its sound-producing component is a cone of stiff paper or similar light material, carrying at its apex a small coil of wire. The coil is located in an intense magnetic field; when the speech and music currents pass through it they cause it to become itself a magnet, and the variations in the currents produce corresponding variations in the attraction and repulsion effects between the two magnetic fields. These forces set the cone vibrating in a fashion which causes a nearly perfect copy of the original sound to be emitted.

FUNCTION OF THE LOUDSPEAKER

Many electrical devices are reversible; the moving-coil loudspeaker is one of them, for it can be used as a microphone. Strong sound waves can set the paper or fabric cone vibrating, and so cause the coil to move in and out in the magnetic field. This in turn causes currents to be generated in the coil, currents which are the electrical counterparts of the original sounds, and which can be used to operate a radio transmitter.

A simple experiment will demonstrate the principle if a receiver, with pick-up terminals, is available, and a spare loudspeaker. Connect the latter to the pick-up point, and talk into it from close range; good quality reproduction will issue from the receiver's loudspeaker. (Beware of placing the microphone too near the receiver, or directly facing it, lest the whole system should start to howl.)

For microphone use, of course, the physical make-up of the device is somewhat different. The large cone is not as a rule used, but some smaller form of diaphragm, and the magnets may be smaller and lighter.

In a still lighter and more compact form the same device may be used as a gramophone pick-up. In this case no diaphragm or cone is required, for the coil is agitated directly by the movement of the needle running in the record grooves.

Neither microphones nor pick-ups are always of moving-coil type, naturally. There are many other forms, but the moving-coil example serves to illustrate that process of generating electric currents to represent sounds which is the first step in transmitting speech and music over a distance.

CATHODE-RAY TUBE

The cathode-ray tube is one of the most potent of modern electronic inventions. It serves countless ends in electrical research and engineering, and it made high-definition television practicable, not to mention such applications as radar and aircraft navigational aids.

The only working part in a cathode-ray tube is a tiny focused beam of electrons, shooting with immense velocity through a vacuum in a big glass vessel, roughly pear-shaped. The beam is indeed no more than the thinnest of pencils, perhaps a millimetre or so in diameter. It is shot out from an electrical device termed the "gun," located in the neck of the vessel, and passes lengthwise up the evacuated tube to strike the big end. This end of the tube is coated inside with certain fluorescent materials, which glow brightly when electrons strike them. The beam, therefore, makes a bright spot where it strikes the end of the vessel; the brightness of the spot depends on the strength of the beam.

A beam of electrons has no inertia, for it has no weight in the ordinary sense.

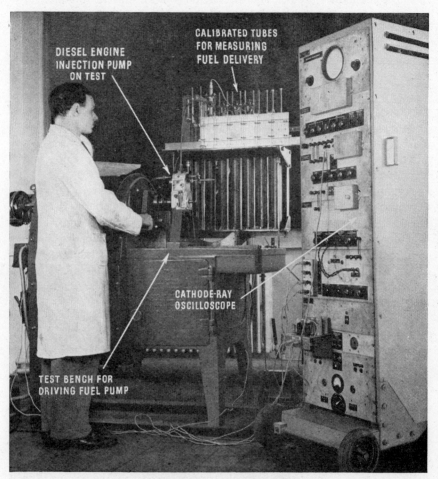

DIESEL ENGINE INJECTION PUMP ON TEST

CALIBRATED TUBES FOR MEASURING FUEL DELIVERY

CATHODE-RAY OSCILLOSCOPE

TEST BENCH FOR DRIVING FUEL PUMP

CATHODE-RAY IN RESEARCH

In addition to its wide applications in television, the cathode-ray tube is being increasingly applied to many forms of scientific research. In the illustration above an operator is seen with a cathode-ray oscilloscope which is being used in a laboratory to record the injector needle lift of a single-cylinder injection pump.

Consequently it can move almost instantaneously when a diverting force is applied, and herein lies the special virtue of the cathode-ray tube. The beam in its flight to the fluorescent screen passes between further devices inside the tube which can deflect the electrons from the straight path when suitable electric currents or voltages are applied. Since the beam is without inertia it moves instantly, and the spot of light flicks to a new position on the screen so fast that it can follow faithfully any changes in the applied electric current, even if they happen in a millionth of a second.

The cathode-ray tube can be regarded in some uses as a time microscope. It enables us to see true-to-scale pictures of electrical events which occur too fast for any other device to record them.

When thus used, the tube presents a static picture of the events, with time

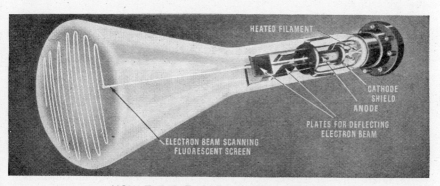

HOW THE CATHODE-RAY TUBE WORKS

Electrons emitted from the filament are directed on to the fluorescent screen and are deflected by the plates owing to the charge on them. The moving spot is, therefore, a visible measure of the charge in the plates.

intervals denoted by physical dimensions or spaces between indications on its face. One can actually see the timing of events.

In another important application the tube enables us to see the shapes of electric currents, in the sense that it will display a picture of their variations in intensity and direction in relation to time.

To do these things, the bright spot on the tube screen must first be made to move in some rhythmic way in synchronism with the cycle of events that we wish to see. This is important; the normal use of the cathode-ray tube is to show a stationary picture of some event of a repetitive nature. A simple example occurs in a radar station. Here there are two electrical occurrences of importance, and everything depends on measuring their time-interval with accuracy. The first event is the dispatch of a brief pulse of radio energy by the sender. The second is the return of a much weaker version of the pulse, in the form of an echo which has bounced back from some distant aircraft; if we can measure the time the pulse took to go and return we can find the range of the aircraft, the speed of radio waves being well known.

The steady repetition of the process at a constant rate enables the measurement to be made. Each time a pulse of wave-energy is sent out, the spot of a cathode-ray tube is caused to run swiftly across the face of the tube in a straight line and at a uniform speed. It might, for instance, be arranged to take two milliseconds to cross the screen. Suppose the echo comes back after one millisecond, and is applied to the tube's control devices in such a way as to deflect the beam momentarily from its normal straight swing across the tube. The result will be that the spot will flick aside for an instant in the middle of the screen, and then resume its straight-line travel.

Since this happens over and over again, perhaps hundreds of times a second, the eye cannot see the separate runs of the spot. Instead it sees, by virtue of persistence of vision, a steady bright line with a wriggle in the centre. This last, of course, represents the lateral excursion made by the spot when its flight is momentarily interrupted as the return pulse jerks the beam aside.

USES OF THE CATHODE-RAY TUBE

This is one of the basic ways of using the cathode-ray tube. It can be employed in investigating all sorts of electrical phenomena which repeat themselves at a regular rate. All that is necessary is to ensure that the spot runs across the screen in step with the repetition cycle, and does so at a pace suitable for showing the time intervals between the stages of each cycle of events.

In applications of this kind the tube is chiefly a means of measuring time intervals. Accordingly the picture it displays is often just a bright line, with excursions here and there produced by the electrical phenomena. When it is required to show the shape of a rhythmically varying current or voltage the picture is somewhat different. Matters are now so arranged that the path of the spot is, so to speak, all excursion, the extent of its divergence from the straight line at any point being proportional to the strength of the electric current at a given instant; very much like a graph, in fact. For example, if it were being used to investigate the nature of a single cycle of an alternating current the spot would trace out on the fluorescent screen the sine-wave shape so familiar to students of electrical engineering.

In all these applications it is necessary to ensure that the spot's movement across the screen shall be under close control. Its repeated flights must be made at exact and regular intervals, and at a constant speed; both speed and repetition rate must be adjustable. Special control circuits known as time bases have been developed for the purpose, the actual track of the spot across the screen is also called the time base.

Space will not permit description of all the principal uses of the cathode-ray tube, but some idea of its potentialities can be gained from what has been said. The possible scope widens enormously when it is realized that many happenings, not in themselves electrical, can yet be submitted to the tube's scrutiny by suitable techniques. Sounds, for example, can be picked up by a microphone and the resulting electric currents can be investigated. In a similar fashion, light phenomena can be brought into the view of the tube, in this case with the aid of a photo-electric cell in place of a microphone.

RADAR IN WAR AND PEACE

It is doubtful whether even now there are many people who realize how much they owe to radar. It can be truly said that if the Battle of Britain turned the tide, and made an ultimate Allied victory possible, certainly radar enabled the fighter squadrons to win it.

The Battle of Britain was possibly the most spectacular instance of the way Britain's lead in radar altered the course of the war, but it contributed in many other less known ways. It was, in fact, put to innumerable defensive and offensive uses by all three services, not least by the navy, who with its aid won actions under extremely bad conditions. The equipping of Coastal Command aircraft with radar had much to do with the ultimate defeat of the submarine attack, and was mainly responsible for the little-realized fact that towards the end these aircraft were sinking more U-boats than were the surface ships. Radar and its cousins, the Gee navigational system and the Oboe blind bombing guide, made it possible to develop a night bombing offensive of sufficient weight and accuracy to shorten the war.

But it is, however, in peace that radar should yield its greatest benefits. When obvious difficulties of cost and international co-operation have been overcome,

BRIGHT MASSES REPRESENT GROUND AND DARK MASSES REPRESENT THE SEA OR OTHER MASSES OF WATER

SCANNER

ECHO IMPULSES

DIRECT IMPULSES

PLAN POSITION INDICATOR
An aircraft fitted with P.P.I. from which impulses are radiated by an oscillating scanner aerial. The impulses are reflected from the ground and are recorded on the screen in the cockpit. As will be seen from the inset, built-up areas are shown vividly, open country to a lesser degree, and the sea distinctly dark.

This diagram shows the principle involved in the propagation of directive radio pulses. These are radiated as a continuous beam, and on striking an object in their path are reflected back into the scanner whence they are transmitted to the indicator in the navigating-room.

CONTROLS

SCREEN

THE INDICATOR UNIT ON THE BRIDGE

MAP OF SOLENT SHOWING RANGES OF RADAR

3 MILE ←RANGE

12 MILE RANGE→

radar will eliminate many of the risks of civil flying, for no aircraft equipped with suitable gear should ever fly into a hillside in bad visibility, nor fail to locate such landmarks as coastlines and cities.

It is probably at sea, however, that radar is most valuable. Fogs lose their terrors, even their ability to slow up a vessel carrying the device, and such mishaps as collisions, whether with other ships or with icebergs, become practically impossible. Navigation in narrow waters can be undertaken almost as confidently at night or in fog as in clear daylight.

Some hint of the working principle of this remarkable invention was given in describing the cathode-ray tube. Essentially it is simple. Short bursts or pulses of radio waves are sent out, and these are reflected back as echoes from objects within range. The time taken for the pulse to go and return is measured, giving the distance of the object, and the direction from which it reappears as an echo is also determined, so fixing the actual position of the reflecting object.

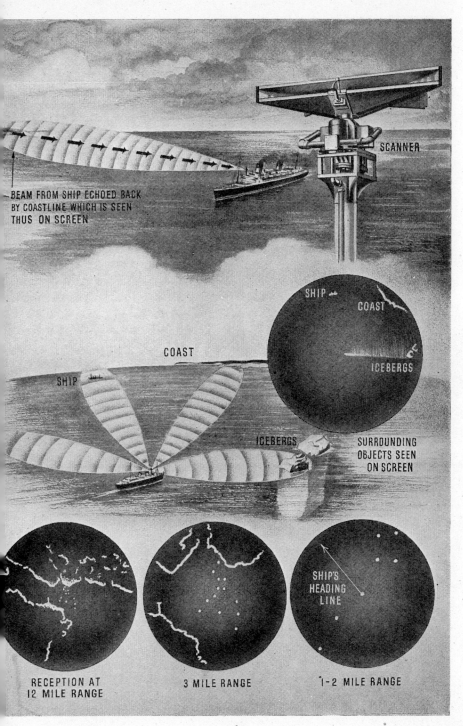

BEAM FROM SHIP ECHOED BACK BY COASTLINE WHICH IS SEEN THUS ON SCREEN

SCANNER

SHIP

COAST

ICEBERGS

COAST

SHIP

ICEBERGS

SURROUNDING OBJECTS SEEN ON SCREEN

SHIP'S HEADING LINE

RECEPTION AT 12 MILE RANGE

3 MILE RANGE

1-2 MILE RANGE

The pulses of radiant energy used in radar are a somewhat unfamiliar conception, and some actual figures may help one to visualize them. The length of each pulse is usually a very small fraction of a second; it varies in different types of equipment from about a quarter of a microsecond to perhaps fifteen or twenty microseconds. Between pulses the equipment's sender is quiescent, to give time for the pulse to go out and the echo to be reflected back. The interval between pulses must accordingly be long enough for a radio wave to travel to the expected maximum range and back again. In short-range radar stations, therefore, the interval may be short, the pulses following each other as rapidly as 1,000 times a second, whereas in long-range equipments it may be 500 or 250, or even less.

These figures suggest that the sender is kept busy, but when the extreme shortness of each pulse is remembered the picture changes; in fact, the sender works hard for a brief instant, then takes a relatively long rest before emitting the next pulse. Herein lies the explanation of something which is apt to be puzzling when a radar sender is seen for the first time, namely, its small size in relation to its power, for example, a sender no bigger than an average size suitcase may be rated to give 100 kilowatts output.

BEAM-TYPE RADAR STATION

For peacetime purposes the beam type of radar station is used, radiating a narrow focused pencil of waves which sweeps like a searchlight across the area to be examined. For this, centimetric wavelengths are chosen, so that they can be emitted from a metal horn or parabolic reflector of convenient size. The resulting beam is passed repeatedly over the field of view, either back and forth over a limited arc or in complete circular sweeps like the traverse of a lighthouse.

This method of scanning the area permits the use of that fascinating device, the Plan Position Indicator, P.P.I. for short, as a means of displaying the result. In this system, the spot of the cathode-ray tube no longer runs across the tube face from side to side, but starts from the centre and flies out to the rim, so drawing a radius rather than a diameter on the circular screen. The radial line is made to revolve, like one spoke of a wheel, in exact step with the sweep of the sending beam; at any instant the spot is tracing out a line on the tube face at the exact relative angle to the direction in which the beam is pointing. Then, when a returning echo is picked up by the receiving gear and appears on the tube, its position thereon gives a complete indication of the range and bearing of the object that sent back the reflection.

In the P.P.I. system the echoes are not indicated by the spot making an excursion from its normal straight-line travel, but by a brightening of the spot itself. Over the rest of its course the spot is dimmed until it scarcely marks the screen, then where an echo is being shown it makes a brilliant spot or patch, according to the size of the object being seen by the equipment.

The fascination of the Plan Position Indicator, however, lies not so much in its ability to show a complete positional "fix" directly, as in its adaptability to

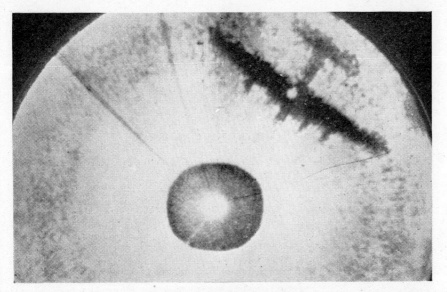

RADAR'S PENETRATING EYES

Unique photograph of the main outline of a low-flying, four-engine aircraft caught in a radar beam, and recorded on the indicator screen.

interesting tricks such as the one often used in ship sets. Here an arrangement of mirrors enables the navigator to see the P.P.I. superimposed on a chart of the area, so that he can at once estimate his own position and that of other ships, identify landmarks on the coast, and get an accurate radar picture of his surroundings, with each detail appearing in its proper place over the chart. Moreover, the whole picture can be displayed at once, by using for the P.P.I. a cathode-ray tube with the property of "afterglow" which causes the bright spots and patches produced by echoes to persist for some seconds after they have been marked. If the scanning beam traverses fairly quickly it comes round again before the bright marks laid down on the tube at its previous passage have died away, and so there is a continuous display of all that the radar set can see; typical images are illustrated above and on pages 268-9.

Just how much a ship's radar can see depends mainly on the height of the aerial device above sea-level, with the power of the sender and the sensitivity of the receiver as secondary factors. Assuming reasonable power and sensitivity, the equipment should indicate the presence of any object projecting more than a foot or so above the sea's surface at distances up to a little beyond the optical horizon as seen from the radar aerial. Suppose the latter to be mounted, as it may well be on a vessel of some size, at 50 ft. above the water-line. Good equipment should then detect small and low-lying objects up to some eight or ten miles distant, and taller ones at longer ranges in proportion to their height and bulk.

Labels on illustration: VISION TRANSMITTING AERIAL; SOUND TRANSMITTING AERIAL; BATTERY OF LIGHTS; STEEL MAST; CONTROL ROOM FROM WHICH PRODUCERS GIVE DIRECTIONS TO STAFF; CLOSE-UP CAMERA; CATHODE-RAY MONITOR TUBE; CENTRAL CONTROL; CONTROL; TRANSMITTER; LONG RANGE CAMERA; TITLES AND CAPTIONS CAMERA; MICROPHONE ON ADJUSTABLE BOOM

BROADCASTING A TELEVISION PROGRAMME

As will be seen, the lay-out of a television studio resembles a film set, the main differences being that in television the action is directly relayed to its audience, and the means of reproduction is electronic, and not chemical as in the case of the film. The output of the camera is taken to amplifiers, mixers and feeders, and then to the transmitter. The range of frequencies required for transmitting television is much greater than that required for sound: the actual frequency used by the B.B.C. is 45 million cycles per second.

For aircraft use the needs are somewhat different. Ship's radar is required to search merely the surface of the sea, so has only to sweep its narrow pencil of rays in one plane, but the aircraft set must explore a considerable volume of space in order to obtain information about the surface beneath and ahead of the machine. It can do this by imparting a more complicated sweeping motion to the same kind of pencil beam, but for some purposes the desired end is more simply achieved by using a fan-shaped beam. This is radiated from a suitably shaped reflector, with the width of the fan arranged vertically. When swept from side to side such a beam covers a wide range of country ahead of the aircraft, and at the same time gives warning of the presence of other craft in the vicinity.

Watching a television screen enables even the hardened radio technician to recapture something of that sense of wonder which most of us felt in the early days of sound broadcasting. To see something happening very far away seems always more remarkable than merely to hear it. Technically, the processes of television transmission and reception hold one's interest after the first wonder has staled. They are more complicated than those of sound broadcasting, but the layman can readily understand at least their outlines.

TELEVISION TRANSMISSION

First in the chain of transforming operations in television transmission comes the equivalent of the work done by the microphone in a sound transmission; electric currents must somehow be produced which shall represent the picture. The microphone's task is, by comparison, a simple one, for it has merely to produce electric currents equivalent to a series of sounds following each other in natural sequence. Its television counterpart must deal with multitudinous picture details which are present all the time. Obviously it cannot handle them all simultaneously. It must deal with them one by one, relying upon certain imperfections of the eye to build them up again into what appears on the receiver to be a continuous picture.

All the known systems of television employ this piecemeal principle, dissecting

APPARATUS USED FOR TELEVISING FILMS

The technique used in television is very similar to that of cinema projection, but in this case the image is cast on to a photo-electric screen. A set of oscillating mirrors reflects the light from the 1,000-watt lamp on to the images. The Emitron camera interprets the film as a series of electrical images.

the scene into small units which are transmitted one by one and reassembled to form the received picture.

In the pioneering days of television the dissection or scanning was done by combined mechanical and optical methods. These ultimately gave place to purely electronic systems without physical moving parts. The only moving parts in these systems are electron beams; the advantages in speed and accuracy of movement will be apparent from the preceding notes on the cathode-ray tube.

PHOTO-ELECTRIC EFFECT

The production of electric currents to represent variations of light intensity, that is, the light and shade of a picture, depends on a phenomenon known as the photo-electric effect; certain metals and their compounds have the property of emitting electrons when illuminated. This effect is the basis of the photo-electric cell, a device which does for light almost exactly what the microphone does for sound, but is not in itself sufficient for the dissection of the light and shade of a scene. As it stands, a photo-electric cell can merely sum up the light from the scene as a whole, and yield an electric current proportional to the total brightness. To obtain currents proportional to each little section of the scene would call for myriads of photo-electric cells, each so blinkered that it accepted only light from its own special bit of the picture.

Impracticable as that may sound, it is almost what is done in the television cameras in general use. The myriads of photo-electric cells take the form of a mosaic of minute globules, usually of a silver-cæsium compound, coated in a single layer on a sheet of mica. Each globule, tiny as it is, forms a separate photo-electric cell, insulated from the rest. If now an image of a scene is focused on the mosaic with a lens like that of a camera, each globule will develop a minute electric charge exactly proportional to the brightness of the particular bit of the image resting upon it.

The next problem to be solved in the television camera is the obvious one of extracting the charges from the mosaic globules when required for transmission. An electron beam provides the means. It is emitted from the same sort of gun as that used in the cathode-ray tube and is focused down to an extremely thin pencil, much less than a millimetre in diameter. This narrow ray is then set to explore the surface of the mosaic in a series of accurately timed and positioned sweeps, in the manner already described in the case of the cathode-ray tube. The process must, of course, be carried out in a vacuum, so all the parts except the lens are enclosed in an evacuated glass vessel.

The effect of sweeping an electron beam over the mosaic surface is, roughly speaking, to discharge each cell in turn, and this is caused to produce a current in an external circuit proportional to the charge in the cell. In this way the exploring electron beam extracts momentary electric currents, exactly equivalent in strength to the light intensity of each detail of the picture focused upon the mosaic. It remains for these currents to be transmitted by radio, and then at the

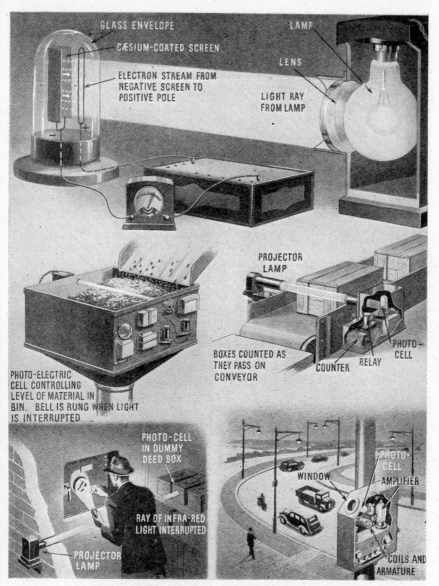

GLASS ENVELOPE

CÆSIUM-COATED SCREEN

LAMP

LENS

ELECTRON STREAM FROM
NEGATIVE SCREEN TO
POSITIVE POLE

LIGHT RAY
FROM LAMP

PROJECTOR
LAMP

BOXES COUNTED AS
THEY PASS ON
CONVEYOR

COUNTER   RELAY

PHOTO-
CELL

PHOTO-ELECTRIC
CELL CONTROLLING
LEVEL OF MATERIAL IN
BIN. BELL IS RUNG WHEN LIGHT
IS INTERRUPTED.

PHOTO-CELL
IN DUMMY
DEED BOX

WINDOW

PHOTO-
CELL

AMPLIFIER

RAY OF INFRA-RED
LIGHT INTERRUPTED

PROJECTOR
LAMP

COILS AND
ARMATURE

PHOTO-ELECTRIC CELL AND ITS APPLICATIONS

When light falls on cæsium, electrons are emitted. Now, because of this it is possible to construct a valve in which the emission of electrons is solely the result of its exposure to light. The photo-electric cell consists of an evacuated envelope containing a cæsium-coated screen. The electrons are collected on the positive pole or anode. The electronic eye has many applications, four of which are illustrated above. Controlling the filling of bins (centre left), counting articles on a conveyor (centre right), burglar alarm (bottom left), and a device for turning on street lights at dusk and switching them off again at daybreak (bottom right).

receiving point to be used to adjust the brightness of the cathode-ray spot to the correct relative intensity. If the sweeps of the cathode-ray tube's beam are kept in precise synchronism with those of the electron camera, then an image of the original picture will build up on the receiver screen.

SCANNING AND CONTINUITY

To secure the illusion of a continuous, complete picture the scanning spot must cover the whole image area at a considerable speed, and repeat the process more than a certain minimum number of times a second. This is a subject on which there is much popular misconception, for the problem is not in fact soluble by applying some hard and fast mathematical rule; it is complicated by factors for which allowance is difficult. Practically, the problem is in two parts. The necessity of presenting a continuous picture is one, and the avoidance of the irritating phenomenon of "flicker" is another.

Experience with the cinematograph shows that an illusion of continuity and reasonably smooth motion of moving objects in the picture can be obtained with some fourteen repetitions a second, but even this is not a definite rule. It must be qualified with a stipulation that moving objects must not move too fast, or they will show motion flicker. Silent films were, therefore, projected at sixteen frames a second.

Avoidance of flicker, not merely of moving details but of the whole picture, calls for a still higher rate of repetition, and the question is complicated by the fact that the necessary rate varies in a far from simple way according to the brightness of the picture. It is even affected by such factors as the darkness of the screen's surroundings and the state of the viewer's eye. Here again empirical rules based on experience are the best guide. In the cinematograph projector a higher rate of repetition is simulated by momentarily cutting off the light with a moving shutter during the showing of each frame of film. It is also cut off while the film is being snatched from one frame to the next, so, if the actual picture repetition rate is twenty-four a second, the talkie rate, there will be forty-eight blinks of the light in each second, and this, under normal conditions, is enough to ensure an illusion of steady, flickerless illumination.

INTERLACED SCANNING IN TELEVISION

These analogies from the cinematograph are helpful in understanding the more difficult problems of television. Here it is not possible to blink each frame, and so double the apparent repetition rate, because the picture is never present as a whole at any given moment. The system known as interlaced scanning gives much the same beneficial effect, however. In this method, the electron beams in the camera and the receiving cathode-ray tube trace out first every other line of the scanning plan, then go back and trace out the lines they missed the first time. Put in another way, the scanning covers first the odd-number lines, then goes back and runs over the even lines. Thus, although the two stages of each scan may be completed only twenty-five times a second, the effective rate of repetition is equivalent to fifty times so far as flicker is concerned; this is the B.B.C. standard speed for television broadcasting.

It is noteworthy that in one way the television screen is inherently less liable to flicker than the cinematograph. When the light of the latter is cut off by the shutter, it vanishes instantly from the screen, but when the cathode-ray tube spot has completed a scan, the brightness of the screen does not necessarily disappear at once. A trace of afterglow, often a useful property of the tube, causes it to die away gradually, and so help to smooth out the tendency to flicker between frames.

So far we have assumed that the moving spot of the receiving tube is kept in step with that of the transmitting camera, but no consideration has been given to the "how" of it. In fact, the process is simple enough in principle. The electrical circuits which move the cathode-ray are of a sort which requires to be "triggered" to set it in action, and, each time the transmitter comes to the end of a line or of a frame, it interjects special impulses which excite the appropriate

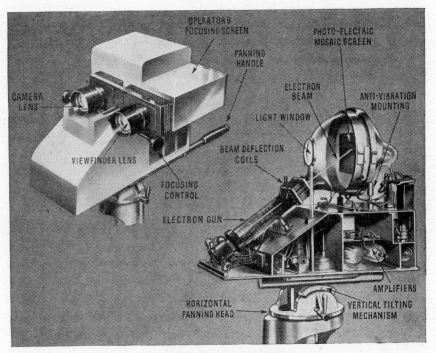

TELEVISION CAMERA

The lens of the television camera focuses the image on the photo-electric mosaic screen. An electron beam playing on the screen transforms the image into a series of electrical impulses which are passed on to the transmitter.

control circuit in the receiver to shift the cathode-ray tube's spot as necessary.

When account is taken of these special synchronizing impulses and all the variety of currents associated with the details of the picture proper, it is evident that the radio sending apparatus must be kept busy. Indeed, it has to deal with such a wide variety of impulses that for technical reasons very short wavelengths are essential. With present systems of television there is no escape from this requirement, and, if the fineness of scanning were increased above the 405 lines into which the B.B.C. picture is now dissected, it would be advisable to go to still shorter waves. Instead of wavelengths of six or seven metres, it would seem that the transmission would probably be shifted to waves of the order of one to two metres.

The effect would be to restrict the service area of a television sending station somewhat more closely. With waves of the present order the range is usually somewhat beyond the distance calculated on the basis of the optical horizon, and at times of "anoprop" (see page 255) it is considerably beyond. On the still shorter waves "anoprop" conditions would still occur, but at other times the range would probably be reduced, while shielding and absorption effects from buildings and hills would be increased.

This matter of range is one of the problems of television. In effect it means that a given sending station can serve only one main area of population, and each such area must have its own station. Unlike sound broadcasts, television signals cannot be passed over ordinary telephone lines for radiation at a distant station, so the organization of a programme distribution system from a central point is difficult and expensive. It necessitates either extremely costly cables to carry the signals to each distant transmitter, or a system of radio relay links.

GEE, LORAN AND DECCA NAVIGATING SYSTEMS

Less spectacular than the wartime achievements of radar, but with great potentialities for safe navigation by sea and air, the modern position-fixing systems represent one of the most advanced applications of the science of electronics. The idea of determining geographical position by radio means is an old one, but the previous systems based on direction-finding lacked accuracy and dependability when operated on board ship or aircraft, while when the "fix" was obtained by shore stations and transmitted by radio to the craft asking for its position the business was slow and cumbersome, and still not of truly adequate accuracy.

Such systems as Gee, Loran and Decca, on the contrary, give their answer in a matter of seconds, are extremely accurate as a class, and enable a ship or aircraft to fix its position without need to communicate with the land at all. All alike provide a service of continuously radiated special waves which actuate the sea or airborne instrument, ready to give a position at any hour of the day or night.

Both Gee and Loran use pulses of radio energy much like those of radar, and likewise depend on measurement of the time taken by the pulses to travel certain

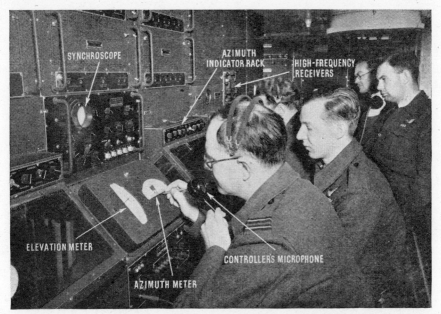

INTERIOR OF MOBILE GROUND CONTROL APPROACH TRAILER
Operators at their stations, and controller in the foreground who gives the final instructions to the pilot at a quarter of a mile from the touch-down point.

distances. In fact, the two systems are almost identical, but Gee was planned to give extreme accuracy at moderate distances, whereas Loran, adapted by the Americans to suit their conditions, covers greater areas, but with less accuracy.

In each case the method is to measure the difference in the time of travel of pulses from two or more sending stations. The absolute time of travel would be more useful, but this cannot be determined at a distant point. Suppose, for instance, a navigator finds that pulses from a pair of stations take the same time to reach him. That does not fix his actual position, but it does tell him that he is somewhere on a line passing midway between the two senders, and running in such a direction that every point on it is equidistant from them. If, on the other hand, he had found that one pulse arrived at a certain time-interval after the other, he could deduce that his position lay somewhere on a line such that all points upon it were farther from one station than from the other by a certain fixed distance equal to that which a radio wave can travel in the time-interval he had measured. To fix his actual position, the navigator must repeat the process on another pair of stations. This gives him another "position line," and where this line crosses the first one is his "fix." In practice all this is simpler than it sounds, for the navigator is provided with a chart whereon all the necessary position lines are already drawn. He has merely to make his measurement of pulse arrival timing on two pairs of stations, identify the appropriate lines on the chart, and run his pencil along them to see where they intersect. An expert can carry out this operation in less than a minute.

The measurement of time intervals between the arrivals of pulses is done on a special form of cathode-ray tube whose spot travels at a precisely adjusted and accurately known speed. The physical distance between the indications made by the pulses is, therefore, the exact measure of the difference in their time of arrival. Suppose the pulse from station A appears farther along the tube's trace from the pulse originating at station B by a distance known to represent 10 microseconds. This means that the path from station A is longer than that from station B by the distance a radio wave can travel in 10 microseconds, since pulse A arrived that much behind pulse B. As a matter of interest, 10 microseconds difference indicates that one path was three kilometres longer than the other. Here again matters are simplified for the navigator, for he has no need to calculate the meaning of the time-intervals, nor even to measure them directly in terms of fractions of a second; his indicating tube displays a series of marker units which enable him to read off the intervals in certain special units whose real meaning he need not know. He uses them merely to locate the correct position lines on his chart, these being marked on the same special system.

PRINCIPLE OF THE DECCA SYSTEM

The Decca system works on a different principle. Instead of pulses, the senders radiate continuous waves so related to each other in length that they set up a sort of stationary pattern in space. An indicating device being carried through the pattern experiences a series of maximum and minimum effects at definite geographical positions which form the basis of special charts and from which a navigator can locate himself.

A particular feature of this system is that the navigating information is continuously displayed on scaled indicating dials. At any given moment, therefore, it is only necessary to note the figures being shown on the instrument and then turn to the chart to see what geographical position they denote.

THE ELECTRON MICROSCOPE

The ordinary optical microscope as frequently used in the laboratory reaches its limit with a magnification of some two or three thousand times. Beyond that point it cannot go, for it comes up against a barrier inherent in the principle of the instrument. The sizes of the objects it is then revealing are approaching the wavelength of the light by which they are seen, and nothing smaller can be clearly defined.

There for many years research was halted. Clear evidence showed that important discoveries could be made if still smaller objects could be seen, but the wherewithal was lacking; research workers had to be content with indirect investigation of such things as the ultra-microscopic viruses, those strange and at first hypothetical organisms which appear to cause influenza, the common cold,

ELECTRON GUN
CHAMBER

INTERMEDIATE
TUBE

ADJUSTMENT FOR
PROJECTOR LENS

VIEWING WINDOWS

CAMERA

PHOTOMICROGRAPH OF MAGNESIUM
OXIDE SMOKE

CONTROL CUBICLE HOUSING ALL ELECTRICAL
CONTROL AND INDICATING EQUIPMENT

USING ELECTRONS TO MAGNIFY

The electron microscope consists of an electron gun which projects a gradually expanding beam of electrons through a magnetic condenser lens (see page 282) on to the object to be examined. The beam then passes through the magnetic objective lens which further magnifies the object, and finally through the projector lens to the fluorescent screen where it can be observed or photographed. The inset shows a typical photomicrograph taken in an electron microscope. This instrument has proved of great value to research workers in almost every scientific field because it makes possible the study of minute particles too small to be seen with an optical microscope usually found in a laboratory.

Drawing comparing the lens system of a normal optical microscope, and the system employing magnetic lenses and a stream of electrons. Note the basic similarity.

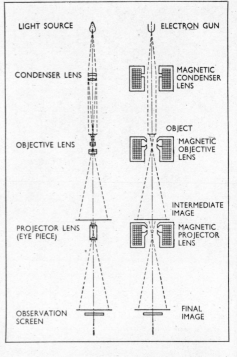

LIGHT SOURCE

ELECTRON GUN

CONDENSER LENS

MAGNETIC CONDENSER LENS

OBJECT

OBJECTIVE LENS

MAGNETIC OBJECTIVE LENS

INTERMEDIATE IMAGE

PROJECTOR LENS (EYE PIECE)

MAGNETIC PROJECTOR LENS

OBSERVATION SCREEN

FINAL IMAGE

and a host of other animal and plant diseases.

To this unsatisfactory state of affairs the invention of the electron microscope put an end. It extends the research worker's vision down to a new range of infinitesimal sizes, for it gives magnifications of the order of 30,000 diameters. Viruses have become visible, along with details of the structure of many small objects hitherto only surmised.

The secret of the electron microscope lies in the small size of the electron itself in comparison with the size of the objects it outlines and displays in the so-called microscope. Small as are such things as viruses, the electron is yet millions of times smaller still. Imagine, therefore, a focused beam of electrons shooting past a small object so as to cast a shadow of it on a fluorescent screen; the edges of the shadow will accurately trace the shape of the obstruction, simply because the electrons are so minute in size by comparison with it.

Electrons are subject to the electric forces of attraction and repulsion, and when in motion can be influenced by magnetic forces also. They can, therefore, be made to follow paths dictated by those forces, and in such ways they are focused and made to exhibit enlarged images, very much after the fashion of rays of light in a microscope.

There are, in fact, electrical and magnetic devices which are closely analogous to the lenses of ordinary optics, and with their aid the magnifying system of the electron microscope is set up. Unlike an image formed with light rays, however, the electronic image cannot be seen with the unaided eye. Special devices, for example the fluorescent screen, must be employed in order to display it.

The whole system must operate in a vacuum, so that the electron rays may travel freely without being impeded by air molecules. The need for maintaining a high degree of vacuum during the working of the apparatus, and for restoring it when the instrument has been opened, adds to the complexity of what is

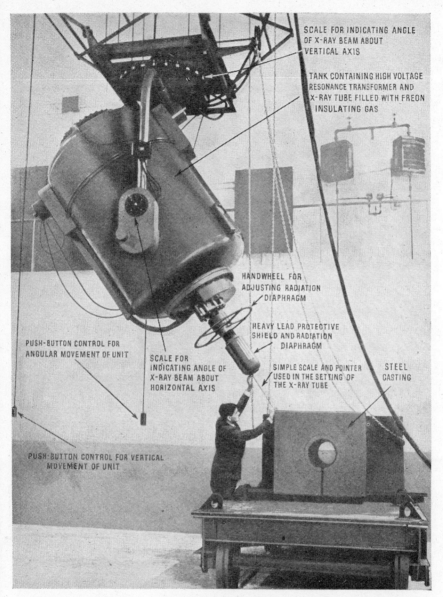

SCALE FOR INDICATING ANGLE
OF X-RAY BEAM ABOUT
VERTICAL AXIS

TANK CONTAINING HIGH VOLTAGE
RESONANCE TRANSFORMER AND
X-RAY TUBE FILLED WITH FREON
INSULATING GAS

HANDWHEEL FOR
ADJUSTING RADIATION
DIAPHRAGM

HEAVY LEAD PROTECTIVE
SHIELD AND RADIATION
DIAPHRAGM

PUSH-BUTTON CONTROL FOR
ANGULAR MOVEMENT OF UNIT

SCALE FOR
INDICATING ANGLE OF
X-RAY BEAM ABOUT
HORIZONTAL AXIS

SIMPLE SCALE AND POINTER
USED IN THE SETTING OF
THE X-RAY TUBE

STEEL
CASTING

PUSH-BUTTON CONTROL FOR VERTICAL
MOVEMENT OF UNIT

X-RAYS IN INDUSTRY

During the past ten years X-rays have been increasingly used as a means of inspecting the internal structure of metals. Above is shown one of the latest 2,000-kilovolt installations being prepared to inspect a large steel casting. The tank containing the X-ray tube is pivoted so that it can be set to any point in the horizontal and vertical planes, its movement being controlled by push-buttons. The spectacular radiograph of a jeep on pages 284-5 was taken on an X-ray machine similar to that illustrated here.

283

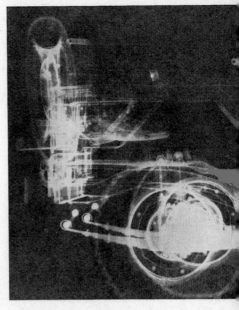

Four matched sections of film make up this unique radiograph of an entire automobile. The jeep was 60 ft. away from the X-ray machine during the 90-minute exposure.

already a somewhat elaborate piece of apparatus. The necessary pumping equipment, which may be built in as an integral part of the design of the electron microscope, calls for skilled handling, and the instrument is indeed one for the advanced research laboratory. Its technical problems, curiously enough, do not seem to be the main obstacle in pressing beyond the threshold of the new sphere of discovery to which the electron microscope will certainly lead us in time. The difficulty is an unexpected one arising from the great jump in magnifying power between the optical and electronic types; it is a matter of knowing what one is looking at when magnifications such as 30,000 diameters are in use for the first time on a new subject. Patient work in this new field of research will solve these problems in due course, and then an exciting extension will take place in our knowledge of the infinitesimal things in the universe.

X-RAYS AND THEIR APPLICATIONS

Far below the shortest of the radio wavelengths there are some radiations whose waves are so short that the actual figure as a fraction of a familiar unit like the inch are practically meaningless. In practice such wavelengths are expressed in millimicrons, this unit being a millionth of a millimetre. Visible light ranges from about 400 to 700 millimicrons. Somewhat shorter than these waves are those of the invisible ultra-violet light, then after a transitional region comes the X-rays, with wavelengths round about a thousandth of those of visible light, and finally the shortest waves, associated with cosmic rays.

With so great a difference in wavelength it is natural to find a correspondingly great difference in properties. Of these the most striking and perhaps the most valuable is a difference in the substances which are transparent to the rays. Whereas light is apparently erratic in its choice of the materials through which it will pass freely, X-rays are more methodical in their ways. To them a larger number of materials are transparent or at least translucent, and there is a simple rule governing the matter: the less the atomic weight of the material, the greater

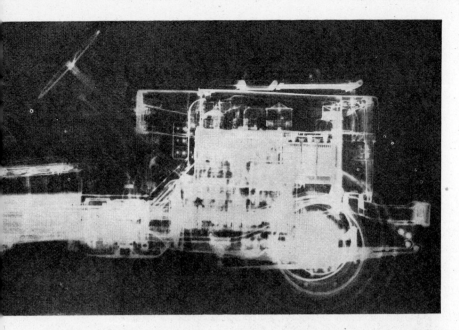

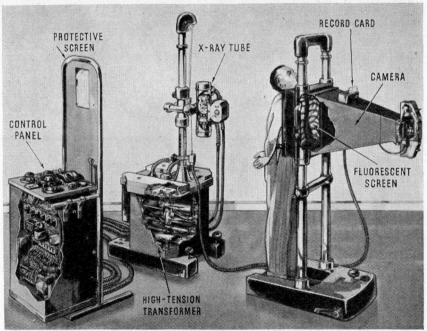

PROTECTIVE SCREEN

X-RAY TUBE

RECORD CARD

CAMERA

CONTROL PANEL

FLUORESCENT SCREEN

HIGH-TENSION TRANSFORMER

X-RAYS AND MEDICINE

X-ray apparatus employed for mass miniature radiography. It consists of three main components, the transformer unit, camera unit and control table. This recently developed technique is being widely used in the fight against tuberculosis.

its transparency to X-rays. Thus lead, with its high atomic weight figure of 207, is densely opaque, iron (55·8) much less so, while aluminium (27) is almost transparent. Most substances except those of highest atomic weight can be penetrated by X-rays to at least a moderate degree, and this property is of immense value in medicine, surgery and industry. It enables an inside view to be obtained of many inaccessible details in the human body, and in such things as metal castings, to mention but one industrial use. Its value to the surgeon is familiar and obvious, but some of the more recent applications of X-rays in

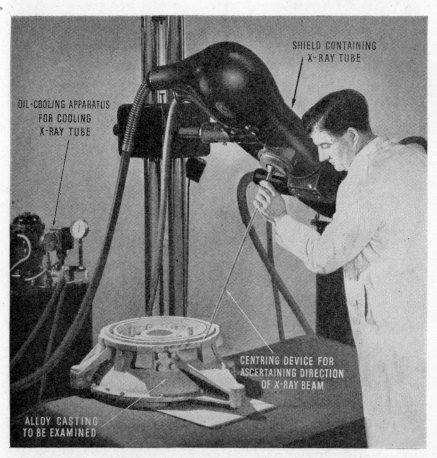

INSPECTING ALUMINIUM-ALLOY CASTING

A 220-kilovolt X-ray apparatus of the type generally employed in factories producing light and medium-size alloy castings. It is capable of penetrating up to approximately eight inches of aluminium. In the view above, the operator can be seen adjusting the centering device before inspecting a component—in this case an aluminium-alloy casting for a Mamba jet engine.

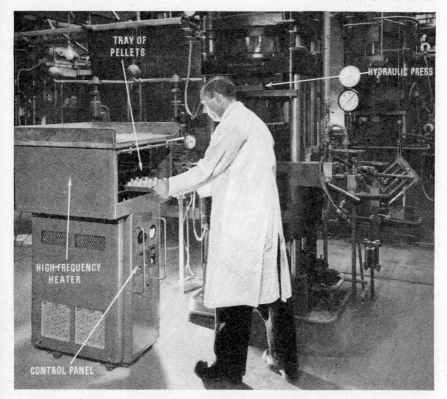

HEATING BY RADIO WAVES

Electronic heating is based on the principle that when a material is subjected to an alternating electric field, heat is generated throughout its mass. In practice the material to be heated is placed between two electrodes, and when a high-frequency alternating voltage is applied to the electrodes from a generator an electric field is set up between the electrodes and in the material to be heated. In the illustration above, pellets of plastic material are being placed in the heater. After heating, the pellets will be ready for moulding in the hydraulic press.

general diagnosis have, in their way, produced even more striking results.

X-rays differ from light, too, in their effect on living tissue. Whereas light, in particular ultra-violet light, has beneficial effects, X-rays are mostly destructive. Since, however, they have some power to destroy or check the growth of certain forms of morbid tissue while having a less marked effect on surrounding healthy cells, they have certain therapeutic applications.

The inherent danger of rays with these properties needs no emphasis. Elaborate precautions are now taken to screen the operator from them, but in the pioneering days little was known either of the danger or of protective measures and there were many casualties. Of the early research workers a high proportion

INPUT CONNEXIONS FROM
HIGH-FREQUENCY GENERATOR

CYCLE SPROCKET
WHEEL

HEATER COIL

HEATING BY EDDY CURRENTS

A cycle sprocket wheel being heated by high-frequency current, illustrating what is known in this field of electronics as "skin-effect." The most intense heat generated by the heater coil is concentrated in the outer skin of the teeth, the rest of the material being heated by conduction outwards.

met a painful and lingering death, yet the work never flagged, even when the danger became fully known. It should be made clear that there is no risk to the patient in the ordinary diagnostic use of X-rays, since the exposure is only momentary.

The generation of X-rays is done in an evacuated glass vessel through which a high-voltage electric discharge is passed. The process, in fact, is one of bombarding a suitable electrode, usually of tungsten, with high-velocity electrons, the emission of X-rays being a natural consequence. The wavelength of the resulting rays depends on the electron velocity, which is governed by the voltage that impels the electrons. The higher the voltage the greater the electron velocity and the shorter the wavelength. Also, the shorter the wavelength the greater the penetrating power of the rays. In some high-voltage plants the penetrating power of the X-rays is so great that the walls of the room in which the tube is housed are specially constructed to absorb the penetrating X-rays and protect the operators.

Examination of the X-ray picture of an object can be done directly with the aid of a fluorescent screen, but more often a permanent record is made by photographic methods. In either case a shadowgraph results, much as it does if you hold your hand in front of a piece of white paper in sunlight. With X-ray illumination, of course, the shadow is no longer solid black, but full of graduations of tone representing the varying transparency of the bones and tissues.

HEATING BY RADIO WAVES

Success has been achieved in treating various forms of rheumatic conditions by means of short-wave radio energy; a technique known as radio-therapy. It is wrong to assume, however, that high-frequency currents of this kind have some therapeutic property. In fact, the effect is purely thermal. The special characteristic of these currents is that they can induce a heating effect deep down in the tissues, and this heating effect has been found to alleviate some forms of rheumatism to a marked degree; wherever heat is beneficial, high-frequency currents provide an excellent means of applying it. They do not overheat the surface before reaching an effective depth, as radiant heat is apt to do, but produce a uniform warmth through a considerable volume of tissue, and the degree of heating can be controlled to a fine degree. The wavelengths which have been tried for this purpose range from six to sixty metres, ten metres being found a convenient wavelength.

This method of heating has many potential uses in industry. It is already widely employed for heating rubber and plastic products as a preliminary to treatment at a higher temperature, with consequent saving of time, and for tempering small steel objects such as knives, scissors and saws. For such purposes the method has the advantage that it can readily be applied to produce the requisite degree of heat in one particular part of the object, and to do this so quickly that the rest remains cool. A hacksaw blade, for example, can have just its teeth hardened, while the rest retains the toughness and elasticity of lightly-tempered steel. An extremely interesting example of surface heating by means of high-frequency currents is shown in the photograph on the opposite page.

COOKING BY RADIO WAVES

Attempts have been made to popularize this form of heating for domestic purposes. Cooking by high-frequency currents is already practicable, and so-called electronic cookers have been demonstrated. Their principal advantage appears to reside in the speed with which, say, a joint can be cooked; it is a matter of a few minutes only, and is practically independent of the size of the piece of meat. Most of the normal cooking time is spent in getting the joint hot right through to the middle. Once hot a few minutes suffice, and that is how the electronic method scores, for its heat begins to develop all through the object from the moment of switching on the current. Such rapid cooking may certainly be expected to conserve the juices of meat, but whether the cost of an electronic cooker, with its expensive high-frequency generating system, can be reduced sufficiently to come within the reach of the average citizen remains to be seen.

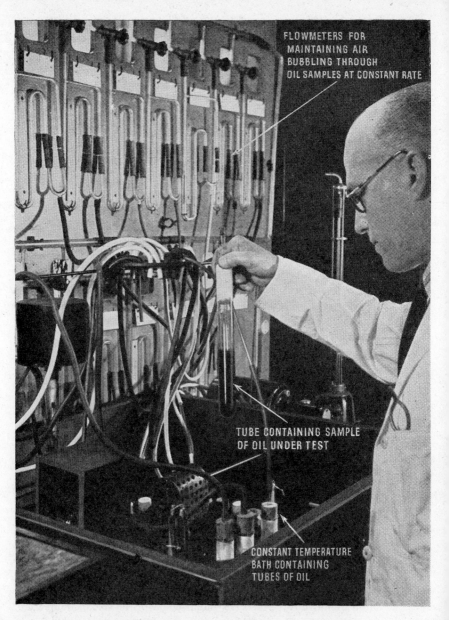

FLOWMETERS FOR MAINTAINING AIR BUBBLING THROUGH OIL SAMPLES AT CONSTANT RATE

TUBE CONTAINING SAMPLE OF OIL UNDER TEST

CONSTANT TEMPERATURE BATH CONTAINING TUBES OF OIL

RESEARCH AND THE FUTURE OF TRANSPORT

Behind every new development in land, sea, and air transport is the research engineer and scientist. The scientist in the photograph above is one of this army of researchers, and is conducting tests on lubricating oils which are so essential to all forms of transport. In fact, many developments in modern transport, such as the jet engine, would not have got very far without corresponding developments in lubricating oils to meet the very high speeds and temperatures.

CHAPTER **9** **The future of transport**

FEW fields offer such scope for revolutionary developments as transport. Rocket, jet or gas-turbine propulsion has already made possible higher speed in the air, on land and at sea. Radar, greatly improved radio equipment and other electronic devices have given us more accurate navigation and, consequently, greater safety. Increased knowledge of the stratosphere means improved economy for air-liners and greater flying comfort for passengers. Last, but not least, space-travel outside limits of the earth's atmosphere is no longer the far-fetched dream of a small band of rocket enthusiasts.

With such a bewildering wealth of scientific marvels to choose from, it is difficult to find one aspect which will provide the key to the future of transport. Perhaps it is logical to begin with power, engine power, for on this depends the increased speed which is the chief factor in the progress of transport.

AIRCRAFT TODAY AND TOMORROW

The designers of the aircraft of today and tomorrow, for instance, demand fantastic engine powers to drive great air-liners at high speeds. It has been calculated that a fifty-passenger transatlantic air-liner, flying at a speed of 600 miles an hour in the stratosphere, will need a total engine power of nearly 120,000 h.p.; only 38,000 h.p. less than is required to drive the *Queen Mary*, which weighs nearly a thousand times as much as the air-liner.

Most engine designers agree that the practical limit of power of the conventional type of piston engine is in the region of five thousand horse-power, and that an engine of this power output may need over forty cylinders. This tremendously complicated power unit naturally incurs heavy maintenance costs, and even then will not be sufficiently powerful to satisfy aircraft designers in the future. What, then, is the answer? A multiplicity of multi-cylinder engines in the aircraft, with still greater complexity in design, and, more important perhaps, service and maintenance? No, the solution lies in a much simpler power unit: a rocket, jet, or gas-turbine engine.

These power units share a common principle. They derive their power from the reaction caused by allowing heated gases to escape at high velocity from a jet tube. Let us first consider the rocket; the simplest form of reaction motor.

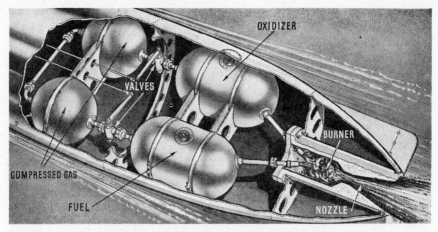

BI-FUEL SYSTEM OF ROCKET PROPULSION

Of the several systems of rocket propulsion, the bi-fuel system is one of the more important and more widely used for aircraft propulsion. In this system two separate fuels are used, and are forced out of the tanks and along the pipe-lines to the combustion chamber by the action of the inert compressed gas. Of the two fuels used one is termed the oxidizer, which is a liquid containing a high proportion of oxygen; the other being a normal combustible fuel. When the gases are mixed they spontaneously react and release a great amount of heat. The resultant hot gases form the exhaust to propel the rocket in its flight.

Rocket propulsion depends on the principle that action and reaction are equal and opposite. How do these twin forces actually drive a rocket?

When a gun is fired the force of the explosion does two things: it sends the shell on its way, and makes the gun recoil. The forward force on the shell is the action, and the backward force of recoil is the reaction. As the explosion causes both action and reaction we say that they are equal and opposite.

Though action and reaction are equal, they are not always equally useful. For instance, in the case of a gun being fired, a high velocity cannot be imparted to the shell without a violent recoil. In other cases it is often the reaction that produces the required motion and the action which is not useful.

In fact, reaction is a force which, like gravity, we are constantly using. Every time we take a step, we press backwards with our foot, but it is the reaction with the ground that moves us forward. Whenever we apply a force in one direction in order to get an equal force in the opposite direction we are using reaction, and we do this times out of number in the course of our normal lives.

It was an old teaser to ask someone how he would get off a perfectly smooth floor if he found himself sitting in the middle of it, assuming that he would not be able to walk, crawl, or slide away, because he could get no grip and, therefore, no reaction to help him. This particular problem is, of course, theoretical.

One answer is that the man should sneeze. If he did this, and then held his breath for long enough, the same force which expelled air from his nose would finally push him to the side of the room.

It is a rocket's sneeze, then, which drives it along. A fuel burned in the combustion chamber develops gases which pass out at great speed through the exhaust. The combustion of the gases, and their sudden and great expansion, provides the reaction which propels the rocket forward.

Imagine what is happening inside the casing of the rocket. The expanding gas is pressing with great force all over the inside of the casing or combustion chamber. At the outlet, however, the gas can escape, being hindered only by the pressure of the atmosphere, which is just under fifteen pounds per square inch at sea-level. At the forward end of the combustion chamber, opposite to the outlet, the gas is exerting a pressure of many hundreds of pounds per square inch. The difference between this pressure and the negligible pressure at the outlet forces the rocket forward.

It is necessary to understand this principle, since many people believe that it is the thrust of the high-velocity jet of gas against the atmosphere which

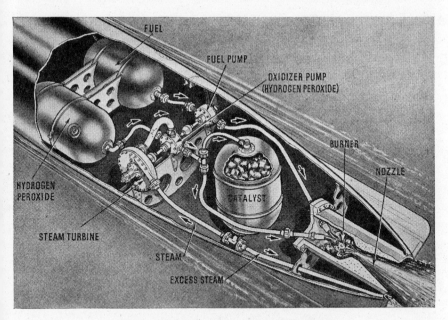

BI-FUEL ROCKET WITH AUXILIARY PUMP

In this variant of the bi-fuel rocket system the fuel is fed by an auxiliary pump. The hydrogen peroxide in passing over the catalyst produces steam which drives a turbine, and this pumps the remainder of the oxidizer and the second fuel into the combustion chamber where it is burnt. A suitable catalyst is formed of stones impregnated with manganese dioxide.

NOSE BALLAST WEIGHT
(JETTISONED WITH
TAKE-OFF OF ROCKET)

DETACHABLE FRAME FOR
TAKE-OFF ROCKETS,
JETTISONED BY MEANS
OF EXPLOSIVE BOLTS

TAILPLANE
WITH
ELEVATORS

FIN (RUDDER IS
NOT FITTED)

TAKE-OFF ROCKETS –
JETTISONED 1½ SECS.
AFTER TAKING OFF

FUSELAGE

WING-TIP
FLARE FOR OBSERVATION
DURING FLIGHT

VENTURI OF
MAIN
PROPULSION
ROCKETS

CONTROL
COLUMN

ADJUSTABLE
LAUNCHING RAMP

ROCKET-
FIRING
TERMINALS

REMOTE CONTROL RADIO SET
TO GUIDE ROCKET FROM GROUND

BRITAIN'S FIRST RADIO-CONTROLLED MISSILE

Radio-controlled, rocket-driven missile, known by the code-name "Stooge." An automatic pilot controls the missile in flight, and is in turn controlled by radio signals from a small ground transmitter fitted with a control column.

drives the rocket forward. A moment's consideration will show that the atmosphere is a hindrance rather than a help. Reduce the atmospheric pressure, as happens when a rocket climbs into the stratosphere, and the difference between the internal and external pressures becomes still greater. The rocket, therefore, travels faster still; remember, too, that the higher it climbs, the less resistance it will meet from the less dense air. Theoretically, the rocket will reach its maximum efficiency in a vacuum.

The bigger the sneeze, the more violently will a rocket be impelled forward. The German V2 rocket, for example, sneezed away 2½ cwt. of gases every second that combustion was taking place. The reaction was so powerful that, with a firing time of 65 seconds, the 12-ton missile was launched from a standing start into the upper air at a speed of a third of a mile a second.

What is the bearing of this on the rocket propulsion of the future? Aircraft powered by rockets gain in efficiency with altitude, while, as the air becomes rarer, their more conventional competitors, and these include jet-propelled planes, becomes gradually less effective. Flight by civil and military aircraft in the substratosphere is an everyday experience, but the sky-way of the future is the stratosphere itself; the region that lies roughly between altitudes of six and thirty miles.

A rocket plane has no ceiling, but practical considerations show that its best service is likely to be in the stratosphere rather than farther out in the ionosphere. A climb of over six miles is not worth while unless the rocket plane can take full advantage of the rarefied air. To do this, it must cover a great distance at very high speed.

Is the speed likely to be greater than humans can stand? To this question we can answer a confident no, for even in our own homes we are moving with the earth at a speed of over eighteen miles a second round the sun. No rocket has yet travelled at much more than one mile per second. The human limitation lies in the acceleration, or build-up of speed.

The effect of violent vertical acceleration on the human body can be sufficient to cause temporary unconsciousness, as proved by the "black-out" experienced by pilots of high-speed aircraft during a sharp turn, or when pulling out of a steep dive at high speed. Just as a weight whirled around at the end of a string

ROCKET-ASSISTED TAKE-OFF

One-hundred-and-eighty-passenger Lockheed Constitution being aided at take-off by six rockets. These give an additional power of 3,500 h.p., and reduce take-off by 24 per cent. This principle has been successfully used for assisting aeroplanes when taking off from the decks of aircraft carriers.

tries to fly outwards, so centrifugal force acts on the human body in a similar way. This force is compared, for the purposes of measurement, with that of gravity. During a high-speed turn, the pilot's body may be subjected to a centrifugal force amounting to four times that of gravity, and forces of seven or eight times that of gravity are not unknown in high-speed manœuvres in fighter aircraft.

Most healthy young pilots can withstand a force of four times gravity, expressed as $4g$ for brevity. At $4\frac{1}{2}g$, however, the blood in the body can no longer return through the veins to the heart; instead, it tends to collect in the legs and the lower parts of the body. The brain and upper parts are thus drained of blood, vision becomes grey, and eventually the pilot blacks out.

Vision and consciousness return, however, as soon as the excessive g force is relieved. By equipping pilots with special flying suits having inflatable legs and waistbands which prevent the accumulation of blood in the veins, the onset of black-out can be delayed, since the legs and abdomen can be tightly constricted during violent turns and when pulling out of dives. A similar effect can be

EXPERIMENTAL STRATOSPHERE AIRCRAFT

Rocket-propelled Bell X-1 was designed for investigating supersonic flight problems. Its estimated maximum speed is 1,000 m.p.h. at an altitude of 60,000 ft.

obtained by providing the pilot with a special type of seat which allows him to lie prone during high-speed manœuvres, although this is a less practicable method.

How does this compare with the acceleration of a rocket? The V2 accelerated from a standing start at about $20g$, and this, even for a firing time of a few seconds only, would be beyond the capacity of a man to withstand. A slower rate of acceleration for a rocket craft would mean a slower expenditure of fuel, so that some of the fuel would have to be raised to a considerable height before it was

DESIGN OF THE FUTURE

Armstrong Whitworth A.W.52 jet-propelled tailless aircraft photographed in flight. It is propelled by two Rolls-Royce Derwent turbo-jet engines, and is a true all-wing aircraft, except for the wing-tip rudders.

used. Lifting fuel against the pull of gravity is exceedingly wasteful, especially as such a high proportion of the initial weight of a rocket craft is due to the fuel it carries. About 70 per cent of the weight of a V2 consisted of fuel.

It follows, then, that for a rocket carrying a non-human load, for example a mail rocket, it is best for the firing to last a few seconds only, so that the stratosphere is reached as quickly as possible. In this case the rocket approximates to a projectile, such as a shell, which is given a violent once-for-all send-off.

If mail rockets have for the present ceased to attract experimenters, research on stratospheric rocket flight has been greatly intensified. In the lower reaches of the atmosphere a rocket motor is relatively inefficient. Here it is best to use rocket motors for assisted take-off or for boosting the performance of aircraft powered by conventional engines.

For rocket-driven strato-planes, on the other hand, it is more economical to raise the plane on the first part of its journey by means of the internal combustion engine or the jet. When the rocket motor takes over it will work with maximum efficiency, so that the load of fuel needed for the rocket will be a minimum. This is an important practical consideration because, of all mechanical sources of power, the rocket has the greatest fuel consumption.

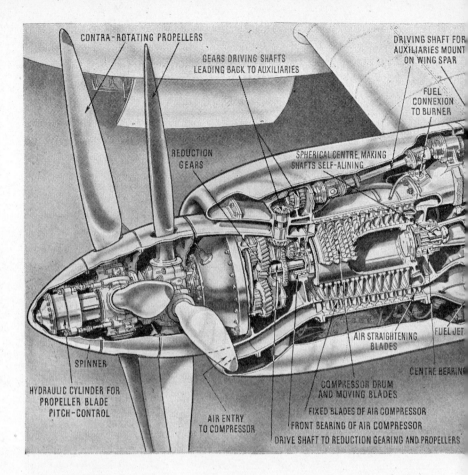

CONTRA-ROTATING PROPELLERS

GEARS DRIVING SHAFTS
LEADING BACK TO AUXILIARIES

DRIVING SHAFT FOR
AUXILIARIES MOUNT
ON WING SPAR

FUEL
CONNEXION
TO BURNER

REDUCTION
GEARS

SPHERICAL CENTRE, MAKING
SHAFTS SELF-ALINING

AIR STRAIGHTENING
BLADES

FUEL JET

SPINNER

CENTRE BEARING

HYDRAULIC CYLINDER FOR
PROPELLER BLADE
PITCH-CONTROL

COMPRESSOR DRUM
AND MOVING BLADES

AIR ENTRY
TO COMPRESSOR

FIXED BLADES OF AIR COMPRESSOR

FRONT BEARING OF AIR COMPRESSOR

DRIVE SHAFT TO REDUCTION GEARING AND PROPELLERS

Many thousands of fuels have been tested in the last few years to find those which give the greatest thrust for the least weight. The most promising are the hydrocarbons, such as petrol and alcohols.

In the future, aircraft driven by propellers will operate the medium-distance routes; jet planes will serve the middle altitudes, going no higher than the lower levels of the stratosphere; while rocket planes, with ranges up to that needed to cover the distance between any two points on earth, i.e. up to 12,000 miles, will assert their supremacy in the upper air.

JET PROPULSION

We have several times had occasion to mention jet planes. Let us now turn to the jet engine. Rocket and jet propulsion both depend on reaction, but whereas a rocket craft carries with it the oxygen needed for combustion, a jet craft draws its supply of oxygen from the air. One result of this is that a rocket can work with maximum efficiency out in space, where there is no air, but the ceiling of a jet plane lies well within the earth's atmosphere.

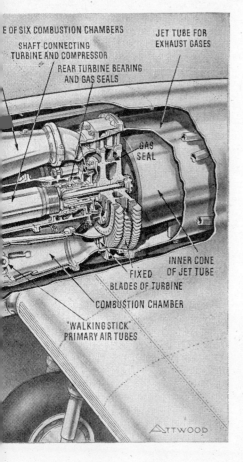

SHAFT-CONNECTING   EXHAUST GASES
TURBINE AND COMPRESSOR
REAR TURBINE BEARING
AND GAS SEALS

GAS
SEAL

INNER CONE
FIXED   OF JET TUBE
BLADES OF TURBINE

COMBUSTION CHAMBER

"WALKING STICK"
PRIMARY AIR TUBES

ATTWOOD

The Mamba gas turbine has an axial-flow compressor which draws air from the air intake and compresses it into the six combustion chambers. The fuel is sprayed into the latter, and after being initially fired by an igniter the combustion is a continuous process.

Work on jet engines designed by Sir Frank Whittle began as long ago as 1933. The first engine ran successfully four years later, and in another four years the Gloster-Whittle *Pioneer* made the first British jet-propelled flight. It should be appreciated that this development was only made possible by the co-ordinated efforts of scientists and engineers. For example, the metallurgist played a leading role by developing new heat-resisting materials for withstanding the terrific temperatures generated in the turbine.

What is the secret of the success of jet-propelled machines ? There is no better or clearer way of answering this question than by taking a typical jet engine apart and seeing how it works. Let us do this to the highly successful de Havilland Goblin engine.

Somewhere in the front of every jet aircraft, usually on the fore part of the fuselage, or in the wings, lie one or more air intakes. When the air enters the jet unit the first thing it meets is the compressor. This is a rapidly revolving fan whose blades are attached at the farther end to a disk, so that the air, instead of passing straight through, is whirled off sideways at a pressure of some forty pounds to the square inch into one or another of the combustion chambers. These lie lengthwise round the central axis of the unit so that they eventually discharge their exhaust gases into the same jet stream.

The fuel is also injected into each chamber, where it mixes with the air, and combustion takes place. The chief effects are a considerable rise in temperature, and such an expansion of the gases that they leave the combustion chamber even faster than they were hurled into it by the compressor.

The ends of the combustion chambers are equally spaced round the circumference of a turbine wheel, so that the rapidly moving gases, in passing between the blades of the turbine, keep it spinning on exactly the same principle that moving air keeps a windmill in motion.

Now the turbine and the compressor are connected by a shaft, so that the gases, besides driving the turbine, also drive the compressor; this ensures a continuous flow of air at pressure into the combustion chambers.

After passing the turbine, the separate streams of gas eventually combine to form a single jet moving at an exceedingly high speed. It is this jet that provides the reaction that drives the aircraft forward.

To get the utmost reaction, the jet flow must be as smooth as possible; eddies, for example, would cause a loss of energy. The streams of gas are, therefore, not

WORLD'S FIRST JET-POWERED AIR-LINER
Vickers Viscount air-liner, propelled by two Rolls-Royce Nene jet engines, seen landing at London Airport after setting up a new record of 34 min. 7 secs. for a flight between London and Paris.

allowed to combine immediately they have passed the turbine blades, but move between the outer wall of the unit and an exhaust cone whose base lies against the turbine wheel. In this way the gases are made to traverse a gradually widening passage and combine with the minimum of disturbance.

It is chiefly for this reason, too, that on most engines there are several combustion chambers. Combustion is made more complete, and its products are taken more speedily away, than would be the case with a single large combustion chamber within which a turbulent flow of gas could hardly be avoided.

A hundred tons of air passes through the Goblin II unit in an hour, and is

BRISTOL BRABAZON

This aircraft is designed specifically as a trans-oceanic air-liner to provide fast travel for a large number of passengers at one time. It is a fully pressurized, high-altitude, long-range monoplane with a wing span of 230 ft. Power is provided by eight Bristol Centaurus 18-cylinder air-cooled engines. As the engines are totally enclosed in the inner wing, it will be possible for inspection and servicing to be carried out while the aircraft is in flight. Passenger and crew accommodation is arranged mainly on one deck, with a half-deck rise over the wing for a dining saloon, lounge bar, kitchen and servery. In the main cabin aft, provision will be made for a cinema projector and radio for passengers' entertainment.

given a jet speed of approximately one and a half times the speed of sound. This is sufficient to give a static thrust of 3,000 lb. The de Havilland Ghost has improved on the Goblin and gives a thrust of 5,000 lb.

It is not difficult to see why jet engines hold such promise for the future. Compared with piston-driven engines they are a miracle of simplicity. They have fewer moving parts, so that wear and tear are reduced, maintenance is easier, and less skilled attention is needed. Their simplicity not only makes for smooth running, so that vibration is eliminated, but allows a smaller and lighter engine to carry a heavier load at a greater speed. Even more important, jet engines do not need the high-grade fuel that is essential for high-speed piston engines. They have the disadvantage, however, of a far greater fuel consumption at low altitudes than normal aero-engines. In this respect they come closer to pure rocket units.

A type of jet propulsion that is being developed now is a compromise between the turbo-jet just described and the conventional propeller drive. By making the turbine turn a propeller, advantage is taken of the fact that a propeller can get a

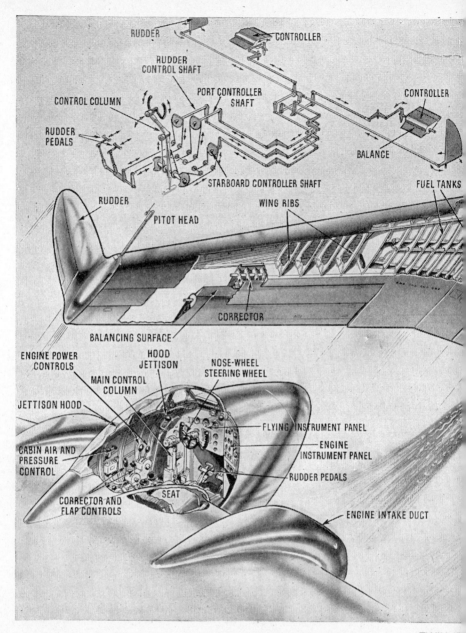

RUDDER

CONTROLLER

RUDDER
CONTROL SHAFT

PORT CONTROLLER
SHAFT

CONTROL COLUMN

CONTROLLER

RUDDER
PEDALS

BALANCE

STARBOARD CONTROLLER SHAFT

FUEL TANKS

RUDDER

PITOT HEAD

WING RIBS

CORRECTOR

BALANCING SURFACE

ENGINE POWER
CONTROLS

HOOD
JETTISON

NOSE-WHEEL
STEERING WHEEL

MAIN CONTROL
COLUMN

JETTISON HOOD

FLYING INSTRUMENT PANEL

ENGINE
INSTRUMENT PANEL

CABIN AIR AND
PRESSURE
CONTROL

RUDDER PEDALS

CORRECTOR AND
FLAP CONTROLS

SEAT

ENGINE INTAKE DUCT

TWIN-JE

This aircraft was specially designed to investigate the future possibilities of tailless or all-wing aircraft. If successful, the data from these experiments will be used to determine the final shape and detailed design of a six-jet tailless airliner. It is powered by two Rolls-Royce Nene centrifugal-flow gas turbines. Directional control is by means of the fins and rudders mounted on the wing tips.

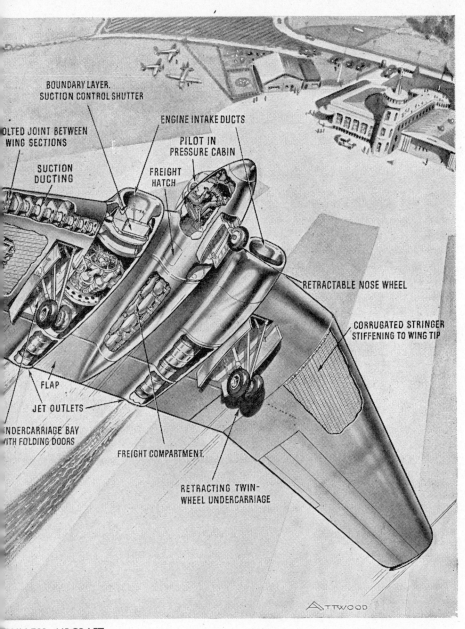

BOUNDARY LAYER.
SUCTION CONTROL SHUTTER

ENGINE INTAKE DUCTS

OLTED JOINT BETWEEN
WING SECTIONS

PILOT IN
PRESSURE CABIN

SUCTION
DUCTING

FREIGHT
HATCH

RETRACTABLE NOSE WHEEL

CORRUGATED STRINGER
STIFFENING TO WING TIP

FLAP

JET OUTLETS

NDERCARRIAGE BAY
ITH FOLDING DOORS

FREIGHT COMPARTMENT

RETRACTING TWIN-
WHEEL UNDERCARRIAGE

ATTWOOD

TAILLESS AIRCRAFT

The cockpit which houses the pilot and navigator or radio operator projects
forward from the centre section of the wing, and is pressurized. The wing span is
90 ft., and the overall length 37 ft. Maximum speed at sea-level is 500 m.p.h.
An advantage of this design of aircraft is that it offers less resistance to the air
than does the conventional aircraft of the fuselage and mainplane combination.

grip on a larger body of air than can be sucked through the jet intakes. While the turbine-driven propeller reduces fuel consumption, it carries the penalty that it cannot be used for really high speeds. As we shall see later, the use of a propeller for speeds approaching that of sound creates more problems than it solves.

The real value of the turbo-prop is to bridge the gap between the operating ceiling of the piston engine and the stratosphere, where the pure jet comes into its own. It bridges the gap in another way, too, for the efficiency of jet aircraft increases with speed, so that the turbo-prop will operate most usefully at speeds up to 450 or 500 m.p.h. where jets are less economical than at higher speeds.

It will take very many years for all the combinations of jets with other forms of propulsion to be tried, and for the full effects of the advances to show themselves. It is already abundantly clear that in the next decade we shall see high-speed stratosphere flight fully established, with craft that can be turned out more cheaply and carry loads at lower cost than any present-day type. Higher speeds mean that aircraft can perform more journeys in a given time, and this fact sets new problems in ground staff work, and in "feeding" airports.

RECENT DEVELOPMENTS IN AIRCRAFT DESIGN

So far we have implicitly assumed that the aircraft is of the conventional high- or low-wing monoplane type, with mainplane, fuselage, tailplane and rudder. In the future, however, we are likely to see quite a number of departures from this accepted rule. The so-called "all-wing" aircraft, for instance, is likely to be widely used, especially for large air-liners. In this case the passenger cabins, pilot's cockpit and power units are built into the huge, triangular wing. Gas turbine engines, driving propellers which protrude from the front or rear edge of the wing, are the most likely means of propulsion, although for smaller aircraft travelling at very high speed pure jet-propulsion units may be used. Several aircraft of both types, the larger ones being in the 100-ton class, are being built both in Great Britain and in America.

TAILLESS AIRCRAFT

These aircraft are often described as "tailless." The rearmost extremities of the swept-back wing generally carry rudders at their tips so that, in effect, the aircraft has two tails instead of none. In some cases the rudders are dispensed with, a special system of controls being used, but the effect is the same. A cut-away view of an experimental tailless aircraft is illustrated on pages 302-3.

An advantage of this type of aircraft is that it offers less resistance to the air than does the conventional fuselage and mainplane combination, while the tapered, swept-back wing also gives considerable advantages at speeds near the speed of sound, which will undoubtedly be approached even by large air-liners in the fairly near future. A further development is the provision of slots on the wing through which air is sucked into the intakes of the gas turbine or jet engines;

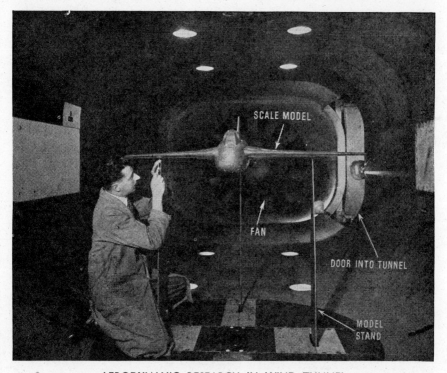

SCALE MODEL

FAN

DOOR INTO TUNNEL

MODEL STAND

AERODYNAMIC RESEARCH IN WIND TUNNEL

Fitting a scale model in a wind tunnel prior to testing. Tests such as these are an indispensable part of all modern investigations into problems connected with aerodynamics. This is especially true in the case of jet- or rocket-propelled aircraft, travelling at speeds close to that of sound.

the removal of the layer of air next to the surface of the wing, or boundary layer, as it is termed, reduces the turbulence of the airflow over the wing under critical conditions of flight, and the more stable airflow gives better control over the aircraft.

That the conventional type of aircraft has still a promising future, however, is proved by several outstanding examples. In a typical aircraft, up to sixty passengers can be accommodated in comfort in the spacious fuselage, enjoying the use of a promenade deck and a cocktail bar, while a galley equipped with a grill-boiler, refrigerator, ice-cream containers, and so on, ministers to their inner needs.

The Bristol *Brabazon* is, of course, a giant by comparison with normal airliners. With an all-up weight of 110 tons, it has wings which measure 230 ft. from tip to tip, and a fuselage 177 ft. in length, while the top of the fin is 50 ft. from the ground. Eight gas turbines, arranged in pairs to drive four contra-

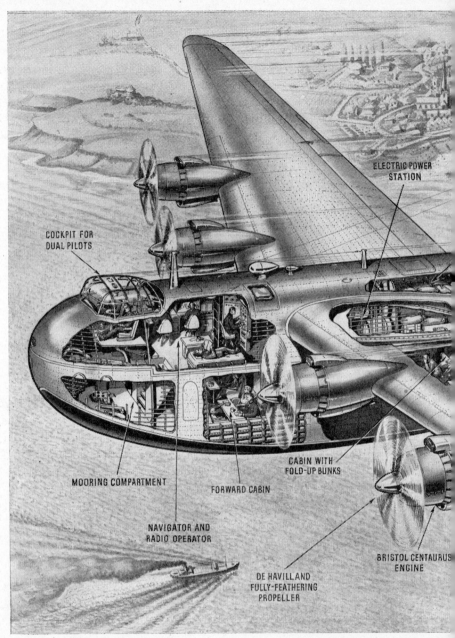

ELECTRIC POWER
STATION

COCKPIT FOR
DUAL PILOTS

CABIN WITH
FOLD-UP BUNKS

MOORING COMPARTMENT

FORWARD CABIN

NAVIGATOR AND
RADIO OPERATOR

BRISTOL CENTAURUS
ENGINE

DE HAVILLAND
FULLY-FEATHERING
PROPELLER

SHORT SHETLAND LON

This commercial flying-boat is powered by four 2,500-h.p. Bristol Centaurus
18-cylinder, air-cooled engines operating four-bladed, constant-speed propellers.
It has a wing span of 150 ft. and is 108 ft. long. All electric power is supplied
by an auxiliary generating plant. The accommodation is arranged in two decks,

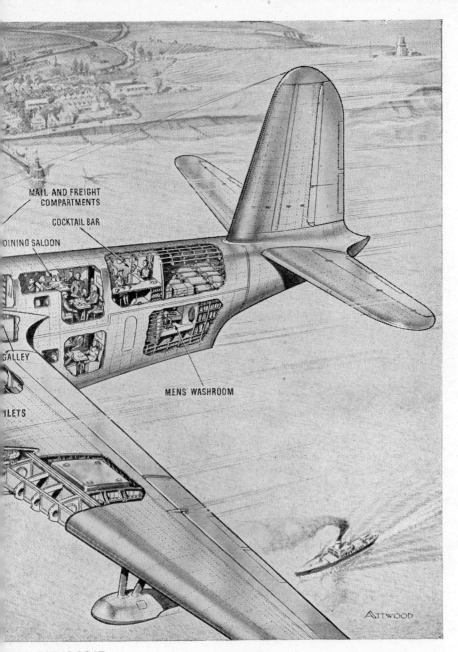

MAIL AND FREIGHT COMPARTMENTS

COCKTAIL BAR

DINING SALOON

GALLEY

...ILETS

MENS' WASHROOM

ATTWOOD

...NGE FLYING-BOAT

and, as will be seen from the drawing, is designed to give a maximum of comfort to the passengers with all the amenities associated with ocean-going liners. One practical advantage of the flying-boat over comparable land-based aircraft is that it does not depend upon expensive aerodromes for its operation.

rotating propellers, enable the aircraft to carry 224 passengers at a cruising speed of 350 miles per hour. American air-liners in the same class are capable of carrying from one to two hundred passengers across the Atlantic in under ten hours; this is true of other long distance routes.

It must not be assumed, however, that the landplane will monopolize the picture. From the earliest days of flight the advantages of an aircraft which could take off from and alight on water were realized. In its earliest form the seaplane was simply a landplane on which floats had been substituted for the ordinary wheel landing gear. This type of aircraft is still widely used, especially in countries where lakes and rivers provide ready-made landing strips, and ordinary aerodromes may be few and far between.

It does not take long to adapt an aircraft with a fixed undercarriage to operate from land with wheels, from the water with floats, or from ice and snow with skis. Generally two main floats are used, attached to the fuselage by streamlined struts, and braced by wires. A single main float is also a popular arrangement in America, but small subsidiary floats must also be attached to the wing-tips to steady the aircraft.

It is a logical step from the single-float seaplane to the flying-boat, in which

HALTERES OR BALANCERS WHICH VIBRATE AT 300 VIBRATIONS PER SECOND

COMMON DRONE-FLY AND GYROSCOPIC ACTION

Research is being conducted on the aerodynamics of insect flight, as it is thought that the principles involved will be of practical use in the development of aircraft. One such field of research is the oscillating halteres on the common drone-fly which have a gyroscopic action, but are not gyroscopes.

PHOTO-ELASTIC STRESS ANALYSIS

In this method of analysing stresses a model of the part is shaped out of a transparent thermosetting plastic and loaded with weights proportional to those expected to be experienced in practice. Then a beam of light, which has passed through a polarizer, is directed through the model. By viewing the model through an analyser it is possible to see colour fringes which indicate how the stress is disposed. This technique is now being used in the aircraft industry.

the fuselage, or hull, provides the necessary buoyancy when afloat. Flying-boat design has developed along entirely separate lines from seaplanes or land aircraft and the hull more nearly resembles that of a ship in design and construction than an aircraft.

It is customary to speak of a "flying ship" when talking about the giant, two-decked flying-boats of today, like the 58-ton Short Shetland, or the new 150-ton Saunders Roe, SR/45, driven by ten gas turbines of 3,500 h.p. each, driving six propellers. Four will be of the contra-rotating, constant speed type propeller driven by a pair of gas turbines, and the two outboard propellers will be driven by single gas turbines.

Beginning at the forward end, or bow, we have the stem, from which the keel runs aft along the bottom of the hull. The bottom is V-shaped, to reduce the shock of alighting on the water at speeds of up to 100 m.p.h., and at the point at which the bottom meets the sides of the hull, called the chine, the plates are curved downwards slightly to throw the spray well clear of the boat.

The most interesting feature, however, is the incorporation of one or more

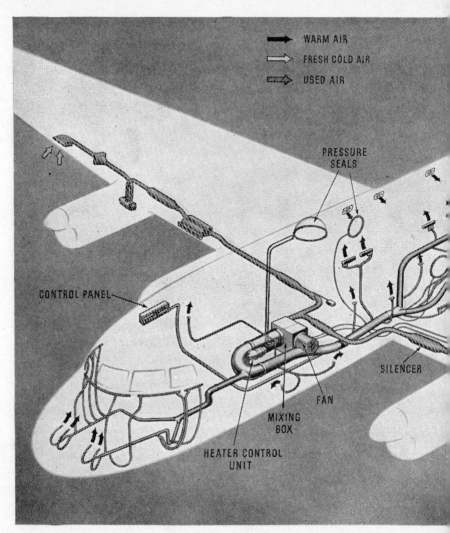

WARM AIR
FRESH COLD AIR
USED AIR

PRESSURE
SEALS

CONTROL PANEL

SILENCER

FAN

MIXING
BOX

HEATER CONTROL
UNIT

AIRCRAFT ATMOSPHE

This drawing shows the installation of an atmosphere-conditioning plant (which includes pressurizing) set against the ghosted outline of the aircraft. This system

steps in the hull below the water-line. It might be supposed that the most effective design for the hull would be a perfectly streamlined shape below water-level to reduce the drag and the engine power required for take-off. Yet a hull having such a shape would never leave the water.

This can be appreciated when the bottom of the hull is compared with the top surface of a wing, but in this case inverted. The water flowing past it behaves in just the same way as air flowing over the streamlined surface of the wing, i.e. it creates a suction. The greater the speed of the hull through the water, therefore,

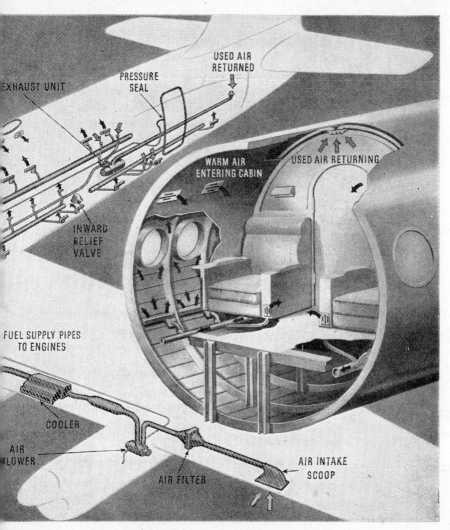

EXHAUST UNIT

PRESSURE SEAL

USED AIR RETURNED

WARM AIR ENTERING CABIN

USED AIR RETURNING

INWARD RELIEF VALVE

FUEL SUPPLY PIPES TO ENGINES

COOLER

AIR BLOWER

AIR FILTER

AIR INTAKE SCOOP

...NDITIONING INSTALLATION

has been developed to maintain a comfortable pressure of air in the cabin at the correct humidity at all altitudes, and in conditions of ascent and descent.

the greater is the tendency of the water to suck it down, a tendency which the lift of the wings cannot overcome.

The step in the hull is intended to prevent this happening. When the flying-boat is taxi-ing slowly, the water flowing past the edge of the step breaks and swirls upwards like an inverted waterfall. As the speed of the flying-boat increases during take-off run, the water breaks farther and farther behind the step, tending to draw in air, and gradually this cushion of air extends back towards the stern of the boat, until eventually the hull is separated from the water, and the lift of the wings causes it to become airborne. On large flying-boats two steps are usually fitted to build up an effective air-cushion.

Since the step causes a considerable increase in drag once the flying-boat is airborne, as compared with a normal streamlined fuselage, a new development is now being introduced. The step is rendered unnecessary by blowing air out of jets at appropriate points in the bottom of a streamlined hull, thus destroying the suction on the plating; this scheme is likely to be used on several flying-boats in the near future.

The roomy, apparently cumbersome fuselage of the flying-boat represents an excellent compromise between buoyancy, internal space and aerodynamic efficiency. Generally the internal accommodation is arranged on two decks. The drawing on pages 306-7 illustrates the lay-out of accommodation in the Short Shetland long-range flying-boat.

The greater freedom of the passengers to move around in the aircraft partly explains the popularity of flying-boats on long-distance routes. From the operator's view, too, the fact that a flying-boat can land and take-off from any suitable stretch of sheltered water is a distinct advantage; it has been estimated that, even if an enclosed lagoon must be built, the cost is only about one-fifth of the average cost of building an aerodrome which will accommodate landplanes of a comparable size, even assuming a suitable area of ground to be available.

AMPHIBIOUS AIRCRAFT

A less commonly-used compromise between the flying-boat and the seaplane is the amphibian, which combines a float or a buoyant hull with retractable undercarriage which can be used for landing or taking off from land. The amphibian can alight on the water, taxi to a slipway or sloping beach, lower its undercarriage, and then taxi up out of the water on to dry land. Alternatively, of course, it can taxi down a slope into the water, retract its land undercarriage, and take off as a flying-boat. This versatility makes it of value for commercial purposes in undeveloped territories, while in the smaller versions it is well suited to the needs of the private owner who requires rapid transport to suitable lakes and rivers for fishing, yachting and so on.

The recently developed helicopter revealed that not only was vertical ascent possible, but that it was also feasible to fly forwards, backwards or sideways at will. On this type of aircraft the wings take the form of two or more narrow blades which revolve horizontally around a central hub. The hub may be driven by a shaft from an engine in the fuselage; or the wings, or rotors as they are called, may be driven by jets issuing from their tips, although this latter system is not very widely used at present.

Now we know that a wing, consisting of an aerofoil section, will develop lifting power if air flows over it quickly enough. Obviously the wing need not move forward in a straight line. It will be just as efficient if it is rotating around a hub, except that, since the parts of the wing near the edge of the circle are moving more quickly than those near its centre, the aerofoil action and angle of attack must vary throughout the length of the blade. With rotors of the correct section, sufficient lift will be developed to raise the helicopter vertically.

One major drawback when an engine-driven rotor is used is that, once the helicopter has left the ground, it will be easier for the fuselage to rotate around the central hub, instead of the rotor doing so and lifting the fuselage. Consequently, it is necessary to provide some form of thrust to counteract rotation of the fuselage. One method is to fit a small propeller to the tail of the machine, pointing sideways to the centre-line of the fuselage. This is driven by an extension shaft from the engine, and the angle of attack of the blades can be altered by a control in the cockpit.

PRINCIPLE OF VERTICAL ASCENT

By increasing the angle of attack, the propeller will develop more thrust and will turn the helicopter against the reaction of the rotor; if the angle of attack is reduced the propeller exerts less thrust and the rotor rotates the fuselage; a compromise between the two positions will keep the helicopter on a steady course. On some machines the steering propeller is fitted to a small stub-wing beside the fuselage and faces in the direction of flight, so that it assists the forward flight of the machine. On others, a jet, or the engine exhaust directed in the form of a jet, is used to give steering thrust instead of a propeller.

It is possible, therefore, for the helicopter to rise vertically from the ground or to hover in the air without rotating about its own axis. How does it fly forwards, backwards or sideways? This is done by arranging the rotor blades on special types of pivot, so that their angle of attack can be altered at any point during their rotation.

Suppose that as each blade sweeps towards the rear of the machine the angle at which it meets the air is increased, and is decreased again as the blade begins to move forwards. The effect will be to give an increased lift over the rear sector of the circle swept by the rotor blades, and this unbalanced lift will attempt to tilt the rotors about their pivots, and will thus exert a thrust which will force the helicopter forwards. The drawing on page 315 should make the principle clear. By increasing the angle of attack of the rotors at any point in the circle, the helicopter can similarly be made to fly backwards or sideways at will.

SPECIAL USES OF HELICOPTERS

It seems likely, therefore, that the helicopter will be widely used for short-distance hops in the future as an adjunct to the main-line air-liner, since its rather low top speed is more than offset by its ability to land or take off from any level space which gives sufficient clearance for its rotors. The smaller helicopters will make excellent private-owner aircraft when the present rather complicated controls have been simplified. The large aircraft at present being developed will have, in addition to ordinary passenger- and cargo-carrying duties, a wide scope in such unorthodox roles as lifting heavy constructional girders or components from inaccessible points and delivering them to the actual spot at which they are required, possibly even hovering above the site while the girder is lowered into position, thus acting as an aerial crane.

So we have seen how the basic idea of the flow of air over a curved wing surface has made possible the huge, 100-ton air-liner, the smaller aircraft for feeder-line services linking the main stopping points on world air-routes with the smaller towns, and the helicopter, ideally suited for short taxi-flights, bringing, say, the centre of a town within a few minutes' flight of an airfield on its outskirts.

FUTURE OF AIR TRANSPORT

It would almost seem that the versatility of the aircraft is likely, in the future, to render all other forms of transport obsolete. How much truth is there in such a prediction?

In the first place, it is true that an aircraft of a suitable type for a given service can offer transport at fares which compare quite favourably with first-class fares for travel by sea or rail. The greater speed of the aircraft is bound to give it an advantage over slower forms of transport, whether it is the passenger who is affected or the business man who wishes to move perishable or luxury goods with the minimum of delay.

Among the many aspects of the problem which render it unwise to be dogmatic, however, are two important factors. The first is that there will always be a large percentage of the travelling public who will choose the more leisurely form of transport for preference: a five-day voyage to New York on a luxury liner, with swimming pools, cinemas, and lavish menus, will always have an attraction if speed is not essential. The second point concerns the carrying capacity of an aircraft. The bulk and weight of cargo which can be moved by air is, theoretically, unlimited; it is simply necessary to build a larger aircraft. Just how much bigger is not always appreciated. The useful load that an aircraft can carry forms only a comparatively small percentage of its total weight, which must include the structure of the aircraft, as well as the load of fuel, oil and other supplies for the flight.

On land and water, and in the air, the new methods of propulsion are proving their worth and providing the data from which fresh advances will come. Speed and distance records are being set up and just as monotonously broken.

Is there any limit to the new speeds made possible by jets and rockets that we can attain? To answer this question we must turn our attention for a moment from objects moving through the air to the properties of the air itself. The sounds that we hear are really waves in the air. These waves consist of a succession of compressions and rarefactions, so that the air is alternately closely and loosely packed.

Sound waves travel at about 760 m.p.h. at sea-level. For the first six miles of altitude the air becomes colder, and as the temperature falls so does the speed of

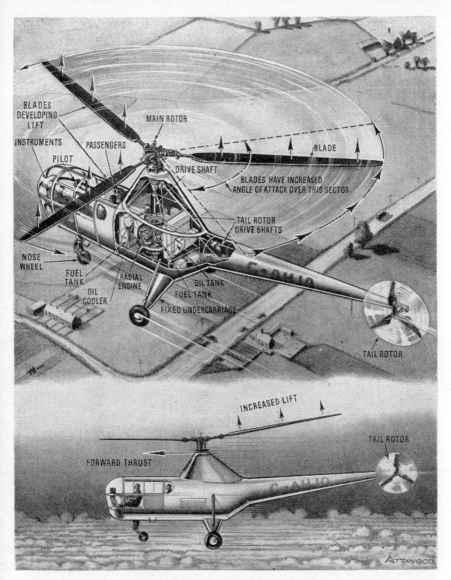

The following labels appear on the illustration:

BLADES DEVELOPING LIFT

MAIN ROTOR

INSTRUMENTS

PASSENGERS

BLADE

PILOT

DRIVE SHAFT

BLADES HAVE INCREASED ANGLE OF ATTACK OVER THIS SECTOR

TAIL ROTOR DRIVE SHAFTS

NOSE WHEEL

FUEL TANK

RADIAL ENGINE

OIL TANK

OIL COOLER

FUEL TANK

FIXED UNDERCARRIAGE

TAIL ROTOR

INCREASED LIFT

TAIL ROTOR

FORWARD THRUST

ATTWOOD

PRINCIPLES OF VERTICAL ASCENT

In the helicopter the wings take the form of two or more narrow blades which revolve in a horizontal plane around a central hub. The hub is driven by a shaft from the engine situated in the fuselage. A blade of aerofoil section will develop lift if air flows over it. Obviously, the blade need not move forward in a straight line. It will be just as efficient if it is rotating around a hub, and, in the case of the helicopter, will develop sufficient lift to rise vertically. Flying forwards, backwards or sideways is done by arranging the blades so that their angle of attack can be altered at any point during their rotation. The tail rotor is employed to counteract the tendency of the fuselage to rotate around the hub.

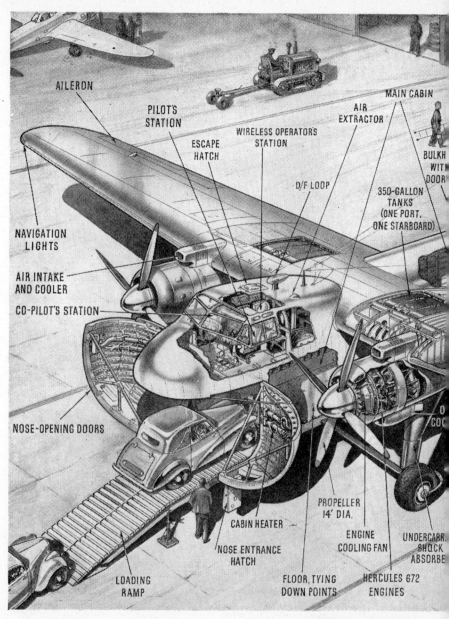

AILERON

PILOTS
STATION

ESCAPE
HATCH

WIRELESS OPERATORS
STATION

D/F LOOP

AIR
EXTRACTOR

MAIN CABIN

BULKH
WIT
DOOR

350-GALLON
TANKS
(ONE PORT.
ONE STARBOARD)

NAVIGATION
LIGHTS

AIR INTAKE
AND COOLER

CO-PILOT'S STATION

NOSE-OPENING DOORS

O
COC

CABIN HEATER

NOSE ENTRANCE
HATCH

PROPELLER
14' DIA.

ENGINE
COOLING FAN

UNDERCARR.
SHOCK
ABSORBE

LOADING
RAMP

FLOOR, TYING
DOWN POINTS

HERCULES 672
ENGINES

BRISTOL FREIGHTER — AL

This interesting aircraft is powered by two Hercules engines developing 3,380 b.h.p. at take-off, and driving two 14-ft. constant-speed, fully feathering propellers. A feature of the engine installation is the new "exit-free" cowl which permits the release of more thrust horse-power for improving the rate of climb. Also, it reduces cooling drag, and improves cooling, especially in tropical conditions.

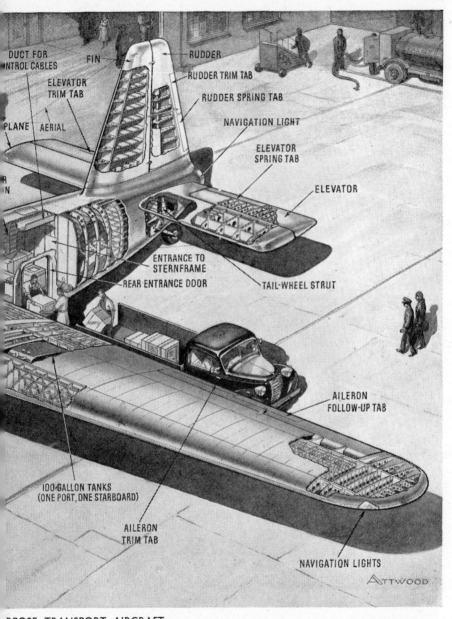

DUCT FOR
CONTROL CABLES
FIN
RUDDER
RUDDER TRIM TAB
ELEVATOR
TRIM TAB
RUDDER SPRING TAB
NAVIGATION LIGHT
PLANE AERIAL
ELEVATOR
SPRING TAB
ELEVATOR
ENTRANCE TO
STERNFRAME
REAR ENTRANCE DOOR
TAIL-WHEEL STRUT
AILERON
FOLLOW-UP TAB
100-GALLON TANKS
(ONE PORT, ONE STARBOARD)
AILERON
TRIM TAB
NAVIGATION LIGHTS
ATTWOOD

RPOSE TRANSPORT AIRCRAFT

*Structurally the aircraft is designed to give maximum room in the fuselage for
freight-carrying. As will be seen from the drawing, the nose of the machine is in
the form of two doors, which give access to the fuselage and are used for loading
motor-cars and other forms of bulky freight. In addition to carrying freight it can
be applied to such jobs as forestry protection, medical services and pest control.*

Armstrong Whitworth Apollo is an all-metal low-wing monoplane of approximately 39,500 lb. laden weight, with accommodation for a maximum of 31 passengers and 7,500 lb. of freight in its pressurized cabin. It is powered by four Mamba gas turbines.

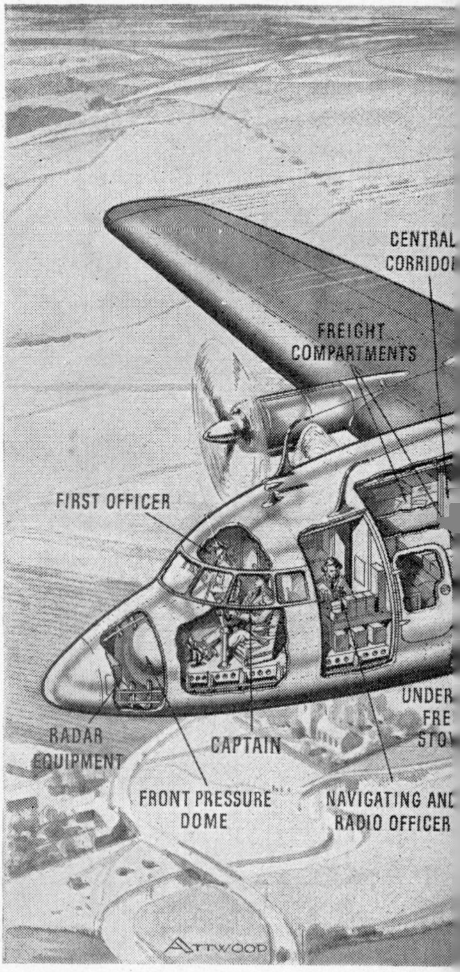
CENTRAL CORRIDO
FREIGHT COMPARTMENTS
FIRST OFFICER
RADAR EQUIPMENT
CAPTAIN
FRONT PRESSURE DOME
NAVIGATING AN RADIO OFFICER
UNDER FRE STO
ATTWOOD

sound. Throughout the stratosphere, where the temperature is constant at minus 78 deg. F., the speed of sound is no more than 660 m.p.h.

High-speed flight at relatively low altitudes has already exceeded the speed of sound and the problems that arise as this critical speed is approached become even more urgent as we venture into the upper air.

It is not hard to see why this speed should be so important. At lower speeds, an aircraft gives notice of its approach because the sound waves it produces travel faster than the aircraft itself. The air in front of it is, so to speak, prepared to receive it. When the aircraft overtakes, or even passes, the sound of its coming, instead of the air parting in an easy flow past the machine, it forms a barrier through which the aircraft has to force a way.

The aircraft, in fact, is in much the same situation as a man who tries to push his way through a crowd of people instead of asking them to make way. The people get crammed together in his path, so that he has to push harder and harder to make headway. An aircraft travelling at the speed of sound piles the air up in front of it, so that all the time it is trying to force its way through a compression barrier.

The shock wave that forms in front of a body travelling at high speed can be made visible to the eye. It does not matter whether the body moves rapidly through stationary air or whether it is the air that streams past the body. In experimental research, therefore, the body is kept stationary.

Suppose, now, that a beam of light is passed through the air across the direc-

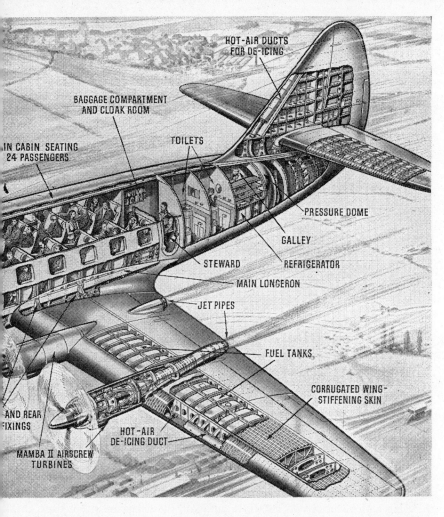

HOT-AIR DUCTS FOR DE-ICING

BAGGAGE COMPARTMENT AND CLOAK ROOM

IN CABIN SEATING 24 PASSENGERS

TOILETS

PRESSURE DOME

GALLEY

STEWARD   REFRIGERATOR

MAIN LONGERON

JET PIPES

FUEL TANKS

CORRUGATED WING-STIFFENING SKIN

AND REAR FIXINGS

HOT-AIR DE-ICING DUCT

MAMBA II AIRSCREW TURBINES

tion of flow. In the area of the shock wave, or system of waves, the air density varies considerably. This variation has the effect of concentrating or diffusing the light, so that a shadowgraph pattern appears on a screen put in its way. The pattern is sometimes rather like what we see in a bath that is being emptied, where the bright lines of refracted light mark the wave-fronts.

The simpler the body the simpler the pattern, and much has already been learned from shadowgraph photographs about the flow of air past aerofoils of different cross-section, and about the shock that develops at the blades of a jet turbine.

For aircraft speeds up to about 680 m.p.h. the air behaves as if it were incompressible, like water, but above this speed compression or shock effects begin to be felt. They are not felt equally all over the aircraft, but appear first at those places where the flow of air is greatest. The tips of the blades of a propeller, for example, move faster through the air than any other part, so it is here that the resistance to motion is felt first. This is one reason why jet planes are more suitable than propeller-driven craft for high-speed flight.

High aircraft speeds are nowadays expressed as a proportion of the speed of sound in air, and this is known as the Mach number. Mach 1 is, of course, the speed of sound itself.

By the time a speed of Mach 0·8 has been reached compression problems have begun to be important, and it marks the threshold of the range up to Mach 1·2, within which speeds are called transonic. Above this, speeds are supersonic.

The importance of this division lies in the fact that the laws that apply to ordinary speeds do not necessarily apply to the transonic flight now under development. In many cases they are reversed. To take an example: the thickest part of a wing designed for moderate speeds is near the leading edge. This edge of a transonic wing is, on the other hand, exceedingly fine, thickening towards the trailing edge.

It is easy to see why this should be so. At speeds above Mach 0·8 the air tends to lose its flow characteristics, and to take on those of a barrier that can only be passed by cutting a way through. Streamlining becomes inappropriate, and a razor-sharp leading edge a necessity.

DESIGN FOR TRANSONIC FLIGHT

Strains and stresses at high speed become intolerable in machines built for work below Mach 0·5, and controls become sluggish and unresponsive. Aircraft have, therefore, to be specially designed for transonic flight. Compactness is essential, so that loads and stresses may be evened out, and the general pattern tends to become either all-wing, so that the barrier is cut by a knife-edge, or else a sharp-nosed cylinder, very much like a needle.

When a needle-shaped nose is fitted to an aircraft of more or less conventional design, the shock front is broken by the needle, and strikes the leading edge of the wing with reduced velocity. If, in addition, the wings are swept back, the velocity is still more reduced. The onset of compressibility problems can, therefore, be delayed. This is important, because the barrier of compressed air increases the drag, or resistance to forward motion, and decreases the lift, by which the machine is held up in the air, and most steps taken to remedy these ill effects only succeed in making the machine less manageable at lower speeds.

The cylindrical shape of the typical rocket is eminently suited to transonic flight, and the external shape of an experimental rocket with its control vanes is often little different from that of transonic aircraft with wings swept back to an angle that is often as great as 45 deg.

Curiously enough, the problem of flying at true supersonic speed is likely to be easier than that of flying at the sonic velocity itself. Once the compressibility barrier has been breached, the air, so to speak, gives up further resistance.

Nearly all the experiments that are taking place on both sides of the Atlantic,

FIXED THROAT WIND TUNNEL

CONTROL PANEL

CAMERA

BALLISTIC RESEARCH LABORATORY

In this wind tunnel models of missiles, bombs and aircraft are tested to determine their behaviour at supersonic speeds, and experiments are carried out to find the correct streamlined forms for bodies travelling in these special conditions.

and these are growing in number, are designed to understand and ultimately to master the turbulent transonic region.

In the Great Salt Desert of Utah, the Boeing Airplane Company of America is conducting for the Army Air Forces a series of test flights of pilotless rocket aircraft. These guided, needle-nose missiles are tracked by radar from various observation posts from the moment they leave the launching tower to the time they bury themselves in the dust of the desert many miles away.

Of the piloted research craft, both the Douglas Skyrocket jet and rocket plane and the Bell XS-1 rocket plane are built for true supersonic speeds. Both are designed to withstand a strain equal to eighteen times the pull of gravity in crossing the transonic region. The XS-1, which is launched from a mother-plane, and has never yet flown full out, is planned to travel eventually at 1,700 m.p.h. at a height of 80,000 feet.

What is the ultimate purpose of these and countless other experiments in high-speed flight? They are collecting the data for the supersonic stratosphere passenger planes of the next decade, and for the space flight which, it is safe to predict, will become a reality before the end of the present century.

It is not only the mechanical problems like acceleration, stability, and control that are being studied, but the human aspects as well. An air-liner can be stressed to resist the shattering effects of flying at high speeds in bumpy air, but the unfortunate passenger, who, unlike a fighter pilot, may not be in excellent physical condition, cannot be expected to withstand similar internal stresses. What, then, is the solution to the problem, if high-speed transport is to be a commonplace in the future?

One answer is to fly at very great heights. Above a height of 36,000 feet, in the stratosphere, the temperature remains more or less constant, and storms are practically unknown, so that flying is very much smoother. Unfortunately, at this height the speed of sound is lower than at sea-level, so that the barrier to high-speed flight is reached much earlier, which means that the aircraft must be specially designed to meet these very special conditions.

Since the density of the air is much lower, too, the cabin of the aircraft must be supplied with air under pressure to ensure that the passengers and crew receive sufficient oxygen, while the air must also be warmed to combat the intense coldness of the atmosphere at these great heights.

Some of these problems can be solved only in actual flight, others will be solved in laboratory conditions in the transonic and supersonic wind tunnels that are in use or under construction.

In a wind tunnel accurate measurements can be made with a stationary aircraft held in an artificial wind moving at any desired speed. For the

The Douglas "Skystreak," powered by a turbo-jet engine, making its first flight. It is designed for true supersonic speeds and to withstand a resistance of up to eighteen times the pull of gravity in crossing the transonic region.

purpose of experiment it does not matter whether an aircraft is moving through stationary air, or whether it is the air that moves past the stationary machine. The advantages of wind-tunnel research are that conditions can be varied to give a wide range of data, there is no risk as there would be if a pilot were actually flying a new machine, and models can be used just as well as full-sized craft. The behaviour of models under test is watched through a window in the wall of the tunnel. Two of the most up-to-date wind tunnels in the world are at the National Physical Laboratory, and the Royal Aircraft Establishment, Farnborough.

At speeds in the transonic range the behaviour of a full-size craft can no longer be deduced from what happens to a model in the wind tunnel. There is another reason, too, why there is no real substitute for flight at really high speeds by full-size craft. At transonic speeds the walls of the tunnel, and the mountings of the object under test, begin to interfere with the actual experiment. To get over this difficulty special tunnels have to be designed.

Tunnels for speeds up to Mach 4, and even over, are now under construction, making use of some of the experience of German research workers, who were ahead of the United Nations in this branch of science during the war.

Present-day research in wind tunnels, with missiles, and with full-size craft, are the signs of a new post-war aircraft industry developing to maturity.

LAND TRANSPORT OF TOMORROW

However important air transport may be, land transport will always play a vital part. Consequently, it is not only to aircraft that gas-turbine engines are being applied. For example, the Metropolitan-Vickers Electrical Co. is building a locomotive in which the turbine drives a generator to provide electric current for the traction motors. This 120-ton locomotive, the first to apply the lessons learnt in the jet propulsion of aircraft, will develop over 2,500 h.p. and have a maximum speed of 90 m.p.h.

This, however, is a project for the future. Of more immediate interest is the tendency to replace the conventional steam locomotive by the more economical diesel-electric type.

Although diesel-electric locomotives have been used for many years for shunting purposes, the introduction of the first main-line diesel-electric locomotive, "L.M.S. No. 10000," marked an important new stage in the development of this type of traction for passenger and goods work in Great Britain.

DIESEL-ELECTRIC LOCOMOTIVE

The design provides for two identical units, each having a diesel engine of 1,600 h.p. and a driving cab at both ends, so that it can operate either as a separate locomotive of 1,600 h.p., or, when coupled to a similar unit, as a 3,200-h.p. locomotive controllable from one end by a single engine-crew of two men. It is capable of working the heaviest expresses at a maximum speed of 100 m.p.h. when conditions permit.

Each 1,600-h.p. diesel-electric unit is powered by a 16-cylinder Vee-type diesel engine, having a maximum tractive effort of 41,400 lb. The engine carries 815 gallons of fuel oil in the main tanks, and 85 gallons in the service tank. The electrical equipment comprises a power unit, the diesel engine and main generator, six electric traction motors which provide the actual motive force for the locomotive, control equipment, and auxiliary apparatus. A master-controller for starting and stopping the unit is mounted in each driver's cab.

The drivers' cabs are fitted with adjustable cushioned seats, electric heaters, wind-screen wipers, de-frosters and sun-blinds. A toilet compartment is also provided for the engine-crew. Air-operated horns are used instead of the usual steam hooter or whistle.

Just as radar and electronic devices are providing navigators and pilots with greater safety in the air and at sea, so automatic electric signalling equipment has been introduced to prevent rail accidents. One of the most interesting

BANK OF EIGHT CYLINDERS

GENERATOR

INTERIOR OF DIESEL-ELECTRIC LOCOMOTIVE

An engineer making final adjustments to the 16-cylinder diesel engine. The engine has a continuous rating of 1,600 h.p. with maximum revolutions of 750 r.p.m. The diesel engine and main and auxiliary generators form one unit, which is mounted on three-point bearings resting on rubber supports.

DRIVING CAB
AT EACH END

CORRIDOR
CONNEXION DOORS
AT EACH END

BOILER, FUEL AND WATER TANKS
FOR CARRIAGE HEATING

MAIN GENERATOR

FOUR EXHAUST–GAS TURBO–
CHARGERS, EACH ONE SUPPLYING
AIR TO FOUR CYLINDERS

10000

AUXILIARY GENERATOR

CAB DOOR

SAND BOX

SIX TRACTION MOTORS
ONE ON EACH AXLE

BATTERIES FOR
STARTING AND LIGHTI[

schemes is that which enables a train to proceed at speed in foggy conditions, when normal visual signalling is impossible.

The track equipment consists of two magnetic inductors, placed fifteen yards apart in the centre of the track, and at a sufficient distance from the stop signal to allow a train to be brought to rest by the automatic application of the brakes. The first inductor is a permanent magnet, whereas the second becomes magnetized electrically only when the distant signal is turned to the "All Clear" position.

The engine equipment consists of a magnetic receiver, mounted five inches above rail level, which responds to the magnetic forces emanating from the track magnets over which it passes. The receiver controls valves by means of which the brakes are automatically applied, and an audible and visual warning is given to the driver.

When the distant signal is in the warning position the inductive action between the permanent magnet on the track and the receiver on the engine puts in motion the following sequence of events. First, a horn in the cab gives an immediate warning to the driver; if, within a period of three seconds, the driver pulls a lever in acknowledgement of this warning, he remains in full charge of the loco-motive, and controls the brakes as required by the traffic conditions.

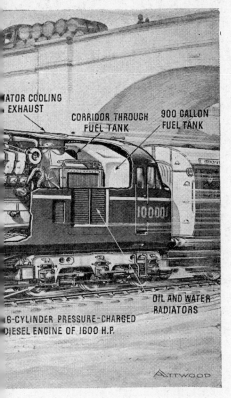

ATOR COOLING EXHAUST

CORRIDOR THROUGH FUEL TANK

900 GALLON FUEL TANK

OIL AND WATER RADIATORS

6-CYLINDER PRESSURE-CHARGED DIESEL ENGINE OF 1600 H.P.

ATTWOOD

This new design of locomotive is provided with two identical power units which can be operated separately, or can be coupled together to give twice the power. The electrical equipment comprises the main generator and six electric traction motors which provide the actual motive force for driving the locomotive. A master-controller for starting and stopping the engine is fitted in each driver's cab. The locomotive hauls from nine to twelve coaches, and has attained speeds of up to 85 m.p.h. At an average speed of 52 m.p.h. over a 128-mile route, the fuel consumption is approximately one mile per gallon of gas fuel oil.

Should the driver fail to operate the acknowledging device, however, the horn will continue to sound, and full application of the brakes will take place smoothly within approximately twenty seconds after passing the inductor, whatever the type and length of the train.

When the signals are in the "All Clear" position the electro-magnet inductor is energized, causing a short reassuring hoot to be given in the cab, but with no effect on the brakes. Laboratory tests have proved that the inductive link is effective at any speed up to 120 m.p.h.

MOTOR-CARS AND COMMERCIAL VEHICLES

Turning our attention next to private and commercial road vehicles, what changes are we likely to see in the near future? Obviously the most radical change would be in the type of power unit fitted. The pure jet-propulsion engine is, of course, totally unsuitable for road use. The effect of the intensely hot, high-velocity jet stream on following vehicles or pedestrians can be imagined. For record-breaking cars, however, the jet-propulsion unit offers real possibilities, and the future will see many outstanding advances in this field.

For normal road use many authorities consider that the gas turbine will eventually replace the piston-type engine. Among its advantages are its freedom from vibration, low maintenance cost, absence of carburettor and ignition system, small size and weight, and its ability to burn cheap fuels. On the adverse side of the picture, however, are the present high cost of such engines, the necessity for relatively large air-filters to prevent dust and grit being drawn into the compressor, and the lack of flexibility, or ability to develop power at low speeds, of the gas turbine.

These difficulties will probably be overcome, however. The engine is unlikely to drive a normal gear-box, but will be coupled instead to an electric generator, as in the case of the gas-turbine-driven locomotive already mentioned; the current from the generator will be used to drive an electric motor which in turn drives the road wheels. An alternative scheme is to provide one driving motor for each wheel. Yet another possibility is an hydraulic pump driven by the gas turbine, and supplying pressure to drive hydraulic motors connected to the road wheels.

The gas turbine is well suited for installation at the rear of the car, thus enabling a closer approach to a streamlined shape to be obtained. It has already been proved on conventional cars that streamlining confers very real benefits at high speeds; quite moderately powered streamlined saloon cars, in fact, are nowadays capable of reaching speeds approaching, and in some cases in excess of, 100 m.p.h.

THE FUTURE OF SEA TRANSPORT

It is unfair to compare the performance of a vessel which must plough its way through such an unyielding medium as water with an aircraft or road vehicle, particularly in view of the fact that sea transport has been by no means backward in making use of the advances of sciences.

Again jet and gas turbine propulsion is well in evidence, although, as in the case of locomotives and road vehicles, pure jet propulsion is limited to record-breaking craft.

Sir Malcolm Campbell's *Bluebird* was the first application of jet propulsion to water craft. The jet-propelled *Bluebird* was essentially the same boat as that which set up the pre-war water speed record of 141·7 m.p.h., but was re-designed to take advantage of recent research. Under a bulge that makes the boat look like an enormous slipper lies the de Havilland Goblin engine. The air is drawn in through two ducts near the front, and the spent gases pass out through a single jet well above the water-line. To be strictly accurate, the *Bluebird* is, in a sense, less of a water craft than an aircraft which happens to rest on the water, which it touches at no more than three points. At speed the aerodynamic lift may even raise it clear.

For normal use in merchant ships, however, it is generally conceded that either gas-turbine or diesel-electric propulsion is the method most likely to be used in the future. In view of the high speed at which a gas turbine rotates, it is likely that it will be coupled to an electric generator rather than a reduction gear, the current supplied by the generator being used to drive a slow-speed

CHIMNEY

60007

ROLLER BENCH

TESTING A STEAM LOCOMOTIVE

A streamlined locomotive being tested in the new British Railways' testing station at Rugby. On the roller bed the engine can be tested up to 120 m.p.h. while stationary. The smoke from the fire-box is directed away by the chimney.

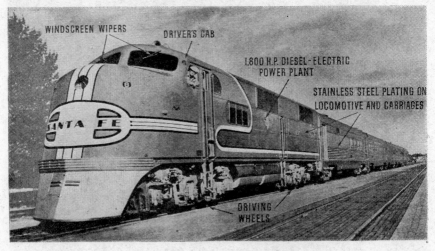

STREAMLINED LOCOMOTIVE

In addition to making every effort to increase the power of engines, the locomotive engineer has been influenced by the researches of the aircraft designer into streamlined forms to reduce head resistance. The photograph above shows a typical example of streamlining as applied to locomotives.

electric motor coupled to the propeller shaft. For maximum efficiency, a large, slowly turning propeller is to be preferred to one which rotates at high speed; a speed of about 150 r.p.m. is often used.

The first marine gas turbine to go into service, however, was a Metropolitan-Vickers unit coupled to a reduction gear which reduced the power turbine shaft speed of 3,600 r.p.m. to 1,200 r.p.m. Needless to say, such a high propeller speed is only suitable for a fast craft, and the gas turbine was, in fact, installed in a naval motor gunboat, No. 2009, which will thus go down in history as the first vessel to be propelled at sea by gas turbine, see illustration on page 331.

The gas turbine developed about 2,500 shaft h.p., and was installed centrally in the boat, with a 1,250-b.h.p. Packard petrol engine on each side of it. Thus the total power installed in the boat amounted to no less than 5,000 shaft h.p. Air was drawn into the turbine at the rate of over $1\frac{1}{4}$ tons per minute through a rectangular opening in the deck, and the exhaust was discharged into the funnel. The particular design of gas turbine used was by no means ideally suited for such an installation, but it enabled experiments to be carried out with the minimum of delay, the object being eventually to install a high-powered turbine in an escort vessel of larger size.

The gas turbine and electric generator combination, mentioned earlier as being the most suitable for merchant ships, will probably be used when an engine developing more than 5,000 h.p. is needed, or when two or more such engines are required to provide the necessary power. On smaller ships the gas turbine is unlikely to be a serious rival of the diesel-electric power unit, which is now being increasingly used.

This arrangement has a number of advantages. First is the economy of the diesel engine, especially in view of the fact that it is now possible to run these engines on the boiler oil used in steamships, providing that suitable filtering and clarifying equipment is installed. Thus advantage can be taken of a cheap fuel available at almost any port in the world.

Taking as an example a 10,000-ton ship, about 20,000 h.p. will be needed to drive it at 20 knots, a very high speed by normal merchant-ship standards. Using ten diesel engines of 2,000 h.p. each, driving electric motors supplying current to two propulsion motors coupled to twin screws, the fuel consumption would be about a little over one-third of that of an oil-fired steamship, and under a quarter of that of a coal-burning steamer, which is a considerable economy in fuel.

GAS-TURBINE-DRIVEN VESSEL

View of the engine-room in the first naval vessel to be propelled by a gas turbine. The power plant comprises a gas generator consisting of a compressor, followed by a power turbine, mechanically independent of the compressor turbine, and coupled by a reduction gear to the propeller shaft. The compressor is a nine-stage axial flow machine with aerofoil-section blades, while the turbine driving it is of the two-stage type. The power turbine is of the four-stage type, and drives a double-helical single-reduction gear. The control of the power output is effected solely by the regulation of the fuel admitted to the combustion chamber of the gas generator, which is done by remote control from the control desk.

Reliability is increased; should one or more of the engines break down, the ship can continue at reduced speed while repairs are carried out, for the component parts of the engines are small and easily handled. While in port, one or more of the engines can be run to supply power for electric winches and other auxiliaries, while the waste heat from the exhausts is used to generate steam for heating and power. In addition, the propelling motors can be directly controlled from the bridge, a very great advantage when manœuvring in harbour.

The use of atomic energy to drive ships is already being discussed, and some authorities believe that the first marine atomic power plants will be in use within the next five or ten years. As described in Chapter 7, the use of atomic power implies the conversion of the heat liberated by atomic fission into steam in some form of boiler, the steam then being used to drive a conventional turbine. The possibility of some form of gas turbine operating on the products of atomic fission cannot, however, be entirely ruled out. The great weight of the shielding material surrounding the atomic power plant must, of course, be a serious drawback, but this will be, to some extent, offset by the negligible weight and

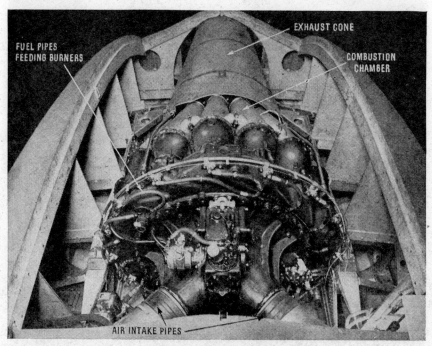

JET-DRIVEN MOTOR-BOAT

Location of the Goblin jet engine in the Bluebird. The air is drawn in through two ducts near the front, and the spent gases pass out through a single jet well above the water-line. At speed, the craft only touches the water at three points and, because of aerodynamic lift, may even rise clear of it.

ENGINE-ROOM OF THE R.M.S. *MAURETANIA*

This view shows the lay-out of the steam-driven turbines which propel this 35,677-ton liner. They are of the combined reaction and impulse type. Each unit comprises one high-pressure, one intermediate and one low-pressure turbine, each driving a pinion which engages with the main gear wheel.

bulk of atomic fuel, as compared with the large quantity of fuel oil or coal which has to be carried.

Apart from power unit developments, improved speed and economy will be obtained by devoting greater attention to streamlining, an aspect of ship design which has, until recently, received little consideration. It is true that, at the relatively low speeds at which ships travel, streamlining may not appear to confer any great benefits: yet a wind of 30 m.p.h., which is not unusual at sea, or a relative wind speed of 30 m.p.h. caused by a ship steaming at 15 m.p.h. into a 15 m.p.h. head-wind, will cause a pressure of one ton on an area of 560 sq. ft. Such an area is represented by a surface of 56 ft. wide, which is less than the beam of a large cargo ship, and only 10 ft. high. Since the height of the bridge alone exceeds 10 ft., it will be obvious that the wind resistance caused by the upper decks and bridge alone will amount to several tons. By reducing the height, streamlining the forward-facing decks and the funnels and removing all unnecessary deck-house ventilators, and so on, it is possible to increase the speed of a ship by several knots. Of greater importance, however, is the very appreciable fuel saving on a long voyage when the maximum speed is not used.

ARTIFICIALLY PRODUCING SNOW AND RAIN

This photograph shows snow turning to rain. It was made by sowing dry ice pellets from an aircraft above the clouds, and extended over an area of from five to ten square miles. It should be understood that artificial rain-making requires that the atmosphere contains sufficient moisture, special conditions of temperature, and clouds of the type that, when treated, will produce rain.

CHAPTER 10 Weather and the earth's atmosphere

SCIENCE has made vast strides during the last hundred years, and not least in those branches devoted to the study of the earth's atmosphere. Speculation about the nature of the atmosphere began as early as the middle of the eighteenth century, and for nearly a hundred and fifty years the results were sketchy and generally inaccurate.

As knowledge of the atmosphere grew more detailed an allied science called meteorology, the science of the weather, began to attract more attention. The needs and experiences of two wars gave an enormous fillip to research into weather forecasting and, based on the new knowledge obtained, methods of prediction have been completely revolutionized.

In this review we shall sketch the results of modern experiment and research into the nature of the atmosphere and show how they are related to the principles of weather forecasting.

The atmosphere is a blanket that envelops the earth and extends to a height of two hundred miles above it; though on account of the air thinning out, the upper limit is indefinite. The density of the blanket is much higher near the face of the earth than it is higher up. Its most important functions are to tone down the rays of the sun, and to prevent the heat stored in the earth from escaping when the sun is not shining on it. In this case the analogy of the blanket is exact. If it seems odd that a blanket helps to keep us cool as well as keeping us warm, we need only remember that the Bedouin's way of dealing with great heat is to swathe himself in layers of blankets from head to foot when he walks out in the open under the broiling sun of the Sahara.

Another thing the atmosphere provides us with is water. Without water life again would be impossible. If the atmosphere did not exist, then all the water on the earth's surface would be lost. As it is, the water part of the earth's surface is in a constant state of change—what is lost by evaporation is returned in the form of rain or dew. It does not necessarily return to the same area as that from which it is withdrawn by evaporation, but all the forces at work together ensure that the total volume is constant. If it were not for the circulation of the atmosphere all the land masses of the earth would be barren desert. By far the greater part of the moisture content of the atmosphere is drawn up from the surface of the seas,

335

DEVASTATING EFFECTS OF DROUGHT

Scene showing the devastation wrought in a field of corn-cob (maize) by drought. This would happen over the whole surface of the earth if it were not for the precipitation from rain clouds formed in the atmosphere.

and it is the constantly moving masses of air which transport and release it.

We can observe what is likely to happen where rainfall is not heavy or constant enough in those few parts of the earth's surface which have less than their due share of moisture; such areas we call deserts. This condition results from the soil drying out, losing its coherence, particle with particle, and liable to become windborne. The characteristic appearance of desert country is an alternation between dunes of shifting sand and bare rock face, which may be swept from time to time by sandstorms, or, as we should more properly call them, dust storms.

This is just what would happen to the whole of the earth were it not for the rain clouds formed in the airstreams. Even a drought of two or three months in temperate climates, such as those of Great Britain and parts of the United States, will cause vegetation to wither and the lighter soils to disintegrate. Where drought is prolonged agriculture of any kind becomes impossible. No crops can grow, which means that no cattle can be fed. In such conditions life would be impossible, even though, by the exercise of science, some small parts of the earth's surface could be made habitable by irrigation. Irrigation is the answer of science to local failures of the earth's atmosphere to supply the so necessary rain. Quite large areas of the North African continent have been brought under cultivation by this means and, with the swelling of the earth's population, this means of increasing the area of cultivatable land will be increasingly adopted.

We will now consider a little more precisely the nature and composition of the earth's atmosphere, which, in the light of modern research, is divided into three layers. The total thickness of the blanket is approximately two hundred miles, but it is very diffuse on top, and by far the greater proportion of the weight of the atmosphere lies within the first 36,000 ft.

This first 36,000 ft. is known as the troposphere, and is the region in which most meteorological activity takes place. Its chief characteristics are the presence of clouds, and an average fall in temperature of about three degrees to every 1,000 ft. of ascent. The fall of temperature is by no means constant, and varies with the point of the earth's surface from which measurements are begun, and with such factors as the amount of moisture which is held in suspension in the air. This fairly consistent fall of temperature is known as the lapse rate. It means that if the temperature near the ground is 60 deg. F., then it will be about 57 deg. F. at 1,000 ft. above the ground, 54 deg. F. at 2,000 ft., and so on.

DESERT LANDSCAPE

Deserts result from the soil drying out and losing its coherence through lack of moisture. Under this sand-sea are just bed-rocks which are exposed when the sand is blown to other areas during a sandstorm.

The pioneers who ascended in balloons suffered torments from cold long before they reached a height where the atmosphere was so thin that it would not provide them with enough oxygen to breathe. It is a phenomenon, too, which is within the range of almost everyone's experience. For instance, Europeans in India invariably retire to the hill country during the hot season.

Why does this fall in temperature take place? The answer follows from the fact that when a gas expands its temperature drops. Now, in the free circulation of the atmosphere, air is constantly rising from lower to higher levels. In the higher levels there is less weight of air above, in technical terms the barometric pressure is lower, and the air which rises to the more rarefied region expands and in the process becomes colder. If the air is perfectly dry the "lapse rate" will be at a rate of 5·4 deg. F. for every 1,000 ft. of ascent, and this is a rate of cooling which is realized quite often in dry climates on hot summer afternoons, when there is little or no horizontal breeze. This has been well demonstrated by thermometer readings taken at the same time from the top of the Eiffel Tower and near street level.

In actual fact there is always a degree of moisture in the air. In continental countries, and in well developed anticyclonic conditions, i.e. conditions of settled fine weather, it may be very low. The presence of moisture in the air reduces the rate of fall of temperature with ascent from the ground. When the air is saturated the lapse rate of 3 deg. shows little variation. As we shall see later, however, the normal lapse rate is sometimes completely upset by the presence at varied levels of horizontal currents of abnormally warm or cold air masses.

VARIATIONS IN ATMOSPHERIC TEMPERATURE

Variations in the speed at which the temperature falls as we ascend into the atmosphere are of the utmost importance to weather forecasting, as they condition the stability of the atmosphere. Accordingly, as a part of the normal weather forecasting service, daily or twice-daily ascents are made from different points to measure the temperature at various heights. From these measurements another interesting fact has been discovered about the troposphere, namely, that it is very much thicker over the Equator that it is over the Poles. Over the Poles the regular fall of temperature ceases after about five miles. Over the Equator it continues to a height of very nearly ten miles.

Since the lapse rate over Poles and Equator alike is approximately the same, it follows that, just as the surface temperature at the Equator is higher by 60 deg. F. or more than it is at the Poles, this higher temperature continues at all equal heights up to the limit of the troposphere in polar regions, i.e. to a height of about five miles. Over the Equator, however, this decrease of 3 deg. F. per 1,000 ft. continues for another five miles, and means that at the extreme limit of the troposphere over the Equator the temperatures are materially lower than they are at the extreme limit of the troposphere over the Poles.

We will next consider the types of clouds which are found at various heights,

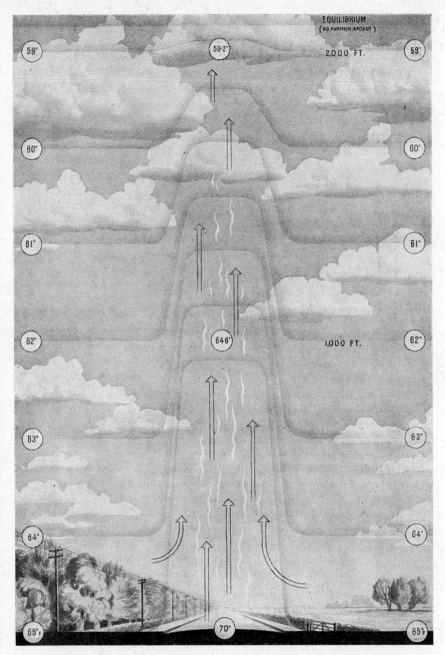

HOW HOT AIR RISES OVER THE SURFACE OF THE LAND

*Air which has been heated by the sun-heated surface of a road rises upward
(a convection current), and, as it rises, cools until it reaches the temperature
of the surrounding air and ceases to ascend any farther.*

AERIAL VIEW OF CLOUDS

This view shows the top of large cumulus clouds. The difference between these and the fair-weather cumulus, illustrated on page 345, is that tops bulge upwards to form rising heads instead of remaining rounded. Ranging above the cumulus formations are banks of cirrus. From the ground cirrus clouds appear so thin that when they cross the line of the sun or moon they do not seem to diminish the strength of the light. Also, they usually indicate that unsettled weather is not far away.

as this knowledge will help us to understand how it is that different clouds are associated with different kinds of weather, and how observation of the clouds at various levels materially assists the weather forecaster in his task.

Cloud formations are divided into four families, a classification advocated by the International Commission for the Study of Clouds in 1930.

PORTENT OF BAD WEATHER

These ragged low clouds, collectively known as fractonimbus, show up very dark against the sky or relatively light clouds. Another characteristic of these clouds is that they appear to be feebly illuminated from the inside. Precipitation from this type of cloud is in the form of continuous rain or snow.

Starting from the ground, there are three types of cloud which are generally below 6,500 ft.; this and other heights mentioned are average heights for temperate regions, but vary enormously at both the Poles and towards equatorial regions. The lowest of all the cloud formations is stratus cloud, which is a kind of fog, a uniform belt or layer relatively thin and with very little vertical motion of the air within it. Most of us have seen the top of a bank of fog from the summit of a hill and will have noticed the sharp distinction and clear outline which exists between the fog bank and the clear dry air above it. Fog, in fact, is a kind of sheet laid on the earth. Stratus cloud is a similar even sheet, distinguished from fog in that its lower edge does not rest on the ground. It occurs at any height up to about 6,000 ft., and is commonly associated with dry weather, although it sometimes gives rise to drizzle, especially in winter. During winter in temperate regions it is often the sign of a long spell of settled dry weather and can only occur when there is considerable stability in the atmosphere.

The other important cloud of the low levels is the nimbus. This is an irregular swiftly moving cloud, with ill-defined edges, usually seen in association with a thick layer of solid cloud above, from which it sometimes develops with amazing speed. It is the typical rain cloud of spring, autumn and winter in temperate regions. At times its lower edge may reach almost to sea-level and often covers high ground. In these circumstances it is frequently misnamed fog, although it is clearly distinguished from fog by the speed at which it moves and its turbulence. The high roads over the Pennines are particularly subject to this kind of cloud which may persist for days. In these areas the wind may be quite strong, or even reach gale force. In true fog the movement of the air is usually imperceptible, or if a wind springs up a rapid clearance can often be predicted with some confidence. Nimbus is very seldom noted above 3,000 ft.

The second group of clouds is those which are generally found up to a height of about 20,000 ft. These are the altocumulus and the altostratus, of which the former is most frequent in tropical regions, the latter in temperate regions.

ALTOSTRATUS AND CIRRUS CLOUDS

The altostratus, as its name suggests, is really a form of stratus, but at a much greater height. It is like a grey veil, which may cover the whole sky, and is sometimes distinguished by long parallel lines or striations. Generally the sun or moon will show through it feebly, and it is always a sign of bad weather, though rain does not fall from it directly, as nimbus cloud tends to form below it before the rain starts. Altocumulus, though most common in low latitudes, occurs fairly often in temperate regions. It consists of a series of rather small lumpy masses, often arranged in groups or lines, and occurs in rather unsettled, changeable, but not really bad weather.

The third group, the group of high clouds, occurs generally above 20,000 ft. and at heights up to the extreme limit of the troposphere, i.e. up to 30,000 ft. or more. This family of clouds is called cirrus, a word derived from a Latin word meaning a curl, and is a very common and well-marked type of cloud in all regions of the earth's surface.

Cirrus clouds are detached and, as the name suggests, look like curly strands of hair stretched across the sky. From the ground they appear so thin that when they cross the line of the sun or moon they often do not seem to diminish the strength of the light. They are generally a sign that bad weather is approaching, and most frequently appear towards the end of a fine settled spell when a depression is moving up from the west in temperate regions. These are the main types of clouds, occurring fairly regularly at specific heights, but there are

Labels within the image:

CIRRUS   CIRROCUMULUS   CIRROSTRATUS

20,000 FT.

ALTOCUMULUS   ALTOSTRATUS   CUMULUS EXTENDING FROM 600 FT. TO ABOUT 20,000 FT.

6,500 FT.

STRATOCUMULUS

1,600 FT.

GROUND LEVEL   FOG, STRATUS AND NIMBUS

CLASSIFICATION OF CLOUDS

The basis of cloud classification is that originally laid down at the beginning of the nineteenth century, namely, cirrus, thread-like cloud; cumulus, heap-cloud; stratus, flat cloud or level sheet; and nimbus, rain cloud. As will be seen from the drawing, the four families of cloud stretch from ground level to over 20,000 ft. This classification does not include the rare mother-of-pearl and luminous night clouds found at very great heights.

343

Cirrus are detached clouds of very delicate and fibrous appearance. They appear in a number of guises; for example, as isolated tufts, fine lines drawn across the sky, branching feather-like plumes, and curved lines ending in tufts.

numerous variations and combinations of the various types; examples are illustrated above and on pages 340 and 343.

There is a fourth family, which is distinguished by strong vertical development, i.e. these clouds are not flat or layer-like, but rise from a relatively low level to a high one. They are known as cumulus, and to the observer on the ground often appear in the distance like mountains rising from a ragged ill-defined base to a clearly-defined anvil. They are characteristic of strong upcurrents in the atmosphere and, therefore, of great instability. Consequently, they are a sign of thundery weather or thunderstorms.

TYPES OF CUMULUS CLOUD

On the other hand, cumulus clouds frequently show only a small amount of vertical development, and then appear as detached masses with flat grey bases and rounded white tops; these are known as fair-weather cumulus and may be observed often on bright days, especially in the afternoons. The most common clouds of all in the British Isles are stratocumulus, which, as the name implies, consist of layers of cumulus. They occur in dry weather, as a rule, and though sometimes well broken up, they often form a continuous sheet and give rise to dull weather. Cumulus and stratocumulus are classed as low clouds, because their bases are usually below about 8,000 ft., though the tops of cumulus are often very much higher. The well-developed cumulus which gives rise to showers or thunderstorms is called cumulonimbus; it has a ragged base and its top may be at the cirrus level.

Although the upper limit of the troposphere is normally the upper limit of cloud formations, modern methods of photography have made it possible to study the rare appearances of clouds at a much greater height. So-called mother-of-pearl clouds were noted in the latter half of the last century at various heights around the fifteen-mile mark—far out of range of the normal clouds of our atmospheric circulation. Another type of cloud was first observed in 1885 at a height of about fifty miles. These latter are generally referred to as luminous night clouds and they and the mother-of-pearl clouds have both been photographed. After sunset they show up in the night sky by contrast with the darkness of the rest of the firmament, when they are illuminated directly by the rays of the sun. It is actually around midnight that the luminous night clouds have been observed, and always during the summer months, although they are not confined either to the northern or southern hemisphere.

Both these types of cloud are very rare phenomena. They can only be observed in exceptional circumstances, and the particular atmospheric disturbance that gives rise to them is not known. Generally the regions above the troposphere are far too dry to admit of the formation of normal clouds. It has been calculated

FAIR-WEATHER CUMULUS

These clouds show only a small amount of vertical development, and appear as detached masses with flat grey bases and rounded white tops. They are generally observed on bright days, especially in the afternoon. Cumulus clouds also appear with strong vertical development ending with an anvil.

ALTOSTRATUS CLOUD

Altostratus clouds cast very little, if any, shadow and usually appear as a greyish sheet. They are always a sign of bad weather, though rain does not fall from them directly, but from nimbus which form below them before the rain starts.

that the diameter of the particles which make up the mother-of-pearl clouds does not exceed 0·0025 of a millimetre.

In appearances both the mother-of-pearl and the night luminous clouds are rather like cirrus, and it has been suggested that they are associated with the magnetic disturbances in the upper atmosphere which are also associated with the aurora borealis. Some idea of their rarity is given by the stated fact that there is no record of mother-of-pearl clouds between the years 1890 and 1932.

The upper limit of the troposphere is known as the tropopause. At this point in the atmosphere there is what is known as an inversion. Inversions, as we shall see later, are liable to occur at any height, but this one at the limit of the troposphere is a permanent one, which, of course, varies in height according to the height of the troposphere itself, being, as we have seen, almost twice as high over the Equator as over the Poles.

When we say that there is an inversion, we only mean that the steady fall in temperature which is normal from the earth upward suddenly ceases, and is replaced for a time by a small rise in temperature, and this inversion of temperature has the effect of enclosing the blanket of air which we call the troposphere in a kind of shell because the up-currents cease there.

Now all of us have seen this effect at levels much nearer the ground. For instance, on quiet winter nights the temperature near the ground always falls more rapidly than the temperature at upper levels, owing to the rapidity with which the earth dissipates its heat after sunset in clear weather. The result of this is a ground frost, in contrast with a temperature, say, at a few feet, which may be appreciably above freezing point. In these circumstances there is a tendency for fog to form, and the smoke of big cities is unable to escape through the inversion of temperature. A pond of cold air, as it were, is formed which remains stationary owing to the fact that cold air is heavier than warm air and so clings to the earth's surface. The whole theory of the turbulence of the atmosphere is based on the fact that air when it is warmed expands and, therefore, grows lighter and rises, whereas air that is cooled contracts and in contracting grows heavier and tends to sink; in other words, convection currents are set up in the atmosphere.

There is always an inversion at the top of any layer of stratus cloud, and

ALTOCUMULUS CLOUDS

This class of cloud usually forms a single layer of cloudlets which are separated by clear spaces. One characteristic of this type of cloud are the patches of delicate green and pink displayed by the translucent edges.

347

airmen are familiar with the sharp contrast between the hazy, misty atmosphere below the inversion and the brilliant sunshine and dry clear atmosphere above it.

The tropopause, as it were, encloses the troposphere. Above it is the second layer of the atmosphere known as the stratosphere, which takes its name, like stratus cloud, from the Latin word meaning a layer. It is, in fact, a wide belt of the atmosphere in which the temperature does not vary appreciably and extends to approximately 100,000 ft., though its upper limit, like that of the troposphere, varies considerably. It may be as high as twenty-two miles above the surface of the earth, approximately 120,000 ft.

Although the air in the stratosphere is very dry and the temperature constant, or nearly so, over many thousands of feet, there are no vertical air-currents and no appreciable cloud formation. It is, nevertheless, an inhospitable region, with an average temperature of minus 70 deg. F., and this temperature does not vary very much between day and night. With very little moisture and a very clear dust-free atmosphere there is nothing to absorb the rays of the sun, which pass straight through it, giving not only a fairly constant temperature as between different heights but a fairly constant temperature also between day and night.

Before scientific exploration of the stratosphere had been carried out it was hoped that this would prove the ideal medium for long-distance, high-speed flight by aircraft. This has proved to be practicable, though a major obstacle has had to be overcome before flying could be carried out at this level as a regular practice.

This obstacle is the low density of the atmosphere. The stratosphere does not contain enough oxygen for human needs. Mountain explorers in the Everest region discovered that their chief enemy was not the height or the difficulty of the final slopes, but the virtual impossibility of breathing or moving at those great altitudes, even though they had the advantage of a long period of acclimatization at intermediate altitudes. For the airman who penetrates beyond the inner shell of the atmosphere the inevitable result is the development of a comatose condition and very soon afterwards unconsciousness.

TEMPERATURES IN THE STRATOSPHERE

So much for the stratosphere. With its upper limit we reach virtually the limit of man's exact knowledge of his atmosphere. As we shall see, a little, but only a very little, is definitely known about the region above the stratosphere, the third layer of the atmosphere, though much has been inferred. We do know now for certain that above the stratospheric region of even temperature there is an upper warm region extending from the 100,000-ft. level to about twice that height. In this the stratosphere ends quite suddenly and thereafter the temperature rises at the rate of approximately 3 deg. F. for every 1,000 ft., or approximately the same rate as that at which the temperature falls in the troposphere. The maximum temperature reached in this region is certainly considerably higher than the highest temperature recorded on the face of the earth and probably exceeds the boiling point of water, 212 deg. F. (at atmospheric pressure).

No means have yet been found of making exact measurements at these altitudes. In fact, above the levels to which free balloons will rise our knowledge is derived from the results of a few unusually great explosions which have taken place on the surface of the earth. For instance, the explosion of an arms dump in the Midland Counties in 1945 provided valuable confirmation of the existence of this upper warm region. The explosion was heard over a radius of nearly a hundred miles, beyond which there was a "deaf" area, i.e. nothing was heard, but outside the radius of this area many observers reported hearing the explosion quite distinctly. Now, the only way this could have happened was by the sound waves being reflected from the warm layer of the atmosphere. It was possible to calculate the height of this upper warm region from the time taken by the sound waves to complete their double journey from the point of the explosion.

LUMINOUS NIGHT CLOUDS

Unfortunately, this and some similar phenomena do not give us any detailed knowledge of the region above the upper warm region, as sound waves which penetrate this warm layer are lost and radiate into the top layers of the atmosphere. It has been inferred, however, from the formation of the luminous night clouds, which were mentioned above, that the upper warm region is succeeded by a cold region extending to a height of about 300,000 ft., yielding temperatures at least as low as those of the stratosphere. But the luminous night clouds are almost the only evidence of this second cold layer. Although it is generally believed that these are true clouds formed from ice crystals (and certainly clouds could not form at this height unless the temperature were cooled to a very great extent), there is the possibility that they are composed of some substance other than water or ice. They might, for instance, be composed of luminous gases, though it must be admitted that there is very little evidence to support this view. Above the upper cold layer the temperature rises rapidly and perhaps reaches the enormous heat of 1,000 deg. F. at altitudes approaching a million feet.

Between 400,000 ft. and 800,000 ft. is the region in which the great majority of auroral displays take place. It is probably right to assume that above this height the earth's atmosphere ends, though there is no sudden transition, and for all that is positively known, the earth's atmosphere, in however tenuous a form, may extend hundreds of thousands of feet farther. All that can be said on the basis of our present knowledge is that beyond this height there are no observable atmospheric phenomena.

The upper regions of the atmosphere are usually known as the ionosphere, and are generally characterized by being good conductors of electricity. The region above the 300,000-ft. mark is referred to as the E-layer, or the Heaviside region. The uppermost region is the F-layer, or the Appleton region (see Chapter 8, which describes the nature of these ionized layers).

Before we consider in more detail the science of weather forecasting or meteor-

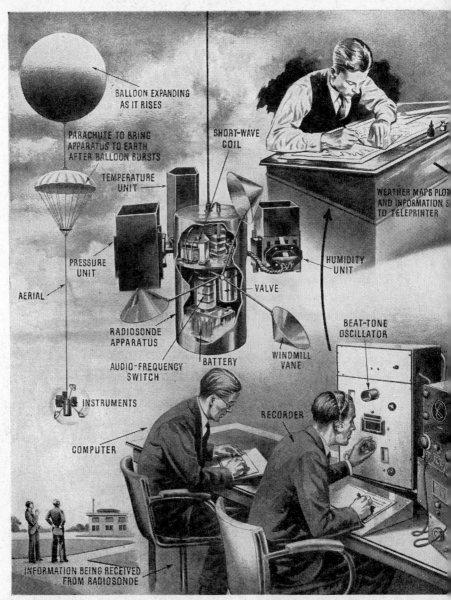

BALLOON EXPANDING
AS IT RISES

PARACHUTE TO BRING
APPARATUS TO EARTH
AFTER BALLOON BURSTS

TEMPERATURE
UNIT

SHORT-WAVE
COIL

WEATHER MAPS PLOT
AND INFORMATION S
TO TELEPRINTER

PRESSURE
UNIT

HUMIDITY
UNIT

AERIAL

VALVE

RADIOSONDE
APPARATUS

BEAT-TONE
OSCILLATOR

AUDIO-FREQUENCY
SWITCH

BATTERY

WINDMILL
VANE

INSTRUMENTS

RECORDER

COMPUTER

INFORMATION BEING RECEIVED
FROM RADIOSONDE

USING RADIO WAVES TO EXPLORE

Radio sonde is an automatic weather station on a small scale, transmitting signals
by radio of the conditions in the atmosphere. The instruments are carried by a
strong rubber balloon up to heights often exceeding ten miles. As the balloon
rises through the air, which becomes progressively thinner, expansion of the
balloon occurs until at bursting point the diameter is about twice that at ground
level. The instrument belongs to the class where oscillations in a valve-driven

TO AIRCRAFT

FORECAST DISTRIBUTED BY
TELEPRINTER EITHER DIRECT
TO RECIPIENT OR FOR ONWARD
TRANSMISSION TO THEM

TO THE
B·B·C

TO FARMERS

TO FILM STUDIOS

TO SHIPPING

‒URE OF THE UPPER ATMOSPHERE

·lectrical oscillating circuit are superimposed and broadcast on a high-frequency ⱱave, known as a carrier wave. This is necessary as it is not practicable to radiate ⱨe low frequencies from such a circuit directly. In other words, pressure, ·umidity and temperature each generate a note of definite pitch which is trans-ⱬitted by radio to a receiving station on the ground, where it is recorded and ⱺmputed. From this information the meteorologist is able to forecast the weather.

A typical chart made by the computer on the basis of information from the signals broadcast by the radio sonde and interpreted by the recorder. It is from the data on the pressure, humidity and temperature of the atmosphere that weather conditions are forecast. Radio sonde flights usually last an hour and are made several times each day.

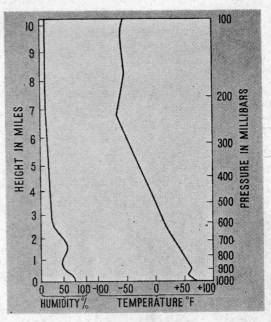

ology, let us devote a little time to surveying one of the most important instruments for investigating the atmosphere and facilitating more accurate forecasting.

The most important aid so far developed for regular study of the atmosphere is the radio sonde. It is for all practical purposes a meteorological station and radio transmitting station in one; yet the whole apparatus in its simplest form does not weigh much in excess of two pounds. It looks like a cardboard box suspended from a small aerial. Attached to the aerial is a closed parachute which in turn is attached to a rubber balloon about 4 ft. in diameter. This is very much like a child's toy balloon and is filled with hydrogen to make it buoyant.

RATE OF ASCENT OF RADIO SONDE

With the apparatus and instruments attached the balloon is released, and rises into the air at about 1,000 ft. per minute. Thereafter it operates in very much the same way as the first experimental air sounding balloons: as it rises into the atmosphere, the pressure on the outer cover of the balloon decreases and the rubber fabric of the balloon expands owing to the relatively high pressure of the hydrogen inside. Ultimately it will burst and it depends principally on the toughness of the rubber how soon this will happen. In general, a balloon is capable of expansion to about twice its original size, and it rarely bursts until a height of about 50,000 ft. is reached. There are cases on record of heights of 100,000 ft. being reached. So every one of these self-contained meteorological stations ascends and records the prevailing weather conditions through the layers of the troposphere and through the tropopause, which is generally at about 36,000 ft., though some penetrate into the stratosphere before the balloon bursts.

The radio sonde has four main functions. First, it enables the speed and direction of the wind at all levels to be estimated; second, it measures the atmospheric pressure at all levels to the top of the troposphere; third, it records the temperature at these levels; four, it determines the relative humidity of the air at those levels at which rain and snow ordinarily form.

By relative humidity is meant the percentage of water vapour which the air holds in suspension at different levels relative to the greatest amount of water vapour which it can contain without precipitating as rain and snow. This latter knowledge makes it possible to forecast when icing conditions, one of the chief bugbears of aerial navigation, are likely to occur.

MEASURING SPEED AND DIRECTION OF WINDS

The methods by which the radio sonde enables the speed and direction of the wind to be estimated will be considered first. In clear weather and in daylight the track of the balloon can be followed by the eye through the telescope of a theodolite; thus its speed and direction from minute to minute can be estimated. In this connexion, observers on the ground are not concerned with the balloon's movement upwards, nor with rising currents of air, but only with its horizontal movement as it is being carried freely by the normal air flow. If it is found that it has moved a mile in a minute from east to west, then we shall know that at the level which it has reached, say, 10,000 ft., easterly winds of sixty miles an hour velocity are blowing.

This is very important information, owing to the extremely high winds which are sometimes found in the upper layers of the troposphere and which may, and often do, blow in directions which bear no predictable relation to the strength or direction of the winds blowing along the surface of the earth.

At night and in cloudy weather the theodolite is of no avail. Then other means have to be found of tracking the course of the balloon. Until recently, radio direction-finding apparatus was used for this purpose. Three stations at known distances apart took a bearing on the balloon by radio, the three bearings were plotted on a scale graph, and the point of intersection of the three lines gave the position of the balloon at the moment at which the three simultaneous bearings were taken. The process was repeated a minute, or perhaps two minutes, later, and the speed and direction of the wind at that level could be worked out in the same way as by the theodolite bearings.

Within the last few years this method has been superseded. With the help of radar the position at any given moment can be worked out without the necessity for taking three separate bearings.

The instruments carried by the radio sonde are a barometer, a thermometer and a hygrometer. These are instruments for measuring the pressure of the air, its temperature and its relative humidity. But the instruments have to be of such a kind that variations in pressure or temperature will have a physical result on them capable of being transmitted by wireless. Consequently, the ordinary barometer and thermometer are not suited to the purpose.

Thus, in one very simple form of radio sonde the hygrometer is a bunch of human hair, tightly fixed at one end and free at the other. When damp, human hairs grow longer, and when very dry they contract. So while the fixed end of the bunch does not move, the other end slides outward along its base when the relative humidity is high and inward when it is low. We shall see later how this is transmitted into a radio signal to record the humidity of the atmosphere.

BIMETAL-TYPE THERMOMETER

The thermometer is as unlike the ordinary mercury thermometer as could be imagined. The principle of the mercury thermometer is that the liquid within it expands when the temperature is raised and contracts when it is lowered. These expansions and contractions are exaggerated by having a sizeable reservoir of liquid leading into a narrow tube, the tube being calibrated in degrees, so that rises and falls can be read from it. The thermometer of the radio sonde, by contrast, consists of two thin plates or strips of different metals welded together. Any two metals which expand when they grow warm will suffice, providing they do not expand at the same rate. In practice, brass and steel are generally used, and the two strips are tightly clamped together so that they cannot slide over each other. When the temperature is raised the sheet which expands the faster must be bent outward into a semicircle. These variations from the straight can, like the movements of the human hair of the hygrometer, be transmitted by signals.

MEASURING ATMOSPHERIC PRESSURE

The barometer, even in the most straightforward design of radio sonde, is a rather more complicated piece of mechanism. It consists of a metal box, which is sealed after the air has been pumped out of it. Although three sides of the box are solid metal, the fourth side is a thin, corrugated sheet of metal, which will be bent inwards by a high barometric pressure and will become straight only when the pressure difference is nil, that is, when the pressures outside and inside the box are equalized; this, incidentally, is the principle of the ordinary aneroid barometer, see illustrations of this instrument on pages 376 and 377.

The function of the radio sonde apparatus is to convert the physical conditions to mechanical motions, which are in turn converted to electrical signals and picked up by a special form of radio receiver.

The transmitter, apart from the aerial, consists of a valve, a coil and a condenser. The wavelength of the transmitter, which is entirely automatic, varies with the capacity of the condenser, which itself depends on the distance apart of its two component plates. When one plate of the condenser is attached to the moving part of the thermometer, barometer or hygrometer, their movement in turn will vary the distance apart of the plates of the condenser, so the wavelengths at which the transmission takes place will vary according to the variations

354

PROBING THE UPPER ATMOSPHERE

The instruments trailing behind the balloon record temperature, pressure, humidity, cosmic-ray intensity, and solar radiation up to an altitude of twenty miles. At the end of six hours the instruments are parachuted to earth.

in the recording instruments, and can be measured in terms of the temperature, pressure or relative humidity.

There are three condensers in all, each one attached to one of the instruments, and an automatic switch which connects each one of the condensers to the transmitter in turn; the switch is generally operated by a windmill.

In the type of radio sonde employed in Britain, goldbeater's skin is used in place of human hair for the hygrometer, but it conforms in most respects to the simple prototype which has been described.

The equipment in the radio sonde is expensive, therefore efforts are made to recover it. This is the purpose of the parachute attached to the aerial of the transmitter. When the balloon bursts, the parachute automatically opens and checks its fall. Some come down in the sea, or are more or less damaged in landing. But in practice the majority are picked up by members of the public and returned to the appropriate station through the Post Office. They are reconditioned and returned to radio sonde stations in order to make further ascents.

LOCATING THUNDERSTORMS

Everyone is aware of the nuisance caused by atmospherics in radio reception, but even these have their uses in weather science, for they are the means by which distant thunderstorms are located. The crackles which interrupt the radio programme are each caused by a lightning flash. With sensitive receivers, tuned to a wavelength of about 30,000 metres, well outside the range of wavelengths used in broadcasting, atmospherics up to 1,500 miles distant can be not only detected, but their position can be determined with considerable accuracy.

The receiver is provided with two large frame aerials, one set in the north-south direction, the other east-west. Lightning discharges produce electrical impulses in these aerials which, after amplification, control the indications of a cathode-ray tube, which is essentially a television receiver. The screen is graduated to indicate direction, like a navigator's compass. In the absence of atmospherics, when the receiver is switched on, a stationary spot of light shows in the centre of the screen. The impulses in the two frame aerials which result from a lightning discharge differ in power from one another in a way depending upon the direction in which the discharge occurs, and the electrical circuits are so arranged that the combined impulse causes the spot of light to jump from the centre towards the edge of the screen, along the graduations in the direction in which the flash lies. A single detector station, therefore, tells the direction of a flash. To locate the flash, however, at least two stations are required, and in practice three or four stations are used, for greater accuracy. The stations are in telephonic communication with one another all the time they are in action. Suppose, for example, that the control station in London detects a flash occurring due east, while a subsidiary station in Edinburgh detects the same flash east-south-east. If on a map a line is drawn east from London and east-south-east from Edinburgh, it will be seen that they intersect at a point in eastern

DISPLAY OF LIGHTNING FLASHES

Fundamentally lightning is a gigantic spark jumping between the earth and a charged cloud, or between two charged clouds. It occurs when the charges are strong enough to break down the resistance of the intervening air.

Germany, near Breslau; this point of intersection is the location of the flash.

The particular value of radar for weather study arises from the fact that raindrops, hailstones and snowflakes are reflectors of radar impulses, and as such can be seen in their correct positions on the plan position indicator. Thunderstorms and isolated showers appear as well-defined light patches on a dark background, while areas of continuous rain appear as larger ill-defined light patches. If the observation is continued over a period of time, the movements of rain areas may be recorded. Like the radio thunderstorm detector, radar shows the occurrence and travel of adverse weather conditions over areas from which meteorological observations are not available. It has a valuable application in short-period forecasting of showers or thunderstorms at a particular station.

Now let us look at the factors which cause variations of climate in different parts of the world. These factors are the result of the general circulation of the atmosphere. It was pointed out as early as 1887 by the Hon. Ralph Abercromby that to find the causes of this circulation we must look to the heat of the sun. Although it is now known that the heat of the sun is not the only causative factor, the statement remains true, subject to a number of modifications.

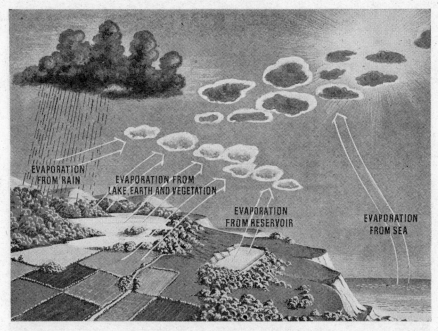

HYGROLOGIC CYCLE

The humidity of the atmosphere, that is, the amount of water vapour it contains, depends upon the evaporation of water by the sun. The main sources of water are the sea, lakes, reservoirs, vegetation and rain. In desert areas where there is no water, and hence no evaporation, the atmosphere is dry and parching.

What happens when the sun's rays fall directly on the earth's surface? The surface layers of the air are warmed and as their temperature rises they expand and, therefore, tend to rise. So we should expect the air to be constantly rising at the Equator and falling at the Poles. A simple, though theoretical, picture of the circulation of the air can be constructed by imagining the warm air rising in equatorial regions and moving northward and southward towards the poles in the upper layers of the atmosphere, there sinking and returning towards equatorial regions, being pushed along the surface of the earth on its return by the sheer weight of air pressing down on it in polar regions.

In the northern hemisphere, then, we should expect a south wind in the upper layers of the atmosphere and a north wind near the surface of the earth. These directions would be modified by the spinning of the earth upon its axis, and the fact that there is far greater movement in rotation at the Equator than at the Poles. Our simple picture can be completed by allowing for these factors, which give a south-westerly current at high-levels and a north-easterly surface current. In the southern hemisphere we should expect the reverse of these wind directions to prevail. This is not an exact picture of the circulation of the air, although it will provide the basis on which the true picture can be built up.

Pressure in the Tropics is generally low and at the Poles generally high, but two intermediate belts have to be taken in consideration, a high-pressure belt in subtropical regions and the low-pressure belt in temperate regions. No one has satisfactorily explained the physical causes for the existence of these two belts, but what seems to happen is that the air which is heated and rises near the Equator drifts northward at high altitudes and falls again in subtropical regions, while the heavy, cold air which drifts southwards from the Poles is heated by the increasing power of the sun as it enters the temperate zones and rises there.

The storm areas of the temperate zones are thus caused by a conflict between

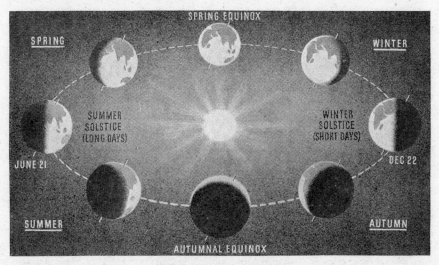

CYCLE OF THE SEASONS

The amount of heat received by any one part of the earth's surface is determined much less by the distance the earth is away from the sun than the inclination of the earth's axis. This accounts for the yearly cycle of the seasons and the amount of heat and light received during each season.

the polar air from the north and the subtropical air from the south, which tend to meet at various altitudes and give rise to a marked instability within the low-pressure belt itself. This instability is represented by a series of depressions, that is to say, areas of particularly low pressure which generally have their origin in the North Atlantic, and move more or less rapidly eastward or north-eastward, separated by ridges or belts of high pressure. It is this alternation of high and low pressure which gives rise to the changeable unsettled weather characteristic of the seaboard of the eastern Atlantic, including the British Isles.

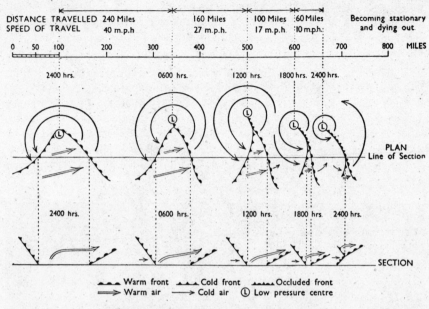

DISTANCE TRAVELLED 240 Miles   160 Miles   100 Miles   60 Miles   Becoming stationary
SPEED OF TRAVEL   40 m.p.h   27 m.p.h.   17 m.p.h.   10 m.p.h.   and dying out.

0   50   100   200   300   400   500   600   700   800   MILES

2400 hrs.   0600 hrs.   1200 hrs.   1800 hrs. 2400 hrs.

PLAN
Line of Section

2400 hrs.   0600 hrs.   1200 hrs.   1800 hrs.   2400 hrs.

SECTION

▲▲▲ Warm front   ▲▲▲ Cold front   ▲▲▲ Occluded front
⟹ Warm air   ⟶ Cold air   Ⓛ Low pressure centre

GROWTH AND DECAY OF A DEPRESSION

This diagram shows the position of the centre and the form of the fronts of a depression recorded at intervals of six hours. In this example of a rather rapid occlusion the warm air has been lifted off the ground within twenty-four hours by the cold front first overtaking and finally overriding the warm front.

In the low-pressure belt near the Equator there is no marked conflict of air currents of polar and equatorial origin and, consequently, far less activity. In this region rapidly moving depressions divided by ridges of high pressure do not exist. It is true that small intense cyclones sometimes form, and are often far more destructive than the less intense cyclonic depressions of temperate zones, but the over-all picture is one of a nearly uniform belt of low pressure moving northward and southward with the seasons. In June it lies near the Tropic of Cancer, having moved northward from the Equator with the sun; in June the sun is overhead at noon at the Tropic of Cancer. By December it has moved southward past the Equator to the Tropic of Capricorn, where again the sun is overhead at noon. It follows that the belt of low pressure moves twice across the Equator, once in March and once in September.

Generally speaking, low pressure is associated with rainy weather, high pressure with dry weather. At the Equator there are two rainy seasons round about the two equinoxes, while towards the two Tropics there is only one main rainy season at the summer or winter solstices. Rainfall takes a quite different form in these regions from what it does in temperate climates. In temperate climates we are accustomed to belts of rain moving eastward or north-eastward in association with the moving depressions, and they seem to have little connexion with the time of day. The position is very different from that which prevails in the Tropics, where, in the absence of moving depressions, day follows day with very little variation. In the morning it is likely to be bright and sunny. Then as the air near the surface of the earth is heated, it rises and condenses into clouds. By the early afternoon there are heavy, torrential showers. In the wetter districts they link up with each other, so that rain may be continuous from near midday until the early evening. As the sun begins to set the air returns to greater stability, cools slightly, partly owing to the failing power of the sun, and partly due to the cooling effect of the rain. When the rain stops, the storm-clouds flatten out and by midnight the sky is nearly clear.

Conditions similar to these occur in temperate climates during the summer when depressions are generally less vigorous and move less swiftly, that is, when the wind dies down and close, thundery weather supervenes.

In the region of the subtropical belt of high pressure, the general climatic picture is opposite to that in the equatorial belt of low pressure. Here rainfall is low and sunshine continuous for weeks or even months. The belt of high pressure moves north and south with the equatorial low, with the result that regions which lie on its fringe have a long dry season, and a wet season of varying duration as the equatorial low-pressure belt approaches.

Regions which are within the influence of the area of high pressure are almost

CLOUD	WEATHER		
CIRRUS	SHOWERS	HAIL	CLEAR SKY
CIRROSTRATUS	RAIN	SNOW	OVERCAST SKY
CIRROCUMULUS			
ALTOSTRATUS	HEAVY RAIN	DRIZZLE	MIST OR FOG
ALTOCUMULUS	CONTINUOUS HEAVY RAIN	CONTINUOUS DRIZZLE	THUNDER AND LIGHTNING
CUMULUS			
LARGE CUMULUS			
CUMULONIMBUS	WARM WIND		WARM FRONT AT GROUND LEVEL
STRATOCUMULUS			
RAGGED LOW CLOUD (FRACTOSTRATUS AND NIMBOSTRATUS)	COLD WIND		COLD FRONT AT GROUND LEVEL

WEATHER SYMBOLS

A selection of some of the symbols used to denote weather conditions and cloud formations. These symbols were standardized at the meeting of the International Meteorological Organization at Warsaw, 1935.

rainless. These regions include deserts of the northern hemisphere, the southern United States, the Sahara Desert and the Gobi Desert. In the southern hemisphere corresponding regions are the Kalahari Desert of South Africa and the Central Desert of Australia. Because of the great dryness of the air, at least over land, the highest temperatures of the world are recorded here, often exceeding by many degrees the highest temperatures recorded near the Equator. Similarly, because of the dryness of the air and the consequent speed at which the earth radiates its heat after sunset, nights are comparatively cool and very great ranges of temperature often occur. In parts of the Sahara Desert, for instance, it is by no means infrequent for an early afternoon temperature of over 100 deg. F. in the shade to be followed by a night during which the temperature falls nearly to freezing point.

The so-called prevailing winds on the earth's surface are intimately bound up with the more or less continuous existence of the four great climatic regions, namely, the areas of relatively low pressure near the Equator and temperate latitudes, and the corresponding areas of relatively high pressure in subtropical regions and near the Poles. What causes wind? Given two masses of unequal density close together, there is a tendency for the masses to fuse and produce a single mass of uniform density. An area of high pressure consists of an area in which the amount of the atmosphere is, by weight, greater above any given spot in that area than in an area of low pressure. There is inevitably a tendency for the over-plus of the atmosphere in areas of high pressure to flow into the comparative vacuum of the areas of low pressure. The direction of the winds, therefore, is outward from areas of high pressure towards the centre of areas of low pressure. This single factor explains the existence of almost every wind current and determines its direction, whether a light breeze or a hurricane.

BUYS BALLOT'S LAW

In estimating the direction of winds, allowance, as we have seen, has to be made for the influence of the rotation of the earth and other factors. These combined effects modify the flow of the air currents so that generally they blow in an anti-clockwise direction round an area of low pressure and a clockwise direction in an area of high pressure. This fact is the basis of Buys Ballot's Law, which states that if you stand directly facing a wind the area of lowest pressure is on your right hand. In the southern hemisphere again this is, of course, reversed. Round an area of low pressure the wind rotates in a clockwise direction; in an area of high pressure, in an anti-clockwise direction.

As an illustration of this principle, when the wind is due south, in Britain, the lowest pressure is likely to be on the Atlantic west or south-west of Ireland. If the wind is south-west, the area of lowest pressure will be farther north on the Atlantic, in the region of Iceland. But if the wind is north, then the lowest pressure will be centred on the continent of Europe.

Where there is an area of relatively constant high or low pressure, the wind circulating round it will also be relatively constant. This is a factor which was of enormous importance in the days of sailing ships, which depended on the strength and direction of the winds to enable them to reach their destinations, and has become of equally great importance in the field of commercial aviation where long-distance flying depends on the availability of this information.

WEATHER FORECASTING STATION
Newly drawn charts being compared with all possible weather patterns, and identified and coded. The information on which these charts are compiled is received from two hundred stations scattered throughout the world.

363

The area of low-pressure near the Equator is a region of comparative calm. This area was dreaded by early mariners and given the name of the Doldrums. It follows from all that has been said that this area of light breezes and flat calms will move north and south, together with the low-pressure system which gives rise to it, northward towards the Tropic of Cancer in June and southward towards the Tropic of Capricorn in December.

The Trade Winds are associated with the boundary area of the subtropical belts of high pressure. What was known to mariners as the area of the Roaring Forties is the area to the south of the Equator round about the 40th degree of latitude, where the wind flows strongly from the west roughly parallel with the lines of isobars, that is, lines connecting points of equal pressure.

In the temperate regions of the North Atlantic, the existence of the area of generally low pressure between Scotland and Greenland and of the high-pressure system in the region of the Azores set up a strong south-westerly current, which is the prevailing wind of the North Atlantic and of the Atlantic seaboard of Europe.

For this reason the journey by air from the American continent to Europe is so much easier than from Europe to America. Air-liners are commonly routed according to the prevailing distribution of pressure and, therefore, of winds. When the low-pressure systems are centred farther south than usual, giving strong easterly currents in the northern North Atlantic, it is often possible for aircraft to fly from Scotland or Ireland to Newfoundland, or direct to the United States, taking advantage of tail winds almost all the way. To take advantage of these tail winds aircraft are routed on an unusually northern course, going by way of Iceland and the southern tip of Greenland. But generally when pressure distribution is more or less normal the journey from Europe to America involves flying for a large part of the distance against more or less strong headwinds, which, of course, involves a longer flying time, and the carrying of additional reserve of fuel for safety, with a corresponding decrease in the pay-load.

CLIMATIC DIFFERENCES AND LAND MASSES

So far in accounting for climatic differences we have neglected the influence of the land masses in modifying the general weather picture on the earth's surface. In the southern hemisphere, where land masses are small, there seems to be a very close approximation to the orderly succession of belts of high and low pressure, from the equatorial low to the polar high.

In the northern hemisphere, too, there is this close approximation in a sector from the Equator through the Atlantic Ocean to the North Pole. But the great land masses of North America and Eurasia modify the over-all picture to a marked extent and we must now consider the scientific reasons which underlie this factor that influences climatic conditions.

The principal factor to be considered is the unequal heating of land and sea surfaces and, conversely, their unequal cooling. The temperature of the sea is far more stable than that of land surfaces, therefore the lowest layer of the atmosphere is far less liable to variations of temperature over the sea than it is over land.

The sea, then, is a reservoir of warmth in winter and of coolness in summer, and the effects of this reservoir spread over the sea-girt lands on the edge of the

LAND AND SEA BREEZES

During the daytime (above) the land becomes hotter than the sea, so that in the afternoon and early evening the air rises over the land and a cool sea breeze flows in to replace it. At night (below) the reverse obtains and the breeze flows off the land.

continents. The farther we go from the seaboard, the less marked is this tempering influence. The British Isles, in general, even those parts farthest removed from the sea, have what may be called a maritime climate, while places nearer the centre of the great land masses, such as central Russia, have a continental climate.

Starting from the fact that the earth radiates away the heat which it acquires from the sun more rapidly than the sea, it must follow that in winter, when the

CLOUDS AT SUNSET

The clouds shown here may be two definite layers of altostratus and altocumulus. Alternatively, the altocumulus may be thickening into altostratus or the altostratus may be breaking up into altocumulus.

effect of radiation in the long hours of darkness is at its greatest, this process will be speeded up over the land areas. In other words, in the centre of the Eurasian continent, from mid-autumn until early spring, the air near the surface of the earth is being progressively cooled and, in accordance with the physical laws we have considered, is continually growing denser.

So a large area of extreme high pressure is formed, which in this case is roughly in the same latitude as the temperate belt of low pressure over the Atlantic Ocean. Some of the highest pressures ever recorded have been noted in central Siberia, where pressures of 31·5 in. are not uncommon in the late winter months, compared with an average pressure of about 30 in. over the surface of the earth as a whole.

In summer this process is reversed. The reflected warmth of the sun striking off the land masses warms the layer of air next to the earth, so that it becomes less dense, with the result that an area of especially low pressure is formed.

These factors together produce a climate of far greater extremes than any found near the oceans. In winter the weather is very cold and dry, in summer warm and wet, and there is none of the alternation of warm spells and cold spells within a single season which diversify the temperate climates of maritime nations. In Moscow, for instance, frost sets in before Christmas and persists day and night, usually without a break, until March; yet in London, which is in approximately the same degree of latitude, and where, without these special considerations, a similar climate would prevail, even a week's continuous frost day and night is rare.

Most of Britain's very cold weather is imported from the continent, and therein lies the explanation of the weather proverb: "As the day lengthens, the frost strengthens." What happens is that during the early part of the winter the continents are accumulating a great mass of cold air, until, towards the end of winter, the continent literally breathes out and the cold dense air flows out from the centre of the continent to the surrounding oceans. The higher the pressure at the centre of the winter anticyclone over Russia, the more likely are there to be easterly currents over Great Britain and France in February, March and April. Sometimes the centre of highest pressure is displaced or extended westward towards Scandinavia. In that event, long spells of cold weather in western and northern Europe are almost certain. Another important factor in the climate of continental countries is that the normal flow of surface air currents is retarded by friction with the land, and is forced upward when it meets mountain barriers. The result is that winds diminish in strength the farther inland they go, while extraordinary differences in rainfall may occur between one place on one side of a mountain range and another, perhaps only a few miles distant, on the other side of it.

In the light of what has been said, we can now explain some of the local winds of special climatic significance which occur in various parts of the world. The monsoon winds of India will be readily explained by the movement northward and southward of the subtropical belt of high pressure and the equatorial belt of low pressure. The bora and mistral of the Mediterranean coasts are caused by the passage eastward of an area of low pressure along the Mediterranean, with a consequent inflow of air from the north in its rear.

CHINOOK AND FÖHN WINDS

In the New World there is a wind called the chinook, which is a strong warm wind blowing over the districts to the east of the Rocky Mountains. This dry, warm wind is very similar to the föhn, which is felt principally on the northern slopes of the Alps; both may be compared with the relatively warm dry westerly winds which bring pleasant weather to the eastern slopes of the Pennines, as compared with the western slopes. In these three cases, and many others in mountainous districts of the world, what starts as a mild wet wind, when it has crossed the mountain range ends as a dry but still warm wind. It follows that in climates where rainfall is plentiful, living conditions will tend to be more pleasant on the lee side of a mountain range, that is to say, on the side away from the direction of the prevailing winds.

Another European wind sufficiently frequent and dramatic in its effects to

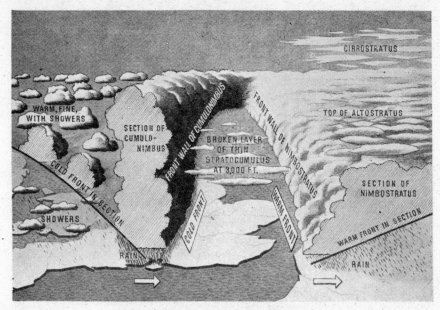

NATURE OF A VIGOROUS DEPRESSION

Air from the cold front thrusts under the warm air on the west side of the warm tongue and reproduces the weather conditions associated with a cold front, forming a narrow strip of squally rain. The cloud walls of the warm and cold fronts are 4–5 miles high; these are greatly exaggerated in the drawing.

deserve a local name is the sirocco, which is really a southerly wind blowing in front of a depression advancing from the mouth of the Mediterranean towards the Egyptian coast. It is thus the opposite of the bora or mistral. The passage of the low-pressure system draws up a lot of intensely hot air from the mainland of Africa, and it is this wind, often laden with fine particles of dust and sand, which becomes further charged with a heavy moisture as it comes across the Mediterranean, which makes its onset on the northern shores of the sea, as in Italy, so markedly unpleasant.

By contrast, the khamsin, which is a wind of identical origin experienced over Egypt, is hot, often almost unbearably dry; its dryness and dust content making it almost as hard to sustain as the characteristic blizzard winds of early spring which blow over the steppes of eastern Siberia. The khamsin is often known as the fifty days' wind, because it sometimes blows for the greater part of March and April. This latter fact is because the depressions moving up the Mediterranean tend to fill up before passing to the north of Egypt, so that the relief of the cool winds in the rear of one of these depressions is long postponed.

Let us now consider the structure of depressions and anticyclones. We have already seen that the term anticyclone is applied not only to the semi-permanent areas of high pressure, such as the subtropical belt of high pressure centred near the Azores, but also to the more limited areas of high pressure which alternate with the passage of depressions in the temperate climates of middle latitudes.

One characteristic of the depressions which move in an easterly direction across the Atlantic is that they travel with a speed which may be as great as sixty to eighty miles an hour, or may be as little as five to ten. As soon as they lose this mobility, it is reasonably safe to predict that they will "fill up" and die. By contrast, anticyclones are often more or less stationary for a period of days, or even weeks or months; when stationary they have a tendency to increase ir intensity.

Another important factor is the regular export and import of air affecting wide areas of the globe. It does not follow that because there is a very deep depression, say in the North Atlantic, that there must be a correspondingly intense anticyclone somewhere in the vicinity. It might be expected that this would be so, for obviously the total amount of air covering the earth's surface does not vary, and air pressure is really only a record of the amount or weight of air over any particular point.

The weight of the atmosphere over the whole of the northern hemisphere has been calculated for all periods of the year, and has been found to vary from

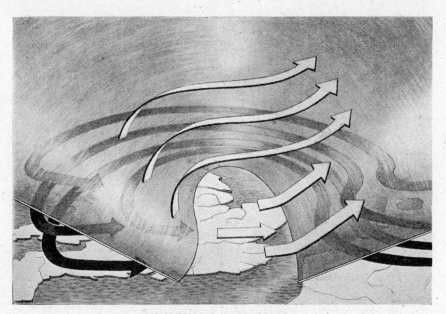

AIR-FLOW IN A DEPRESSION

Warm air (white arrows) above the plane of separation rises gently over the cold air (black arrows) along the warm front and is jerked upwards at the cold front where the cold air turns and thrusts under it.

month to month. In July, for instance, on the average there are ten billion tons less air over the northern hemisphere than in January.

Thus there is a regular process of inflow and outflow as between the northern hemisphere and the southern, and as between the continents and the oceans. In the winter, as we have seen, the oceans export air to the continents and import it again in the summer; so in the summer depressions, or areas of low pressure over the oceans, are either less numerous or less deep than they are in the winter. This fact explains why the winter is the period of the great storms of the North Atlantic, while summer storms are relatively infrequent.

The structure of a continental winter anticyclone is relatively simple. It is of a homogeneous nature, and consists of a mass of relatively heavy air which tends to seep outward from the centre rather slowly, by virtue of the pressure of the air above it. Directly the factors which tend to warm the air exceed those which tend to cool it, it begins to break up, and a consequent decrease of pressure even within the actual area of the anticyclone. This is what happens when the continents breathe out in the spring.

The depression or cyclone, as it is sometimes called, is something very different. There is nothing stable about it. It is in a constant state of motion and change.

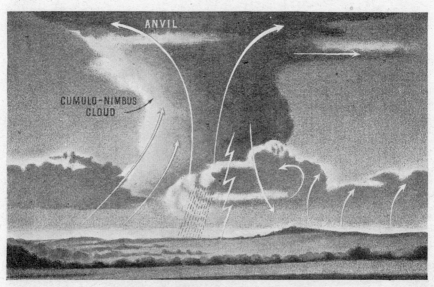

HOW A THUNDERSTORM DEVELOPS

The moisture in the air, carried upwards by violent upward currents, is cooled and forms raindrops or hail. Large raindrops become unstable and break up into smaller drops, causing a positive electrical charge to form on the drops and a negative charge to accumulate in the air in the cloud, the cloud forming a huge static machine. Heavy rain carries the positive charge to the ground, to which a lightning flash may jump.

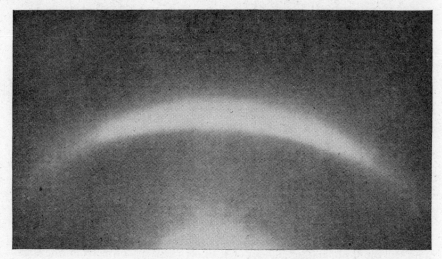

NEBULOUS CLOUD FORMATION

This thin, uniform, nebulous cloud is termed cirrostratus. One of its visual character-
istics is the halo effect it produces round the sun or moon. Sometimes it is quite
diffuse and gives the sky a milky appearance. It also appears with a fibrous
structure with disordered elements. As will be seen from the drawing on page 343,
this type of cloud occurs above 20,000 ft.

In fact, no two depressions are alike, and in spite of intensive research there is still some doubt about the various causative elements, its origin and development, and final decline or filling up. It must be remembered that it is one thing to study the structure of a depression or cyclone, and quite another to give an accurate and detailed account for its origin.

Depressions vary enormously in size and intensity, ranging from areas with a diameter of perhaps no more than fifty miles to some with a diameter of a thousand miles or more. Again, some depressions grow larger and deeper quite suddenly, while others pursue a fairly even and relatively predictable course without any great change of shape or intensity. Some are short-lived, starting their life somewhere off the coast of Newfoundland, moving across the Atlantic at an average speed of about thirty miles an hour, and dying out near the coastline of Europe after a life of no more than four or five days. Other depressions persist and the course of a few has been mapped for as much as six weeks, during which time a depression has passed almost round the temperate and subarctic latitudes of the globe, ultimately reaching a point in the Atlantic very near its place of origin.

In general, a depression may be regarded as an eddy or wave in the atmosphere in which there is constant interplay of masses of air of widely different temperatures. When these masses of air of unequal density impinge on each other there is

371

said to be a "front." A very active depression has at least two fronts, a cold front and a warm front, and two distinct sectors, a warm sector and a cold sector.

The typical Atlantic depression has its two well-marked fronts in its southerly sector. It is this sector that produces the bulk of bad weather. The cold sector, that is, the sector to the north of the centre of the depression, is an area of relatively good weather, often with a few scattered showers, though near to the centre, even in the cold sector, rainfall is often very persistent.

PROGRESS OF A DEPRESSION

If we regard ourselves as observers in the track of the southerly sector of an active depression as it approaches the coast of Ireland, the first sign of its approach will probably be a backing of the wind from some point of west to some point of south. Very high cloud will begin to obscure the sky, and from it will spring low clouds and finally rain. At the same time there will be a sharp rise of temperature, which means that the warm front has arrived. Thereafter the rain will diminish, and for an hour or so to perhaps a day or more, during which the sky is mainly overcast, with occasional drizzle or light rain.

Subsequently there will be a piling up of heavy clouds in the west or north-west, a brief period of heavy showers or rain, perhaps of a thundery type, and with dramatic suddenness the wind will veer to west or north-west, the sky will begin to clear and there will be a marked drop in temperature. This means that the cold front has arrived. These conditions will persist as the barometer rises, with the formation of cumulus clouds and occasional showers in summer, until the advance of the next depression, when the whole process may be repeated with a greater or less degree of similarity.

The analysis of very many depressions of this type shows that the following sequence of events is taking place in the atmosphere. With the approach of the warm front there are masses of warm air climbing up over the colder air which it is destined to replace. The formation of cloud and rain is an inevitable consequent of the rising of the warm air currents. It also explains why the rain tends to stop and be replaced by cloudy weather when the warm air has established itself, because then it is no longer rising and is in a greater state of equilibrium.

Now comes the cold front, a swiftly moving mass of cold heavy air advancing against the warm air in front of it. What happens? It must force itself underneath the warm air like a wedge and force the warm air once more to rise. Because this upward movement will in some cases be very sudden and intense, owing to the strength of the wedge of cold air beneath it, the result will be great instability and the formation of heavy showers and thunderstorms. When the cold air has established itself there is a return to more stable conditions and the formation of showers in this cold air is no more than the normal result of the interplay of hot sun and cold air. It will be noted that these showers in the rear of an active depression are much more frequent during the day than they are during the night and during the summer than during the winter.

MEASURING THE HEIGHT OF CLOUDS

The ceilometer is a photo-electric device for measuring the height of cloud ceilings at any time of the day or night. Its chief application is for airports where the ceiling height and the rate at which it is rising or falling is of vital interest to incoming aircraft. The measurement is made by triangulation of a modulated beam of light projected vertically to the base of the cloud, and reflected from the cloud projector. An electrical signal corresponding to the reflected modulated light signal and the angle at which the detector "sees" the spot of light on the cloud are transmitted to a chart from which measurement data may be observed.

When the depression begins to die out there is an almost invariable sequence of events. The cold front is generally very powerful and has a slightly greater rate of progress than the warm front. In other words, it is constantly tending to catch up with it. At the moment when it does catch up it has cut like a wedge under all the warm air which is essential to the continuance of the depression and has cut it off from the earth. When this condition obtains the depression is said to be occluded, and the line along which the cold front catches up with the warm front is referred to as a line of occlusion. As soon as a depression is occluded, that is to say, when all the warm air in it has been lifted off the ground, it quickly begins to fill up and lose its vigour, though the struggle between the polar air and the equatorial air is continued in the upper atmosphere.

NATURE OF AN OCCLUSION

There is one more thing to notice in the life history of a depression. We have said above that it tends to die out, that is to say, to become occluded very soon after it makes landfall. This may well be because the progress of the warm air is retarded by the normal effect of friction with the surface of the earth and its irregularities, though precisely how this factor works and how important it is has not yet been explained satisfactorily. It is at least known that depressions very rarely cross a high mountain range.

When an occluded depression passes over land it is seen to have lost all its activity. The sequence we have noted above will be modified, and usually there is no more than the onset of rain followed after a time by a gradual clearance. The cloudy weather of the warm sector is lost and there is none of the dramatic clearance as the cold front advances, nor is any noticeable change of temperature recorded at the clearance.

At the point where the cold front catches up with the warm front, that is to say, along the line of occlusion, an interesting phenomenon often takes place. This is the formation of a secondary depression, with its own warm and cold fronts. Now a few secondary depressions appear to rotate round the parent depression, that is to say, starting in its southern sector they move in an easterly and then northerly direction. But the more vigorous secondary depressions show no inclination to do this, but develop a complete independence and move in a generally easterly direction, very often becoming extremely deep and vigorous, and overshadowing the parent depression, which gradually fills up.

Weather forecasts sometimes speak of V-shaped depressions, or troughs of low pressure. These terms refer to secondary forms which are not entirely enclosed within isobars; lines connecting points of equal pressure. If you look at a weather map you will see that the typical depression is represented by roughly concentric lines of descending pressure, with the word "low" marked in the centre. A trough of low pressure is represented by roughly parallel lines inclined towards each other and meeting in a V. That is to say, it is a sort of V-shaped offshoot of the main depression, in shape very like the valleys in mountainous

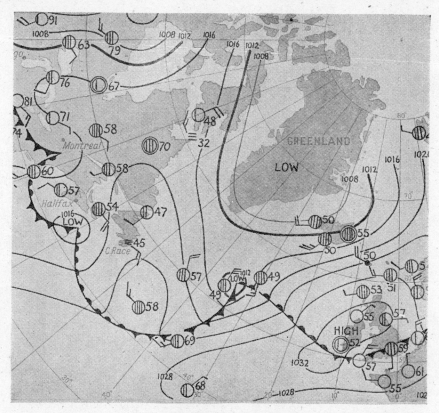

PLOTTING THE WEATHER

*The northward-pointing salients of warm air (see diagram on page 360) are the
centres of a family of depressions separated by southward bulges which are wedges
of high pressure (anticyclones), one of which is crossing Britain.*

countries which branch off from a main valley and lead up into the hills, the hills
on the weather map being represented by the anticyclones.

When we come to consider the origin of depressions, we are faced by a number
of conflicting theories. The most commonly held is that they arise when a large
mass of cold air moving from north-east to south-west flows side by side with a
large mass of warm air flowing from south-west to north-east. Now the line of
demarcation between these two masses of air cannot be precisely vertical. In
practice, the side, as it were, of the warm air mass tilts over and so gradually the
cold air goes underneath the warm and an eddy or ripple on an enormous scale
is set up in the lower layers of the atmosphere, analogous to the ripples on a
sheet of water, or the waves of the sea. Quite how the ensuing vortex sucks out
the air from the centre has not yet been fully investigated.

READING THE WEATHER

A weather observer on a U.S. Coastguard weather ship reading an aneroid barometer. Below it is a barograph, which is an elaboration of the aneroid barometer, and makes a permanent record of the prevailing weather conditions. The arc that carries the recording pen responds to minute variations of the diaphragm and traces a continuous line on the chart fixed to the revolving drum.

Whatever the mechanics of origin, the majority of disturbances in the atmosphere originate through the interplay of cold air and warm air. But these conflicting air masses are not necessarily currents direct from polar and equatorial regions respectively. They may be indirectly referred to their points of origin. In some cases, however, particularly in the winter of the northern hemisphere, when pressure is high in a belt from Siberia to Greenland, there is a direct corridor for the outflow of true Arctic air, and a corresponding outflow of true equatorial air round the Azores anticyclone. When these two currents meet, as they must somewhere in mid-Atlantic, a cyclonic activity of unusual intensity is to be expected, with the formation of depressions which move on a more southerly route than usual and, passing either up the English Channel or into the western Mediterranean, bring snowstorms to most of northern Europe, including the British Isles.

The majority of depressions are formed through the juncture of air masses which, though they differ in temperature, do so to a less marked degree. Apparently it sometimes happens that depressions form entirely in polar air and, though these have a quasi-warm front and a quasi-cold front, they also characteristically bring heavy snowfall. Their movement, too, is almost unpredictable, and they rarely conform to the conventional easterly or north-easterly direction.

Modern weather forecasting is based on this analysis of depressions and anti-cyclones, with a consequent prediction of the movement of fronts, and the weather which these fronts bring with them.

At the present time, twenty-four hours is about the limit of forecasting with any degree of accuracy. Even over this short period there is the possibility of error, particularly in forecasting the occurrence of thunderstorms in summer which is vital for air navigation. In north-western Europe, for instance, conditions in which thunderstorms are likely to form can be predicted with some certainty, but there is no equal certainty in the prediction that the thunder-

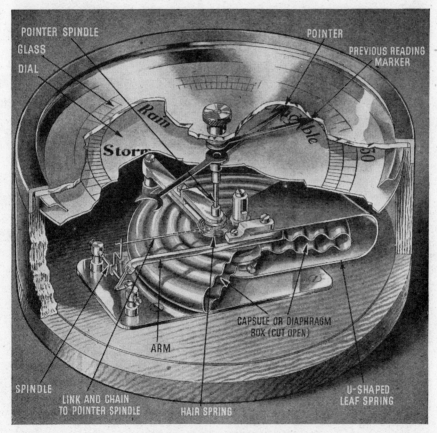

HOW A BAROMETER WORKS

In principle this type of barometer is an airtight box which contracts when the air pressure increases and expands when it decreases. These variations are transmitted to the pointer by means of a small chain and hair spring. By observing the pointer it is possible to make approximate weather forecasts.

THEODOLITE

GYROSCOPIC COMPASS

FLOATING WEATHER STATION

These are situated hundreds of miles out to sea and collect the data so essential to trans-ocean aircraft and liners. The observers on the stern of the cutter are plotting its course and speed with the aid of a theodolite and gyroscopic compass to chart the speed and direction of wind currents.

storm will form on any particular day, or will follow any particular course. Many thunderstorms form in summer in the strongly-heated air over northern France during the afternoon and drift northward across the Channel to reach southern England by late evening. That is why many of the great thunderstorms over London and southern England occur during the hours of darkness.

About once in every five or six years an outsize in thunderstorms sweeps across southern England, developing near the Channel coast in the late afternoon and moving in a north-easterly direction to East Anglia during the night. This particular kind of storm, which is nearly always accompanied by torrential rainfall, is very difficult to predict.

Long-range weather forecasting is a subject which has occupied the attention of meteorologists ever since the science was in its infancy, and in general the results have been disappointing. No one doubts that in time long-range forecasting will be feasible with at least as much certainty as short-range forecasting is today, but that time is not yet in sight.

In general, from the point of view of the British forecaster, weather imported from the continent is easier to determine in advance than weather imported from the Atlantic, but that again is unhelpful seeing that about nine-tenths of Britain's weather has its origin to the west. The most that one can do at present is to recognize a given weather and pressure "pattern," and by analogy with previous similar "patterns" and their subsequent developments forecast along the lines of similarity.

So when the Eurasian winter anticyclone is particularly intense comparatively early in the winter, it is fairly safe to predict that the continent will breathe out with unusual strength and frequency and bring to the western seaboard of Europe and the British Isles recurrent spells of strong easterly winds and a colder than usual winter. Even then analogy can be extraordinarily misleading and prediction may be falsified because of factors outside the knowledge of the forecaster.

BUCHAN'S HOT AND COLD CYCLE

Again, there is an alleged tendency for weather to repeat itself annually at certain approximate dates. A vast amount of statistical research has been carried out in this connexion, a typical result of which is the alleged validity of Buchan's hot and cold periods, which were based on observed annual recurrences of weather in southern Scotland over a limited period. Of these periods the only two which have been substantiated by later observation are the first two cold periods in early February and April respectively. At most stations in England, Wales and southern Scotland the graph of the normal seasonal increase of temperature pauses in its ascent for about ten days in early February, and although there is no certainty about the occurrence of a cold spell at that time, there is a distinct probability that one will occur.

Similarly, in Great Britain there is a marked tendency for a period of fine weather associated with a high-pressure system to occur about the middle of

379

December, and for this to break down between Christmas Day and New Year's Day into a period of unusually stormy weather.

In tropical climates, of course, long-range prediction is far easier, because of the less variable nature of the weather, and the definite north and south movements of the areas of high and low pressure.

Another factor which is a very real one to be taken into account in forecasting is that of weather "moods." The weather may be said to be in a dry mood or a wet mood when a tendency for one type of weather to persist is noted contrary to the normal indications, and such moods may persist for weeks or even months. In some periods of long drought in Great Britain there have been instances of weak secondary depressions moving across the country without producing a drop of rain. No satisfactory explanation for this has been achieved.

Since the turn of the century attention has been focused on the search for a rhythm in weather, and, in particular, the search for a long-term weather cycle. There is a probable connexion between sunspot activity and the weather in temperate zones. The complete cycle of sunspot activity is known to be eleven years. An eleven-year cycle is the most obvious one to propound for weather

RAVAGES OF FLOOD

Corner of a house seen as it collapses into the raging torrent of flood water. A few hours later only one corner of the house remained standing. This photograph was taken during a fen breach at Southery, Norfolk.

This spectacular auroral phenomenon is a permanent feature of the Arctic night, but can at times be observed in more temperate latitudes.

changes and, indeed, statistics support this cycle to a limited degree. As an example of this, it has been pointed out that the winters of 1928-29 and 1939-40 were unusually severe and, in fact, were two of the most severe of the present century in Britain. A large number of similar instances may be adduced and it can be said with some degree of truth that there is a strong tendency to the recurrence of certain types of weather at eleven-year intervals. It is a fairly safe forecast, therefore, that the winter of 1950-51 will be cold above the average.

Though these correspondences are noted, and to some extent valid, they are only so in the most general terms. No possible means can be adduced from these correspondences to forecast weather changes from day to day. Moreover, even the eleven-year cycle often breaks down, and longer cycles have been sought, including the thirty-five-year cycle proposed by Brückner. The difficulty with these longer cycles is that weather records do not extend far enough back to check their validity, and only time and further research can show to what extent they can be depended upon. This much is certain, that the climate in any particular spot of the temperate zone does show marked changes over a long period. It is probable that these changes follow a regular cycle, while their causes are totally unknown, though they may be of world-wide incidence, and be connected with variations in the amount of solar radiation.

It is known, for instance, that at one time the greater part of Britain was covered in glaciers and that these receded from time to time and fresh glaciations took place. This means that the climate over Britain has been very much colder than it is now, though not so much colder as might be thought. The winter climate of Britain is, in fact, a critical one. As it is, there is almost always snow on the upper slopes of Ben Nevis. A fall of ten degrees would bring a return of the ice age. But we are not now in a position to predict whether such changes will take place again or, if they do, when. Until 1939 it was confidently asserted that British winters had become milder, and certainly statistics showed that the nineteenth century showed a far higher proportion of cold winters than the twentieth. Then came the three winters 1939-43, which taken together were the three coldest successive winters since early in the nineteenth century, effectively disproving that the climate had materially changed. And even now it is too early to say whether these three cold winters together ushered in a cycle of relatively cold winters, or whether they were rather an isolated phenomenon. Research is still being carried out into the nature of the recurrent singularities of climate.

Most of the dramatic peculiarities of weather have been proved definitely to be associated with a cycle of sunspot activity. The incidence of thunderstorms and intense cyclones is definitely greater at a time when sunspots are at their greatest development. Similarly, unusually vivid displays of the aurora borealis almost invariably occur about a day after a large sunspot has crossed the centre of the sun's disk.

Of the aurora borealis, for instance, the most salient fact which is definitely known is that it is self-luminous, and occurs at widely differing altitudes in the upper atmosphere, certainly up to a thousand kilometres. The distance at which it is seen depends partly on the height at which it occurs, and it follows, therefore, that only the most intense and loftiest displays are seen in temperate latitudes. The area in which there is the greatest frequency of auroral displays is not, as used to be supposed, at the Pole, but in the neighbourhood of a curved line drawn

TROPICAL WEATHER

A hurricane, or tropical revolving storm, may be from twenty miles to several hundred miles in diameter, while the wind force may exceed 100 m.p.h.

HURRICANE IN PROGRESS

Picture taken during a 100-m.p.h. hurricane that swept the Texan coast. These tropical storms do not cover a very great area, and move very slowly.

through northern Canada, Greenland, Iceland and the northern tip of Scandinavia. North and south of that line the frequency diminishes rapidly. But even in the Shetlands the aurora is seen on an average of nearly a hundred times every year, as it is also in northern Canada and Alaska.

In London the aurora can be observed about seven times a year, but it is rare for any inhabitant of the metropolis to be aware of it, for the lights and the smoke frequently obscure the skyline and preclude any clear observation.

It is often said that the aurora is a form of magnetic storm, and certainly there is some connexion between the disturbances of magnetic instruments and the appearance of the aurora. But the case is not proven. With terrestrial phenomena, such as the tropical cyclone, the tornado and the waterspout, the case is a little different, because they can be studied close at hand.

The tropical cyclone is not so very different from a depression of temperate climates. Its main distinctions are that it is very much smaller in extent than the average temperate depression, moves relatively very slowly, and is generally more intense, with a small area near the centre which sometimes yields extraordinarily low barometric readings of the order of 950 millibars or less. Its destructive effect arises from the prolonged and intense winds which blow in front of it and behind it, where the pressure gradients are very steep. Gusts of a hundred miles an hour or more have been recorded near the Atlantic seaboard of the British Isles, but they are only gusts. The wind never blows at this strength in temperate climates for more than a few minutes. In the track of the tropical cyclone, however, the wind may attain a force of about a hundred miles an hour for hours on end. One other distinguishing feature of the tropical cyclone is the area of calm in its centre, usually accompanied by a clear blue sky, a feature which is usually lacking in depressions in temperate climates.

NATURE OF A TORNADO

A tornado is a phenomenon which can occur in almost any part of the world, but is most frequent in subtropical climates such as that of the Mississippi Valley and parts of India. It occurs near the onset of a cold front, and consists essentially of a very small area of intensely low pressure surrounded by a circular-flowing wind of great intensity. It may measure only fifty yards across, and appears as a characteristic funnel trailing from heavy thundery clouds, the nearer end of the funnel sweeping the earth. The funnel-shaped cloud is caused by the condensation of the moisture in the air due to the fall of pressure. A tornado, then, is essentially a vortex, and the strong uprising currents are capable of lifting quite heavy objects off the ground and depositing them hundreds of yards away; there have been instances of fully-grown men being carried a distance of about a quarter of a mile.

The destructive effect of a tornado is not only due to the hundred-mile or more an hour revolving wind and the lifting effect of the up-currents, but also to the explosive effect caused by the sudden drop of pressure at its centre. The air is sucked out of the vortex, and buildings, particularly wooden buildings of no great constructional strength, collapse outwards in the same way and for the same reason as do buildings in the vicinity of a heavy explosion, just outside the range of direct blast.

A few tornadoes have been observed in the British Isles, and these, as in tropical climates, always arise out of the roll cloud which is frequently seen horizontally at 2,000 or 3,000 ft. at the onset of a cold front. The incidence of the roll cloud shows a vortex, and a tornado forms when the roll is displaced from the horizontal to the perpendicular. Every roll cloud at the onset of a cold front has the potentialities of producing a tornado.

OCCURRENCE OF WATERSPOUTS

A waterspout is similar, if not identical, with a tornado, but occurs over sea. Its characteristic form is given by the water which is sucked up by the vortex. Again, waterspouts are most common in tropical seas, but occur also in temperate regions. For instance, six waterspouts were observed in the North Sea by British ships in a period of twelve years, mainly in August and September, but this number is an underestimate, as waterspouts are usually of short duration and must occur frequently when there is no observing ship in the vicinity.

There is as yet no certainty as to the extremes of temperature which can be recorded on the surface of the earth. It is known that the area yielding the highest temperature is not in the equatorial zone, but rather in the subtropical zone of

A tornado is an advancing whirl-wind which is formed as a result of strongly ascending currents. The prairie tornados of the South and Middle West of the U.S.A. are always associated with a deep V-shaped depression caused by the meeting of tropical air from the Gulf of Mexico with polar continental air from the north-west. It travels east or north-east at a speed of 20 to 40 m.p.h. and cuts a narrow swath of destruction all along its path.

high pressure and dry air in the interior of continents. Similarly, the coldest temperatures recorded are not near the North or South Pole, but rather within the continental area of high pressure in northern and central Siberia.

As far as our present knowledge is concerned, the highest shade temperature recorded in a standard screen under proper recording conditions is in the region of 135 deg. F. in North Africa and also in Death Valley, California. The lowest temperature recorded in northern Siberia is in the region of 125 deg. of frost, or minus 93 deg. F. On 2 February, 1947, a temperature of minus 81 deg. F. was reported from Spag airport in the Yukon, and this is the lowest recorded temperature in the American continent.

In all these regions human life is maintained, though under rather strained conditions. It is safe to say that active life would not be possible for long in an air temperature of 130 deg. F., and is only possible for short periods owing to the extreme dryness of the air in desert countries. Similarly, active life in a temperature of 60 deg. of frost would be scarcely possible were it not for the stillness of the air which prevails near the centre of anticyclones.

It is perhaps surprising to many that the range of temperature over the whole globe is not more than 230 deg. F., yet a small area such as Great Britain, which is justly famed for its equable and temperate climate, lying as it does on the very edge of the ocean and warmed by the Gulf Stream and the prevailing south-westerly air currents, should be able to show a range of well over 100 deg. F. Exact figures of the highest and lowest readings ever recorded in Britain are difficult to agree, because of differences in the conditions in which observations have been made. Official temperatures are those recorded in a screen about 4 ft.

from the ground, and temperatures recorded in older-type screens are not always strictly comparable.

The highest temperature ever recorded is 100 deg. F., at Greenwich in 1911, but this was in an old-fashioned screen, and the true comparable figure would probably be about 98·5 deg. The lowest official temperature recorded is minus 17 deg. F., recorded at Braemar in 1929.

But it is interesting that nearly every weather station in England and Wales has at one time or another recorded an air temperature of zero Fahrenheit or lower; for example, minus 4 deg. F. at Canterbury, and a total range of 100 deg. F. has been recorded at several stations.

Even lower temperatures are frequently recorded on the grass, or, as the case may be, snow. One recent instance was minus 9 deg. F. at Northolt on 29 January, 1947. On the same day, incidentally, Newquay, Cornwall, which ordinarily enjoys an even more temperate climate than the rest of Britain, recorded a maximum day temperature of 23 deg. F., and Falmouth, a maximum day temperature of 25 deg. F., followed by a foot of snow on the following day.

All these figures prove that climate depends far less on latitude or distance from the Equator than it does on the origin of the prevailing air currents, which can travel for hundreds or thousands of miles without materially affecting their nature. The air currents, for instance, which can produce a maximum day

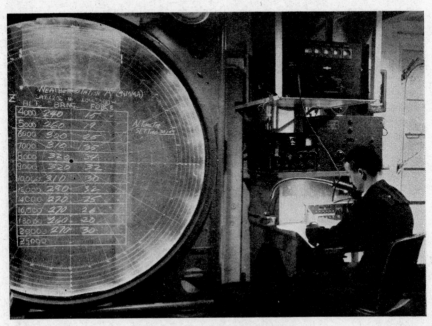

FLOATING WEATHER STATION
Special ships are now used for the purpose of providing weather reports.

ROUGH WEATHER ON THE SUSSEX COAST
Heavy seas are shown breaking over the promenade at Rottingdean, Sussex.

temperature of 23 deg. F. at Newquay are imported from Siberia, via the Balkans and Central Europe. Similarly, when very high temperatures are recorded the air is generally imported direct from Africa, and loses little of its heat in its journey across Western Europe. So much does weather depend on the source of the prevailing airstream that in a temperate climate, such as that of Great Britain, it can happen that the mean temperature of a January day differs little from the mean temperature of a July day. One day in July, in 1946, for instance, the thermometer in London never exceeded 59 deg. F., while there are several instances of a temperature of 50 deg. F. in January. Still more remarkable, many January nights do not fall below 45 deg. F., whereas in July a minimum of 42 deg. F. is not really unusual.

Another factor which has an important relation to temperature is the actual position of a place in relation to its surroundings. As we have seen, temperature normally decreases with height, and where there is a good circulation of the air this is true. But when the surface air currents die out, as they frequently do inland in fine settled weather, more especially in winter, temperature near the earth may fall rapidly at night owing to the effects of radiation. The heavy cold air adheres to the ground in valleys, particularly those surrounded by higher

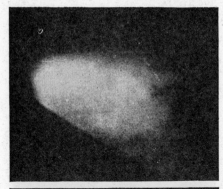

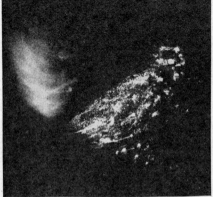

The creation of artificial snow. In the top picture a beam of light shines through millions of "supercooled" droplets. In the middle picture ice germs placed in the cloud have begun to take effect, and in the third stage all the water droplets have become snow.

ground, and act as ponds into which the cold air flows, producing what are known as frost hollows.

Research into the nature of frost hollows is still continuing, but already some extraordinary results have been achieved. In the period between the two wars a recording station was set up in an enclosed valley near Rickmansworth, Hertfordshire. This showed that on still winter nights temperatures are recorded many degrees colder than in places only a few miles distant, and often comparable with those recorded in similar weather in northern Scotland. The average of low night temperatures in January, February, March, and April appear to be almost identical at Rickmansworth and at Braemar, which is situated almost 1,000 ft. above sea-level in the valley of the upper Dee.

The science of meteorology is nowadays clearly linked with industry and agriculture. This intensive study of frost hollows is directly related with research into fruit-growing. Unusually mild winters are frequently followed by heavy frosts in May, and it is the incidence of these frosts which makes a difference of as much as five to one in the final weight of the cherry, apple, and pear crops. In other words, it can and does happen in some years that 80 per cent of the crop of one particular fruit is lost due to this freak of weather.

The incidence of fog is another problem which has been tackled constructively. During the Second World War it was mastered with complete success in a confined area, making landing of aircraft possible at selected airfields even when visibility was nil. This was achieved by the instalment of the apparatus which has become known as Fido, a system of pipes acting as petrol conveyors with jets which are lighted at intervals along the pipes. These burning jets set up great heat, which has a double effect, one of causing the air to rise and thus literally producing a lifting of the fog, and secondly by warming, however slightly, the local air temperature so that the air is capable of holding a greater moisture content without the formation of fog.

PRODUCING RAIN AT WILL

It is certainly beyond the power of man to muster all the forces involved in quite ordinary weather occurrences, but, under favourable circumstances, the forces once assembled by nature may be, so to speak, touched off and rain produced artificially. The process consists simply of sprinkling dry-ice particles into certain types of clouds, from aircraft flying above them. There are scientific as well as observational reasons for believing that clouds will not yield appreciable rainfall unless there is present in them a mixture consisting of ice particles and water droplets.

In spite of being at temperatures below freezing point, most clouds which are thick enough to produce rain consist not of ice but of droplets of liquid water, which are said to be in the supercooled state. These droplets are so minute that they float in the air like a mist, and cannot fall as rain. But if ice particles are present also, the water vapour in the cloud condenses on them, while the water droplets evaporate. The ice particles grow at the expense of the water droplets and, soon becoming sizeable snowflakes, fall out of the cloud, usually melting into raindrops during their passage through the warmer air which lies below the cloud.

The effect of this change from water to ice may be readily observed in thunderclouds, which while they are growing have hard cauliflower-like tops. With comparative suddenness the tops become fuzzy and are blown out into the characteristic anvil shape; this is the change over to ice particles, and not until this has occurred does rainfall usually begin.

SPECIAL CONDITIONS FOR RAIN-MAKING

To produce rain artificially, dry-ice particles are sprinkled into the cloud from above. Showers have been produced in this way in Australia, and some success has attended rain-making experiments in England also. But it must not be thought that the desert can be made fertile or even that such minor droughts as are experienced in the British Isles can be mitigated at will by the use of this means alone.

For artificial rain-making requires not only that the necessary supply of moisture shall be already present in the atmosphere, but also special conditions of temperature and clouds of a type that will react to the stimulus. In most periods of drought the moisture is not available, and clouds of the right type do not form.

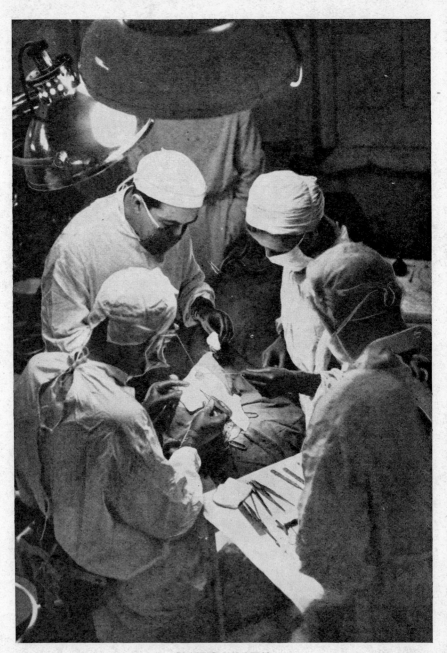

PLASTIC SURGERY

Surgical operations of the kind illustrated above have been the means of making a normal existence possible for those unfortunate people who would otherwise have been disfigured as a result of war injuries or accidents. Some of the results of plastic surgery are little short of miraculous.

CHAPTER 11 Modern science and the human body

MEDICAL and surgical research have advanced at such a speed that the larger textbooks, revision of which is no mean task, are now almost out of date before they are published. The purpose of the following brief account of some aspects of modern medicine is to give a glimpse of some of the more important findings of recent years. The study of medicine falls sharply into two parts, diagnosis (the identification of the departure from the normal in a diseased body) and treatment.

Diagnosis is by far the more important of the two. Without exact diagnosis, treatment is but a fumbling in the dark. It is now realized that the eyes, ears, and hands of the physician are not enough. Chemistry, physics, radiology, and other sciences have furnished him with invaluable aids; even the atom bomb has helped medical diagnosis. In what follows, undue emphasis may be laid here and there on treatment, but it must be remembered that only advances in diagnosis have made the rational application of such treatment possible.

Medicine is based on three branches of science: (1) anatomy, the study of how the body is put together; (2) physiology, the study of the way in which the machinery works; (3) pathology, the study of conditions which prevent the smooth running of the machinery.

The human body is subdivided into the so-called systems. For example, there is the circulatory system, which is simply an arrangement for supplying every nook and cranny of the body with nutriment and the oxygen necessary to burn the foodstuffs and convert them into energy; and the nervous system, which arranges the harmonious working of the infinite number of small parts of which the body is composed. The physician has of recent years rediscovered the truth of the ancient philosopher's dictum, "a healthy mind in a healthy body," and the relation between physical wellbeing and mental and emotional balance is being investigated more and more. A man's body will not function efficiently unless his mind is contented. The disgruntled, unhappy individual is heir to all sorts of illnesses: high blood-pressure, stomach ulcers, and even skin rashes may be caused by emotional stress.

Apart from the troubles we bring about by our own disregard of the simple rules of life, we have nature ever at our elbow, not the kindly nature of the poet, but a grim, ruthless nature striving to stop life through such agencies as the louse, the mosquito, the rat, and the invisible bacteria and viruses. Modern medicine has gone far towards winning its fight against nature. For example, the 1948 cholera epidemic in Egypt was stamped out in a matter of weeks. There now remains the sterner battle against human ignorance and carelessness.

NUTRITION VALUES

In the past, human ignorance and carelessness have both been well illustrated by man's unwise choice of food and drink. Even now the civilized individual knows little, on the whole, about the requirements of his body in this respect. For its smooth running, food and drink are essential. No apology is, therefore, needed for a brief survey of the important subject of nutrition. The essential components of food are proteins (chiefly taken as meat, fish and cheese), fats, carbohydrates (starches and sugars), mineral salts containing sodium, potassium, calcium, phosphorus, chlorine, sulphur, and a number of other substances in traces, and vitamins.

All these components must be balanced in the diet, and none can completely replace any of the others. In times of shortage, rationing systems are designed by experts to give each person the necessary amounts of each component, and to furnish daily a sufficient amount of fuel for his needs. The amount of fuel is calculated in calories, the calorie being a unit of heat. The calorific value of a food is the number of calories which that food will yield when it is burnt up in the human body. Of course, the breakdown of food in the body is not solely used to provide body heat; heat is a form of energy and can be transformed into other kinds of energy. Energy is required to keep the body ticking over at rest, as in sleep when the heart still keeps pumping the blood around, and the muscles of the chest still keep inflating the lungs. Much more energy is needed to do muscular work, though not to do brain work. Furthermore, some of the food, especially protein, is needed to build up new body substance to replace older broken-down tissue. For example, we now know that our red blood cells only last three or four months and must constantly be renewed. It is clear that the amount of food needed for building new tissue must be enormously increased in the growing child or in the woman who has to provide for her infant, both while it is growing in the womb and while she is suckling it.

NOURISHMENT FOR THE INVALID

Of great importance is a knowledge of nutritional needs in disease. We now realize that many of the ideas current on this subject twenty years ago were incorrect. There used to be a great tendency, for example, to starve a patient before and after operation. This is no longer done, because we now know that the patient in these circumstances needs an adequate supply of food to help him overcome the disturbance he has undergone. Modern science has proved that wounds do not heal so readily if the patient has insufficient protein. Again, it has

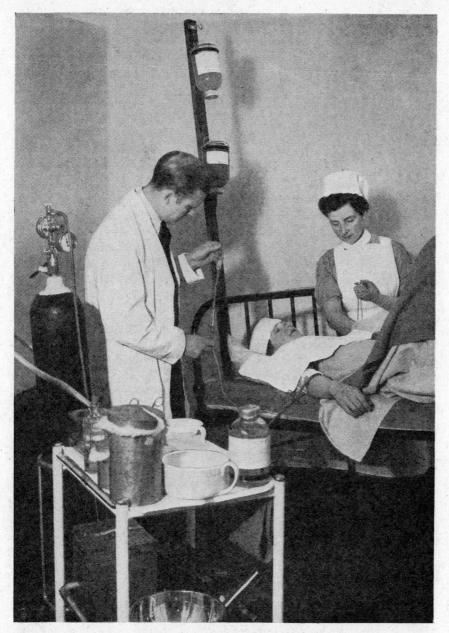

GIVING A BLOOD TRANSFUSION

Blood transfusions are used today for the treatment of ordinary accident cases, anæmia, pre- and post-operatively in surgery, in cases of accident at childbirth, for various disorders of the new-born infant, and for many other conditions. In recent years much progress has been made in this field.

been proved that what dressing is put on severe burns does not matter nearly so much as the amount of protein put into the burned person. But if the patient has no appetite or is unconscious, what then ? Modern science has supplied the answer by giving him the prefabricated substances he needs, directly into his veins. Blood transfusion not only replaces the vital red blood cells lost by bleeding, but also gives the recipient large quantities of protein already built up into the varieties he needs. If he has not bled, and does not need red cells, he can be given plasma (blood without the cells), or he may be given simple building-stones from which his body can construct protein. These building-stones are now becoming available in solutions of protein hydrolysates. Furthermore, so that he will not waste his precious protein by burning it up to supply energy, he may be given carbohydrate, the great energy-producer, in the form of a glucose solution into his veins.

Water is essential to the body; indeed, most of the weight of the body is composed of water, without which no exchange of substances between different parts of the body is possible. The water requirements of a human subject in different circumstances have all been worked out, and the necessary amounts can be supplied either by the mouth or into the veins of a dehydrated individual.

It is now realized that, of the various mineral salts taken into the human body, sodium chloride, and particularly the sodium ion (an ion is an electrically charged particle), is of special importance. What happens to the water in the body depends to a great extent on what happens to the sodium. If the latter is held back in the body, the water is also retained, and vice versa. Hence the value of the common practice of giving patients a solution of common salt (sodium chloride) by infusion into their veins.

VITAMINS

These are mysterious but very important substances. They are mysterious because their presence is unobstrusive, but their absence always spells trouble. They were originally distinguished by letters of the alphabet, but as a result of newer discoveries these letters no longer run in strict sequence. The names in common use now are vitamins A, B, C, D, E, and K. Modern research has shown that vitamin B is not a single substance, but a group or complex of different compounds.

The vitamins have been identified and sorted out by the diseases caused by their absence from the diet. The amounts we require are very small, and the sources of the vitamins are widespread in the animal and vegetable kingdom. They are very fashionable substances nowadays, and many healthy people take supplements of vitamin pills under the impression that their diet may not contain a sufficiency. In the majority of cases this impression is probably wrong. Nevertheless, even under peacetime conditions in a civilized country, cases of vitamin deficiency may be encountered, particularly in elderly persons who are faddy or neglectful as regards the quality or quantity of their food.

EVERYDAY FOODS AND VITAMINS
Four selections of foods arranged according to their vitamin content.

Attention has been focused on the vitamin-B complex during the past few years because so many cases of deficiency of members of this complex were seen in Japanese prisoner-of-war camps. Lack of one of the vitamins B caused a disease called beri-beri, of another, soreness of the tongue and cracked lips, and of another, a peculiar form of lunacy, pellagra. The "jittery legs" complained of by so many prisoners may have been due to a lack of vitamins. Some people think that the neuritis found in drunkards is due to interference with the supply of vitamin B. The important point is that all these conditions, if they have not gone too far, are easily cured by giving vitamin B. If one member of the vitamin-B group is withheld from rats, their coats turn grey, but it is by no means certain that human hair turns grey for the same reason.

The most recent member of the group of vitamins B to be discovered has been isolated in the U.S.A. It has been called vitamin B_{12} and, in doses as small as a few millionths of a gramme daily, cures a disease known as pernicious anæmia. Pernicious anæmia is a rather complicated deficiency disease which was incurable until a few years ago. Then it was discovered that liver contained the missing food substance. A few years ago it was found that a compound present in spinach, called folic acid, would also make good the deficiency in pernicious anæmia in daily doses of a hundredth of a gramme, but since folic acid is not present in liver the cause of pernicious anæmia is still a mystery.

Vitamin C is found in a large variety of fruits and vegetables. If the intake of this vitamin is insufficient, scurvy breaks out, a disease in which bleeding from the gums and other parts is a prominent symptom, and which for centuries ravaged the world's navies on long voyages, because the crews lacked fresh fruit. Nowadays, nearly every baby is given orange juice to protect it against scurvy and the disease is rarely seen. It is also known that wounds will not heal so quickly if the diet does not contain a large amount of vitamin C.

Vitamin K is a vegetable oil which helps to make blood clot. In jaundice there is a lack of this vitamin in the blood, and surgeons used to have endless trouble in stopping bleeding during operations on jaundiced patients. Now they give the patient an injection of vitamin K beforehand and all is well.

Vitamins A and D are obtained from milk and butter, and large quantities are found in cod-liver oil and halibut-liver oil. These two vitamins differ from the others in that the human body can make them if given their precursors. The commonest symptom of vitamin A deficiency is night-blindness; the individual has great difficulty in seeing at night. It is well known that deficiency in vitamin D leads to rickets; the child suffering from rickets has a large head, a deformed chest, bow-legs and a pot-belly, or as someone once said, "the forehead of a philosopher, the legs of a grand piano and the belly of a poisoned pup." A new use for vitamin D was found during the Second World War. Skin specialists in England and France discovered that enormous daily doses of it would cure a once-dreaded form of tuberculosis of the skin called lupus. Experiments are in progress to test the usefulness of the vitamin in other forms of tuberculosis.

ENDOCRINE GLANDS

Obviously such a complicated mechanism as the human body must have an arrangement to regulate all its activities, whether the latter are under the control of the will or not. There are two ways in which a general may deploy the forces under his command. He may send messages to units by means of electricity over the telephone or wireless, or he may employ a messenger. Similarly, the functions of different parts of the body may be co-ordinated by electrical impulses down the nerves or by the dispatch of chemical messengers through the blood-stream. The chemical substances are called hormones, and are manufactured by a small number of insignificant structures scattered through the body and known as endocrine organs or endocrine glands, which may well be compared with the "back-room boys" of the Second World War.

The leader of the endocrine orchestra (page 397) is a tiny gland (a gland is simply a structure which makes a chemical substance or mixture of substances) tucked away in the centre of the skull-cavity beneath the brain, and known as the pituitary body. No other structure of its size has such an important part to play in human affairs. It is made up of two independent parts, a front part and a back part, which have practically nothing in common and each goes about its business without reference to the other.

The back part or posterior pituitary is really a part of the brain and is concerned with the regulation of the flow of urine and also with the onset of labour

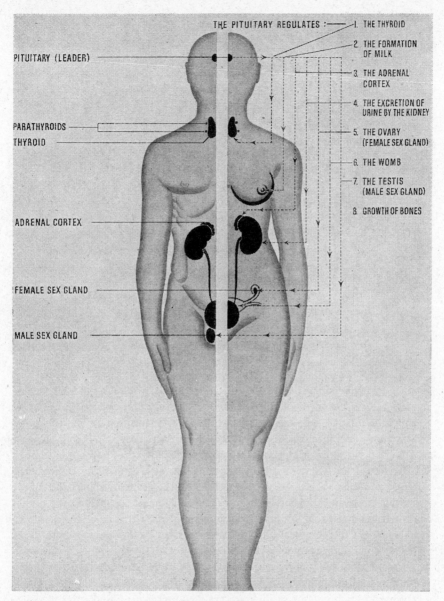

THE PITUITARY REGULATES :——1. THE THYROID

PITUITARY (LEADER)

2. THE FORMATION
OF MILK

3. THE ADRENAL
CORTEX

4. THE EXCRETION OF
URINE BY THE KIDNEY

PARATHYROIDS

THYROID

5. THE OVARY
(FEMALE SEX GLAND)

6. THE WOMB

7. THE TESTIS
(MALE SEX GLAND)

8. GROWTH OF BONES

ADRENAL CORTEX

FEMALE SEX GLAND

MALE SEX GLAND

THE ENDOCRINE ORCHESTRA

*The principal endocrine organs are shown here (left) in the male, and (right) in
the female. It will be seen that the leader, the pituitary, has a very great influence
upon many functions. The differences in the sexes are not restricted merely to
anatomical features, but apply also to the type of hormones manufactured by the
sex glands. Giving a hormone of an opposite sex to an individual will not, of course,
completely change his or her sex, but it will go some way towards it—the female
grows a beard, while the male breast enlarges.*

Typical cretin, or sufferer from thyroid degeneration due to iodine deficiency. The function of the thyroid is to act as a store-house for iodine and to introduce into the blood-stream the thyroid hormone. This hormone stimulates organic growth and metabolism, that is, the chemical and physical changes which are constantly taking place in the body.

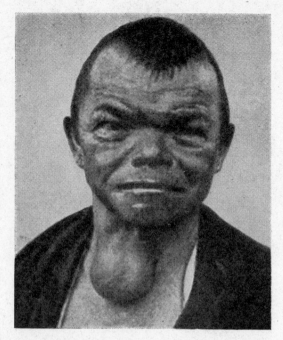

in the pregnant woman. Why the posterior pituitary should suddenly decide to send a hormone to the womb at the end of pregnancy and incite the latter to expel the infant is still a mystery, but the fact remains that only at this point will the hormone, pituitrin, rouse the womb into activity.

The front part or anterior pituitary makes a whole series of hormones, some of which control the work of other endocrine glands, such as the thyroid, the adrenals and the pancreas, while others regulate the growth of bone, the supply of human milk, and the activity of the male and female sex glands. We do not know what controls the pituitary itself, but we do know that no endocrine organ is independent of the others and that messages between them pass both ways. Thus if the pituitary stimulates the thyroid to work harder, the increased output of hormone from the thyroid will circulate back to the pituitary, and slow down its output until the balance is again adjusted.

Disorder of the function of the pituitary may produce a wide variety of symptoms. Thus, too much pituitary hormone may make a man into a giant, because growth of the bones continues indefinitely. In some cases only certain bones are picked out, particularly the lower jaw and the bones of hands and feet, and over a period of years the unfortunate sufferer develops a grotesque appearance with a massive chin and spade-like hands. Too little pituitary hormone may produce a dwarf, who may be well-proportioned and graceful, or fat and stupid. The fat boy in *Pickwick Papers* is an example of pituitary disorder.

398

Another important endocrine organ is the thyroid, which lies across the wind-pipe in the centre of the neck. It makes the hormone thyroxine, whose chief function is to step up the rate of energy production in the body. With more thyroxine life's little candle burns brighter and faster; with less thyroxine it burns dully and slowly, though it never quite goes out. In the latter case, two conditions may be seen: the child becomes a cretin, a stupid, dull, coarse-skinned, dwarfish creature, but the adult changes into a sort of human cabbage, only desiring to sit by the fire and do nothing. The latter condition, myxoedema, can be cured if the sufferer takes thyroid extract daily for the rest of his life.

The outlook for the cretin usually depends on how soon his condition is recognized. If recognition is early, thyroid extract every day of his life may make him into a normal adult eventually. Most fat people have taken thyroid extract at some time in their life in an effort to reduce, but since most fat people do not have a thyroid deficiency they take the extract in vain. The only sensible way to lose weight is to eat less; that this is a certainty can be verified by a glance at photographs of the inmates of a concentration camp. In any case, taking thyroid extract entails a risk of producing the condition of exophthalmic goitre, due to too much hormone. In this condition the most obvious feature is the staring eyes, associated with loss of weight, shakiness of the hands and anxiety.

CALCIUM IN THE BLOOD

The other endocrines are mainly of medical interest. There are four tiny bodies in the neck, called parathyroids, because they lie near the thyroid. They regulate the transport of calcium, a mineral essential for bone formation. If they are accidentally removed at operation, the amount of calcium in the blood falls, and the patient begins to have convulsions of a peculiar kind which can be abolished by taking more calcium. If, on the other hand, the parathyroids begin to over-work, they attempt to raise the level of calcium in the blood by laying hands on the most readily available source of calcium, that is, the bones. As a result the bones become softened, and bend and twist under the strains put on them.

The two adrenal glands sit on top of the kidneys and, like the pituitary, are made up of two parts with practically nothing in common. One part, the medulla, makes a substance, adrenaline, which is poured out into the blood-stream in moments of stress, and acts on various parts of the body so as to put the individual in good fighting trim. The other part, the cortex, is essential to life. The hormone holds the balance between certain salts in the body. It also has some peculiar relation to sex. Overgrowth of the cortex in a male child produces a deep-voiced, hairy infant Hercules; in a girl it changes the appearance completely and transforms her into the typical bearded lady of the side-show.

The male and female sex organs, the testis and ovary, in addition to producing the cells necessary to start the next generation, make hormones whose presence is essential to the proper physical development of the adult. Some of these, or substitutes for them, have now been made in the laboratory and are widely used to make up for deficiencies. The most fascinating field of research at the moment is their relation to cancer. Recent reports from all over the world show that these hormones can, in certain circumstances and in certain types of cancer, hold the tumour in check for a time, and even make it become smaller. The successes so far are small, but we are grateful for small mercies in dealing with cancer.

In this outline, so far, we have hesitated on the borderland that divides the normal body from the abnormal. Let us now pass into the realm of the abnormal and survey briefly some recent marvels of medicine. To recount them all would weary the reader. It is proposed, therefore, to discuss only a few to illustrate the

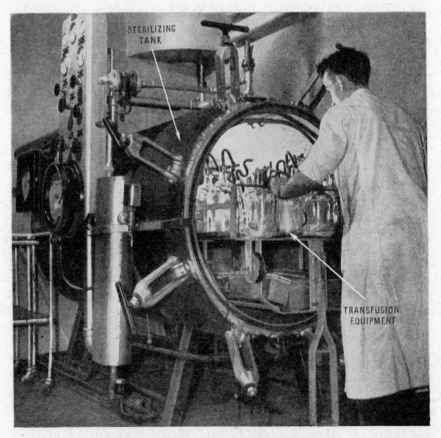

STERILIZATION OF TRANSFUSION EQUIPMENT

It is most important that all equipment used in the collection and giving of blood or plasma should be absolutely free from bacterial contamination. This picture, taken at one of the British Regional Transfusion Centres, shows containers being placed in the sterilizing tank preparatory to being sterilized.

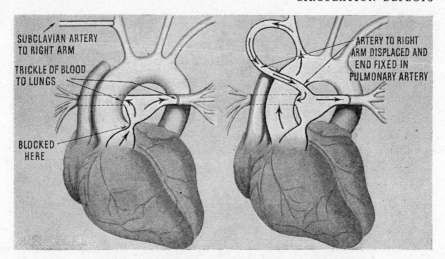

SUBCLAVIAN ARTERY
TO RIGHT ARM

TRICKLE OF BLOOD
TO LUNGS

BLOCKED
HERE

ARTERY TO RIGHT
ARM DISPLACED AND
END FIXED IN
PULMONARY ARTERY

CURING THE "BLUE BABY"

Some infants are born with a block in the artery to the lungs. The location of the blocked artery is shown to the left and the surgical treatment to the right.

types of problem with which the physician and surgeon are confronted. Thus, under the heading of "Heart Disease and the Surgeon," an attempt is made to show how the surgeon tackles the difficulty arising when a human being is actually born with a defect. In the subsequent section on bones and joints, the emphasis is on two common problems arising from injury and from premature wear and tear respectively. Lastly, we revert in the section on infection to the never-ceasing struggle for existence against the forces of malevolent nature.

HEART DISEASE AND THE SURGEON

One day during the late summer of 1947, a crowd of more than a thousand surgeons struggled to gain admittance to the lecture theatre of the Royal College of Surgeons, where an American surgeon was giving a quiet and modest commentary on a Technicolor film. The surgeon was Alfred Blalock, and the film showed him performing an operation which has rescued from death in childhood some hundreds of "blue babies." The "blue baby" is blue because it is born with a defect in its circulation. There are several possible defects of the heart and the great vessels, all grouped together under the title of congenital heart disease. Some do not matter greatly, and do not greatly embarrass the child or shorten his life, but in others the outlook is gloomy and until recently the sufferer rarely lived to adult life.

In 1939, Gross, also an American surgeon, taking advantage of the greatly improved methods of anæsthesia for chest surgery, opened a chest and successfully operated on a case of congenital heart disease. The patient he cured had a

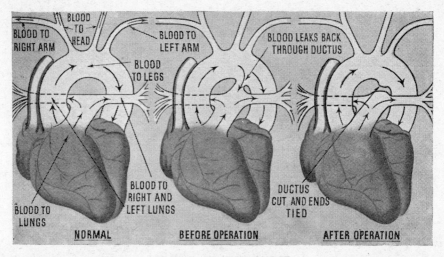

BLOOD TO RIGHT ARM · BLOOD TO HEAD · BLOOD TO LEFT ARM · BLOOD LEAKS BACK THROUGH DUCTUS · BLOOD TO LEGS · BLOOD TO LUNGS · BLOOD TO RIGHT AND LEFT LUNGS · DUCTUS CUT AND ENDS TIED · NORMAL · BEFORE OPERATION · AFTER OPERATION

CURING A HEART DEFECT

On the left is a normal heart. In the middle drawing a duct (ductus arteriosus), which should have closed at birth, has remained open. The resultant leak has been stopped (right) by cutting the duct and by sealing it in two places.

relatively mild type of defect; he had an abnormal communication between the pulmonary artery and the aorta, and Gross succeeded in closing the abnormal vessel by tying it off. In this type of case surgery is not always needed, but may be required if the child's growth is interfered with, or if he gets a blood poisoning, as these children not uncommonly do.

In 1945, Blalock and Taussig successfully attacked the problem of another much more serious defect of the heart, pulmonary stenosis. In this condition the baby is blue and breathless because the pulmonary artery which should be conveying blood to the lungs is blocked. Hence the blood cannot take up oxygen in the lungs and passes to the rest of the body in a blue oxygenless state. The lack of oxygen makes the little victim breathless on the slightest exertion. Blalock decided to feed blood to the lungs by joining another big vessel in the neighbourhood to the pulmonary artery beyond the block (see page 401).

The third surgeon who has helped to lift congenital heart disease out of the textbooks into the operating theatre is Crafoord of Sweden. He has attacked yet another type of defect, coarctation (narrowing) of the aorta. In this condition, the aorta, the great vessel carrying blood from the heart to the head, trunk and limbs, is narrowed down to a mere chink in part of its course. As a result, the trunk and legs are perpetually short of blood. The remedy is boldly to cut out the whole of the narrowed portion and to join up the two ends of the vessel remaining. All these operations are serious and difficult undertakings, but the saving of a number of children's lives makes them well worth while.

The above are only three of a variety of heart defects that can be present, either alone or in combination. A few years ago it did not matter much whether the physician knew exactly what the defect was or not, since nothing could be done about it. But with the new operations a very different state of affairs has arisen. Exact diagnosis is essential. As so often happens, a means of studying these defects accurately has been devised. It consists in inserting a long thin flexible tube (called a catheter) made of rubber or woven silk into a vein, either in the arm or the neck, and pushing it along until the point lies in the heart. The exact position of the end of the tube is found by looking at the chest from time to time through a fluoroscopic screen with an X-ray tube behind the patient. Now, this procedure seems very alarming at first sight, but in practice it is neither difficult nor dangerous in the hands of the expert.

At a Congress in 1946, some Mexican cardiologists showed a series of X-ray pictures they had taken by injecting a substance opaque to X-rays through the catheter (see below). The heart and vessels are beautifully outlined and some types of defect are easily demonstrated. Furthermore, samples of blood can be obtained from the different parts of the heart and analysed; the pressure in the various chambers and vessels can be measured, and an idea can be obtained of the efficiency of the heart as a pump. Thus it is that, in a medical sense, the secrets of the working of the heart are gradually being revealed to mankind.

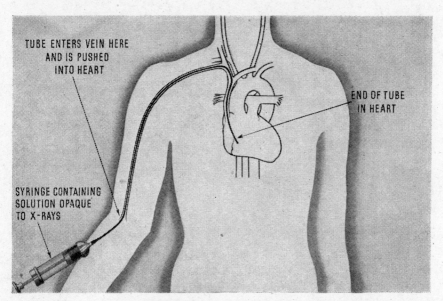

TUBE ENTERS VEIN HERE AND IS PUSHED INTO HEART

END OF TUBE IN HEART

SYRINGE CONTAINING SOLUTION OPAQUE TO X-RAYS

PHOTOGRAPHING THE HEART

A long, thin rubber tube is pushed into a vein so that its end lies in the heart. Next, a solution through which X-rays cannot pass is pumped into the heart. An X-ray picture will then show the size and shape of the heart chambers.

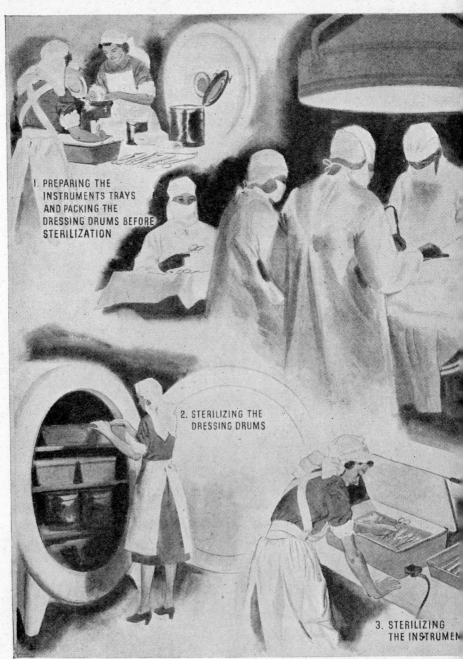

1. PREPARING THE INSTRUMENTS TRAYS AND PACKING THE DRESSING DRUMS BEFORE STERILIZATION

2. STERILIZING THE DRESSING DRUMS

3. STERILIZING THE INSTRUMEN

ROLE OF STERILIZATION AND ANÆSTHESI.

In the picture above, the centre group shows surgeons, anæsthetist and nurses engaged on an actual operation. The smaller illustrations show part of the work which must be done beforehand. Anæsthesia is certainly one of the greatest

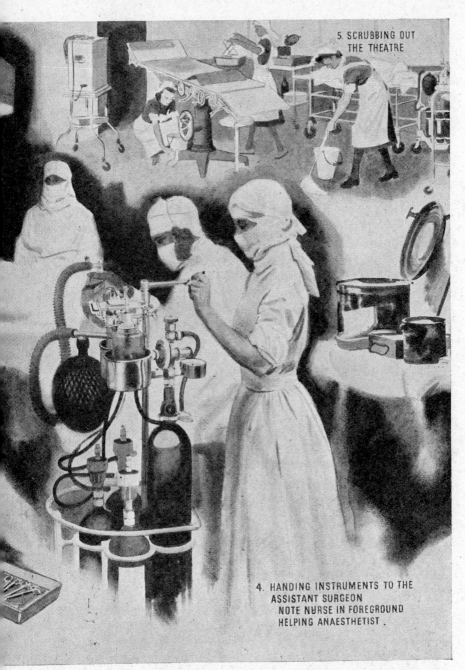

5. SCRUBBING OUT THE THEATRE

4. HANDING INSTRUMENTS TO THE
ASSISTANT SURGEON
NOTE NURSE IN FOREGROUND
HELPING ANAESTHETIST

IN A MODERN OPERATING THEATRE

achievements of modern times, without which the skill of the surgeon would be of little account. Note the emphasis placed on the scrupulous cleanliness of all instruments and the masks worn by those taking part to prevent bacterial infection.

405

It is common knowledge that when a small cut is made in the skin it will bleed for a little while, and then, after a few moments, even if nothing is done to stop the bleeding, the latter will cease. That the bleeding stops is due to two things: (1) the blood has a natural tendency to solidify or clot, and so seal off a cut vessel; (2) the wall of the vessel contracts down and seals up the mouth of the cut portion. Stopping severe bleeding has been a surgical problem from the beginning of time, but recently efforts have been made in the reverse direction, with the aid of two new substances called dicoumarin and heparin. Heparin was found in dog's liver years ago; it is probably present in small quantities in circulating blood, where it may help to stop the blood from clotting during its circulation. Nobody was very interested in heparin until 1935, when a Canadian doctor injected it into a patient's circulation and showed that the patient's blood then clotted less readily.

One of the nightmares of certain types of surgical operation is that while some patients are in bed, recovering after the intervention, the blood in the veins of their legs forms a clot. This is a nuisance, since it interferes with the blood supply to the leg and may cause persistent swelling, but there is worse to come. Sometimes a piece of the clot comes adrift, careers off to the heart, passes through the heart into the lung arteries, and plugs one of the latter. When this happens the patient may die quite suddenly. Obviously, the risk of all this happening may be greatly reduced if, at the first sign of danger, heparin is injected into the blood to reduce its clotting capacity. But heparin is expensive and its action is short-lived. Here the second anticoagulant drug, dicoumarin, comes in.

It was noticed before the late war that cattle which ate spoiled sweet clover developed a tendency to bleed. Analysis of the clover showed that the substance causing bleeding was dicoumarin, which interfered with clotting. Dicoumarin is now used in medicine to delay clotting, and has the advantages that it can be taken by mouth and is cheap. The two anticoagulants have already the saving of many lives to their credit.

BONES AND JOINTS

In 1945, when British Army surgeons were able to go into Germany again, they were anxious to see what advances the surgeons of the Wehrmacht had made, and whether British and German ideas had developed on the same lines. In the main they were bitterly disappointed. German surgery had, in general, lagged far behind Anglo-American surgery, but one man, Küntscher of Kiel, had had a good idea and one of which we shall probably hear more. He had developed a new technique of dealing with fractures of the long bones, by hammering a long vitallium nail down the marrow cavity of both the fragments, and so fixing them immovably in a favourable position for healing.

There is nothing new in the principle of pinning two pieces of broken bone together. Surgeons have been pinning the broken-off head of the thighbone on to the shaft for fifteen years or so, with the result that a lot of elderly persons who would previously have languished in bed for the rest of their days are now walking about. But nobody had had the courage to ram a metal nail over a foot long down the hollow centre of a thighbone broken right across its middle until Küntscher did it. His method is being adopted in Sweden, France, the U.S.A., and elsewhere. One great advantage of this method is that a patient who, under previous methods of treatment, would have spent months in bed in splints can get up in a few days free from pain and start walking.

NEW HIPS FOR OLD

The hip joint has anything but an easy time in life. In doing the job of transmitting the weight of the body to the leg it has to take some powerful stresses and strains, and as a result it often wears out before the rest of the body. Because of wear and tear, the highly polished surfaces of the ball and socket become rough and irregular, and the condition known as osteoarthritis develops. The patient suffers severe pain, drags himself about with difficulty, and may eventually become bedridden.

Twenty-five years ago, Smith-Petersen, a surgeon in Boston, Massachusetts, was already thinking over the problem of giving these sufferers new hip joints

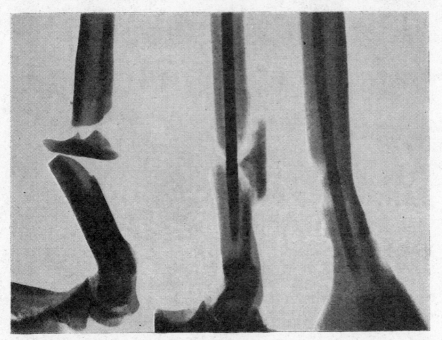

NAILING BONES TOGETHER

Long metal nails are now used to hold together two parts of a broken bone. The X-ray pictures above show how healing proceeds while the limb is held rigid.

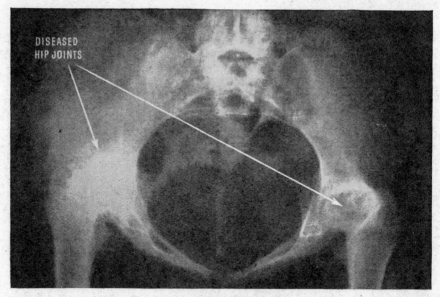

DISEASED
HIP JOINTS

DISEASED JOINTS

Wear and tear on the hip joints can result in a painful condition known as osteo-arthritis. The treatment for this is illustrated on the opposite page.

when he observed that a piece of glass taken from a patient's back had become encased in the body in a smooth sheath just like the lining of a joint. This gave him the idea for the first "mould arthroplasty," an operation in which the old gnarled joint surfaces are first smoothed over with special reamers. The head of the thigh-bone is then covered over with a smooth cup or mould, which used to be made of glass but is nowadays made of vitallium, and the rest is left to nature. Guided by the smooth contours of the mould, the two bones which form the joint obligingly fashion for themselves new, smooth surfaces. As a result, the patient is free from pain, and his stiffness, instead of increasing, gradually improves with the passage of time. Not only sufferers from osteoarthritis, but also younger patients whose hip joints have seized up as a result of injury or disease, have profited from Smith-Petersen's thirty years of study of the problem of providing new hips for old.

PROCESS OF INFECTION

Of the many different perils which beset us in this world, one of the most important is due to the presence of living organisms so small that they cannot be seen by the naked eye. Of these living things, the micro-organisms, some have a benign influence on human life, such as the organisms responsible for the production of beer from malt, some do not affect man, and some have a harmful influence and produce disease. The latter are our chief concern. When they cause

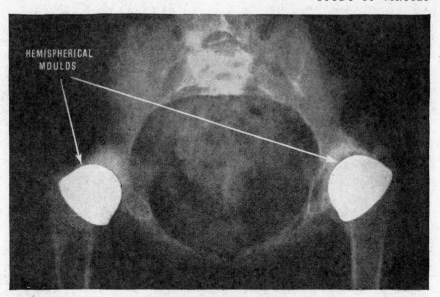

MOULD ARTHROPLASTY
Smooth cups, or moulds, placed between the roughened bone ends encourage the formation of smooth surfaces. This frees the patient from pain and stiffness.

disease the process is known as infection. If they transmit disease from man to man, or from animals to man, they are said to be responsible for an infectious disease. Such diseases kill about one in five of the human race, so that their control is a problem of great importance.

The micro-organisms are of various sizes. The smallest living things are known as viruses and cannot be seen individually with the ordinary microscope. Somewhat larger are the bacteria, which can just be seen under the highest powers of the microscope, and larger still are the bigger one-celled creatures, the protozoa, of which the malarial parasite is the best known.

As one would expect, viruses were the last of these organisms to be discovered, and they have been the object of intense study in the last decade. The story of virus research really begins in 1899, when a Dutchman showed that tobacco mosaic disease in plants was due to a living agent, which could pass through clay filters.

At the end of the First World War, scientific research revealed the existence of a peculiar micro-organism, bacteriophage, which attacks bacteria and dissolves them, and in 1935 Stanley crystallized out the pure virus of tobacco mosaic disease, the first living thing to be obtained in simple crystalline form.

Viruses are parasites, that is to say, they prey on larger plants and animals, whose bodies they invade. They may attack anything from bacteria upwards, but each virus is very particular about the type of host it chooses to dwell in, and about the type of host cell it is going to invade. Thus, for example, the virus of infantile paralysis likes to live in a certain type of cell in the spinal cord, which it may damage; the result of injury to the cell is made manifest by paralysis. How the virus injures its host cell is not known; it may kill the cell or it may, on the other hand, stimulate the cell to grow wildly, and so form a tumour. Furthermore, it need not always cause disease; it may enter a human body and lie dormant there indefinitely, a silent infection. If the individual harbouring the virus transmits disease to others without being ill himself he is known as a carrier of the disease.

It is fairly clear that in some virus diseases the number of infected but healthy people is great. Many children may have infantile paralysis and yet not lose a day's schooling. Clearly, such individuals are a danger; if they were obviously ill they could be isolated, but as things are they go about undetected and spread the virus around.

The electron microscope, which permits magnification of objects to a degree far beyond that of the ordinary microscope, has given a great deal of information about the structure of viruses. They are now found to be a very mixed bunch;

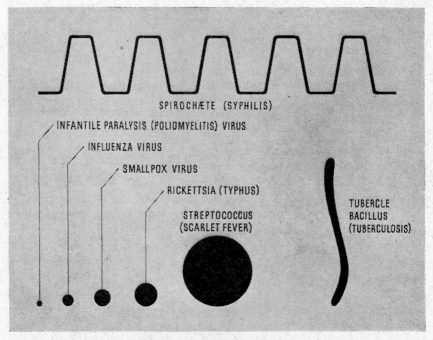

SPIROCHÆTE (SYPHILIS)

INFANTILE PARALYSIS (POLIOMYELITIS) VIRUS

INFLUENZA VIRUS

SMALLPOX VIRUS

RICKETTSIA (TYPHUS)

STREPTOCOCCUS
(SCARLET FEVER)

TUBERCLE
BACILLUS
(TUBERCULOSIS)

COMMON CAUSES OF DISEASE

These living agents of disease are drawn approximately to scale. The three largest can be seen under an optical microscope, but rickettsia and the viruses can be identified only with an electron microscope (see Chapter 8).

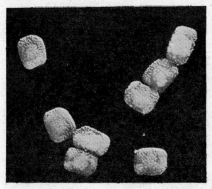 

AGENTS OF DISEASE

Until the invention of the electron microscope no one had seen a virus, as it was not possible to design an optical microscope with a high enough magnification. The photographs above, taken with the aid of an electron microscope, show (left) vaccinia, the cowpox virus; and (right) psittacosis virus, which causes a disease transmitted to human beings by parrots. Viruses vary considerably in size and shape, and for this reason different kinds can be isolated.

some are cubical, some spherical, and some of irregular shape; the bacteriophages look like tadpoles as they swim in head first to the attack on bacteria. Viruses also vary greatly in size; for example, the influenza virus is ten times the size of the virus of infantile paralysis. Viruses of different kinds have been separated off by filtering through membranes whose holes are of different sizes, or more recently by the ultra-centrifuge, an apparatus revolving at very high speed. According to the speed, particles of different sizes tend to fly outwards

The other means of their identification is by immunity reactions. When a micro-organism (virus or bacterium) attacks a patient, his body responds by forming substances known as antibodies which circulate in the blood and attack the invader. The invader is called an antigen, and the reaction between antigen and antibody is the basis of all immunity studies. Some antibodies are present before the invasion; if they are powerful enough, no illness will result from invasion. For example, a baby receives antibodies from its mother. These persist for some months, and so infectious diseases such as measles practically never affect tiny babies. Immunity may be acquired by exposure to the infecting agent. Thus one attack of measles usually confers immunity to that disease for life.

Some viruses, however, do not produce much immunity. It is well known that a cold may be followed within a matter of weeks by a second attack. The cold virus has evoked practically no immunity. There are two methods of proving that an illness is due to a virus: (1) by finding and isolating the virus from the patient—this is expensive and time-consuming and requires elaborate equipment, and (2) by finding antibodies against the suspected virus in the blood.

The treatment of virus disease is very difficult, and progress in this field has been poor compared with the strides made in fighting bacterial disease with sulphonamides (the well-known "M. and B." drugs) and penicillin. The trouble is that the virus gets into the cells, and chemicals must damage the cell before they can get at the virus, while antibodies cannot penetrate the cell at all. Nevertheless, drugs such as penicillin appear to have an effect on some viruses. Production of an artificial immunity has been a great standby in fighting bacterial disease, for example, in diphtheria, tetanus, or typhoid fever (the well-known T.A.B. vaccine), but it is not so easy in virus disease. There are two ways of making a person immune: (1) by injecting a harmless modification of the disease agent to stimulate the patient to produce his own antibodies (T.A.B. vaccine); (2) by giving the patient someone else's antibodies (tetanus antitoxin). The first method confers active immunity, the second passive immunity.

Active immunity is slow to start, but lasts long; passive immunity is conferred at once, but only lasts a few days. Unfortunately, finding a harmless form of virus which will produce active immunity is not easy. The problem has been solved in the case of smallpox (by vaccination), rabies, and yellow-fever. Passive immunity in virus disease is only useful if the antibodies are injected early, before the virus gets into the cell. Recent experiments have shown that most of the antibody in human blood is concentrated in a small fraction of the protein called gamma globulin. Trials are still in progress, but it would appear that small injections of gamma globulin given as a preventive measure during epidemics of such diseases as measles are definitely useful.

COMBATING BACTERIA

Treatment of bacterial disease has been revolutionized since 1936, when the first sulphonamide appeared. Some half-dozen sulphonamides, all chemically related, are in common use now, though penicillin, which appeared some five years later, has stolen some of their thunder. The sulphonamides act on bacteria by depriving them of an essential foodstuff, an organic acid called PABA for short. Strangely enough, it has been found within the last year or two that PABA itself is useful in treating diseases due to micro-organisms called rickettsiae (after Ricketts, their discoverer), which stand half-way between viruses and bacteria for size.

Penicillin (or, rather, the penicillins, for there are at least four of them) does not interfere with the food supply, but prevents the bacteria from multiplying. Penicillin only does this to certain types of bacteria, and unfortunately a great deal of penicillin is being wasted on the wrong bacteria, particularly in the U.S.A., where the public demand to be treated with it is most insistent. The danger of its indiscriminate use is that bacteria become resistant to its action in time, so that it should be reserved for really serious illness alone.

This consideration applies even more to the newer drug streptomycin, which is being used in tuberculosis. In the last few years, many other substances

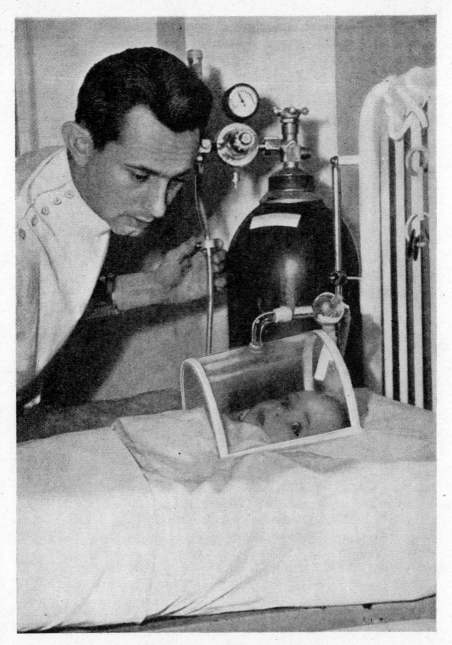

TREATMENT BY PENICILLIN VAPOUR

Under a transparent plastic tent, this seven-month-old child is receiving treatment for a diseased condition of the lungs which has hitherto been incurable. In this method of treatment the vaporized penicillin is first diluted in a saline solution before being pumped into the tent to be inhaled by the patient.

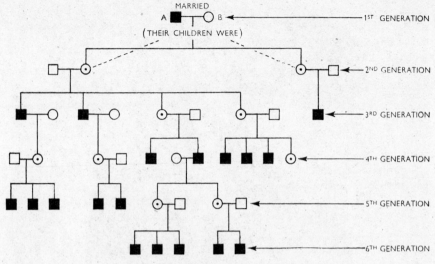

PEDIGREE OF A FAMILY WITH HÆMOPHILIA

This disease, in which the blood has insufficient powers of clotting, is shown only by the male, although the recessive is carried by the female. The white squares, above, represent healthy males and the black squares diseased males. Females are indicated by circles, those with a dot representing a carrier.

obtained from living material have been tried out on bacteria. Such substances, if they injure bacteria, are called antibiotics. Besides penicillin and strepto-mycin, only a very few are promising, because resistance to the others is so quickly developed by bacteria as to render them useless in treatment.

HEREDITARY CHARACTERISTICS

No two human beings, not even a pair of identical twins, are exactly alike in physical and mental make-up. Two factors combine to produce the differ-ences between individuals—heredity and environment. Thus, W. G. Grace was probably a great cricketer because he came of a family whose ruling passion was cricket; his relatives thrust a bat into his hand so soon as he was old enough to hold one and continued to coach him almost from infancy. In other words, the influence of environment was strong. But it is also likely that he was born with an aptitude for ball games, a quickness of hand and eye inherited from his parents.

Genetics, as it is taught in most of the civilized world, is based on the work of an Austrian monk, Mendel, who crossed various types of pea in his monastery garden and studied the results. For thirty-five years his work went unnoticed until in 1900 three scientists independently publicised it. Then other scientists who had made a study of the cell, the unit on which all living tissues are based, were able to relate their microscopical observations to his ideas.

Every cell has as its controlling part a nucleus within which there lies a number of thread-like structures which stain deeply with dyes and are called chromosomes. Every cell in a species has the same number of these; for example, man has forty-eight. When a cell divides into two—and all growth depends on cell divisions—the chromosomes split into two, a half of each chromosome going to each new cell to keep the number constant. There is only one exception to this. The male and female generative cells, the spermatozoon and the ovum, just before they come together to start the formation of a new individual (fertilization) each undergo a division in which the chromosomes do not split, but simply distribute themselves in the new cells on a half-and-half basis. Thus each new cell now has only twenty-four chromosomes and, when the male and female cells unite, the resulting fertilized egg will again possess forty-eight, half of which have come from the mother and half from the father.

Chromosomes contain the physical basis for the transmission of characteristics from parent to offspring. The parts of a chromosome responsible for each character, red hair, for example, are called genes, and each gene lies at a definite point on a chromosome. Thus the infant receives half its genes from each parent. Lack of space forbids discussion of the most fascinating details of gene transmission. Suffice it to say that there are two types of character conferred on offspring by genes, one a dominant, which tends to assert itself, such as premature baldness in men, and the other a recessive, such as red hair, which tends to lie dormant and to come to the fore when near relatives intermarry.

A certain number of diseases can be transmitted by special genes, and will appear from time to time in a family. The disease may arise in a family quite

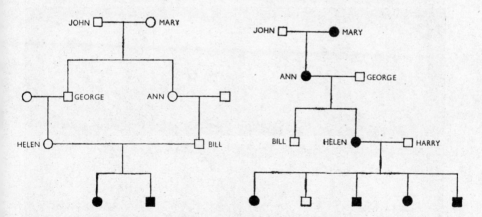

RED HAIR AND NIGHT-BLINDNESS

Red hair is a simple recessive which requires a gene from both parents. Above (left), Mary had the gene but John had not, so George and Ann were not red-haired. But their children, Helen and Bill, both had the gene, and their offspring were red-haired. The pedigree (right) shows how night-blindness (a dominant) can be transmitted. Note that an individual occasionally escapes the gene.

suddenly, because genes are not fixed structures but may undergo change or mutation, and the changed gene may give rise to disease in future generations. For example, a disease called hæmophilia (page 414), which affects males, causing them to bleed abnormally easily, suddenly appeared in the British Royal family. Queen Victoria carried the gene for hæmophilia, and several of her male descendants, such as the son of the last Tsar of Russia, were afflicted. Fortunately, Edward VII did not receive the gene, and so his descendants were not affected. It is now realized that mutations of genes can be brought about by physical agencies such as X-rays and emanations from radio-active substances.

There are four main blood groups which are found in man, labelled A, B, AB, and O. Every human being belongs to one or other of these groups, of which groups A and O are the commonest in Western Europe, although the Soviet Union contains a much higher proportion of group B. These groups are of great importance, because blood transfusion is only safe between certain groups. For example, if the red cells of a group A person come in contact with the serum (the liquid part of blood) of a group B individual, they form a clump and suffer damage. This change is known as agglutination, and it is obviously highly dangerous to introduce into a patient by transfusion red cells of such a group that they will at once agglutinate in the recipient. Hence the need for testing so as to determine the groups to which the donor and recipient belong.

These group characteristics are transmitted in a special gene, and we are, therefore, able to predict the possible blood groups of a child from a knowledge of the parents' groups. These facts are made use of in cases of disputed paternity;

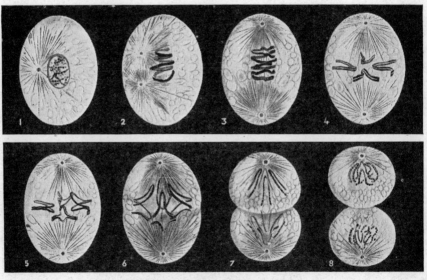

HOW ONE CELL BECOMES TWO
Eight stages of cell division, showing the part played by chromosomes.

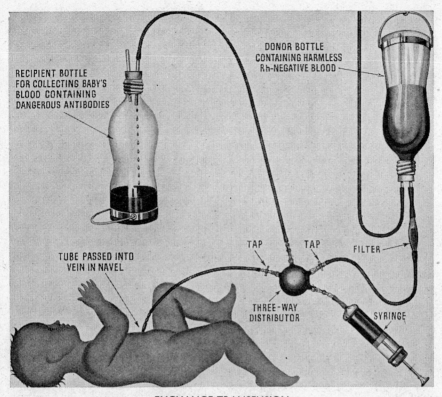

RECIPIENT BOTTLE
FOR COLLECTING BABY'S
BLOOD CONTAINING
DANGEROUS ANTIBODIES

DONOR BOTTLE
CONTAINING HARMLESS
Rh-NEGATIVE BLOOD

TUBE PASSED INTO
VEIN IN NAVEL

TAP TAP FILTER

THREE-WAY
DISTRIBUTOR

SYRINGE

EXCHANGE-TRANSFUSION

Research reveals that Rhesus-negative children born as a result of a union between a Rhesus-positive man and a Rhesus-negative woman have a poor chance of survival. To remedy this, the dangerous blood is replaced by safe blood from a donor.

by their application it is sometimes—not always—possible to state definitely that a man cannot be the father of a certain child. It is, of course, never possible to say that he *is* the father, though a consideration of other transmitted characters may make paternity highly probable.

The most recent development in the knowledge of blood groups is the discovery of the Rhesus (or Rh) factor. This factor, present in 85 per cent of the population, is so called because it is invariably present in the Rhesus monkey. The subject is becoming more and more complicated, and at least eight different Rhesus factors have been identified. Its importance lies in the fact that marriage between a Rhesus-positive man and a Rhesus-negative woman may end in disaster for their infants. It had been noticed for a long time that in some families, although the first child might be normal, subsequent infants became severely ill soon after birth, either with severe jaundice or anæmia. No treatment was of avail and the result was often a succession of infant deaths. It is now known that if an Rh-positive man impregnates an Rh-negative woman and if the resulting child is Rh-negative, the mother's blood may form substances called antibodies which will either kill the child in the womb or exert a delayed action on it soon after birth.

Clearly, the treatment is to get rid of these noxious antibodies from the infant's blood. American experts have solved the problem in brilliant fashion, by draining off as much of the new-born infant's blood as possible and at the same time introducing harmless Rhesus-negative blood to replace it. This is known as exchange-transfusion (see page 417).

In the discussion of endocrines, it was pointed out that the co-ordination of bodily activities was achieved through a dual arrangement, the endocrine glands and the nervous system. The time has now come to consider some disorders of the latter system, and to see what light modern science has cast upon them. The most highly developed part of the nervous system is the brain, and with that organ, as everyone knows, the mind is associated. It is, therefore, logical to follow up the study of the nervous system with some data on the workings of the mind in general and mental illness in particular.

THE NERVOUS SYSTEM

If that great detective, Sherlock Holmes, had been a modern physician he would almost certainly have become a neurologist, that is to say, a physician who deals with diseases of the nervous system. No other branch of medicine is so fascinating to the detective mind. The complex system for the transmission of information from one part of the body to another, and for the regulation of the bodily actions, partly under the control of the will and partly independent of it, has now been studied so exhaustively that the exact position of a diseased portion can often be predicted to within a fraction of an inch by simply listening to the patient's story and performing a careful examination in the consulting room. But, alas, there are penalties attached to its complexity. The more intricate the mechanism, the less easy it is to repair. The value of drugs in nervous disease is limited, and the more brilliant triumphs in this field have been gained by the surgeon, and that only in very recent years. Only sixty years ago, a leading surgeon predicted that nobody would ever be able to carry out an operation on the brain successfully.

He has since been proved wrong by the infinite pains taken by such fathers of modern neuro-surgery as the late Harvey Cushing, the great American who died within the last few years. The work of the neuro-surgeon demands infinite patience and physical endurance; it may take twelve hours to remove a tiny tumour in the centre of the brain.

It is of primary importance that the surgeon should know exactly where a tumour or an abscess lies in the brain. X-rays have come to his help in this problem. The central nervous system, that is, the brain and spinal cord, lies within a bony case and between the two lies the buffer of the cerebro-spinal fluid. This fluid also penetrates into a system of canals and cavities inside the brain. If the space containing the fluid is tapped by inserting a needle between two pieces of the backbone, and the fluid is drawn off and replaced by air, an X-ray picture will show a clear layer around the brain, and may thus outline a suspicious bulge due to a tumour. This is called encephalography. Moreover, air may be injected directly into the cavities of the brain so as to outline them in a radiograph, by making a small hole in the skull and inserting a needle into the brain through it.

Lastly, solutions which cast a shadow on an X-ray picture may be injected into the great artery of the neck, the carotid artery; if a radiograph is taken immediately, a picture of all the blood-vessels of the brain is obtained. This picture may reveal the presence of swellings or aneurysms on the vessels, or may disclose that one or other of the vessels is being pushed aside by a tumour. Armed with the information gained by these methods, the surgeon may open up the skull and either remove the tumour or, if he cannot do this, at least give the sufferer some relief from his intolerable and continuous headache by cutting

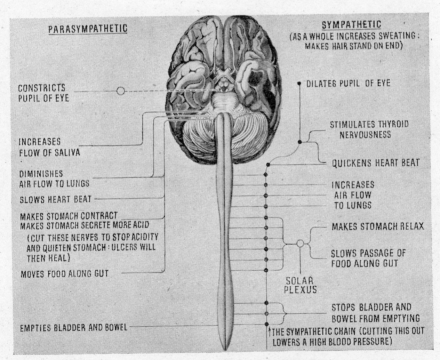

AUTONOMIC NERVOUS SYSTEM

The body contains a number of independent nerve systems, and one of them, comprising the sympathetic and parasympathetic (vagus), is illustrated above. Broadly speaking, the sympathetic nerve-impulses constitute a driving current, while the parasympathetic produce a braking effect upon the activities of the organs.

out a portion of the skull and so releasing the compression on the healthy brain by the diseased part.

Advances were made during the Second World War in the treatment of head injuries. Penicillin has helped to rob brain injury of one of its terrors, that of infection, and the newer metals such as tantalum, and plastics such as lucite, have been fashioned into plates to replace large defects in the skull. These substances are durable, non-irritating, and not attacked by the body fluids and tissues; many a patient will go on happily to old age wearing a metal or plastic skull-cap.

RELIEF OF PAIN

It may be said that the patient's most insistent demand to his physician is for the relief of pain. There are snags in the treatment of persistent and severe pain by drugs. In the first place, there is really only one drug of outstanding value for this purpose, and this drug, morphine, often speedily loses its effect or upsets the patient in other ways. Where such pain is likely to continue, and its cause cannot be removed, as in incurable cancer, there is an increasing tendency to ask the neuro-surgeon's aid in severing the path between consciousness and the source of pain.

Now the neurologists have mapped out very accurately the paths taken by pain impulses from any part of the body to consciousness. We receive the impression of pain in a small portion of the cerebral cortex or outer layer of the cerebral hemispheres of which the human brain is mostly composed. To reach this part the message from the diseased or injured part must travel up in the nerves of the part to the spinal cord, which it enters by means of the posterior nerve roots.

In the cord, the fibres responsible for carrying sensations of pain are bundled together in a special part of the cord to form a tract which ascends through cord and brain stem to the cortex. Thus the path may be severed by cutting nerves or nerve roots outside the cord. This is the easiest method, but surgeons are now abandoning it, because better results are obtained from cutting the pain tracts in the cord itself. This is no mean feat, since it involves an absolutely accurate knowledge of the anatomy of the spinal cord. The cut is made in a certain position to a depth of only an eighth of an inch. If there were the slightest deviation from the correct position, other tracts would be cut and the patient might be left with a paralysis of his legs instead of freedom from pain. The operation is often carried out under local anæsthesia with the patient conscious; when the surgeon's knife has divided the pain tracts, the patient can immediately tell him that his pain has disappeared. Unfortunately, pain fibres from upper parts of the body, such as the neck, enter the cord very high up and access to them is not easy, but since 1941 bold surgeons have been removing portions of skull and attacking the pain tracts within the brain stem itself. Lately the experiment has even been made of completely cutting out that part of the cerebral cortex which receives the pain impressions.

In addition to those parts of the nervous system which perform their many functions under the control of the will, there is a portion, the autonomic (self-governing) nervous system (see page 419), which regulates the humdrum bodily activities which must go on day in day out, such as the passage of food through the gut, the heart beat, and the respiration.

This system is composed of two parts, like the Government and the Opposition, whose function it is always to oppose each other to a certain extent. They are known as the sympathetic and parasympathetic systems; a balance is normally struck between their activities and then, according to the needs of the moment and the site of action, first one and then the other may be top dog. If, for example, a light is shone into the eye, the pupil will contract by parasympathetic action; if the light is withdrawn, the sympathetic immediately dilates the pupil again. Within the last few years the surgery of the autonomic nervous system has become of importance.

Its most interesting development is in the treatment of high blood-pressure. It is appropriate that most of this work should have been done in the U.S.A., since high blood-pressure appears to be a very common complaint in that land of high-pressure living. The malady is encountered frequently in middle age and is by no means harmless. No drug has yet been discovered which will cure or even satisfactorily

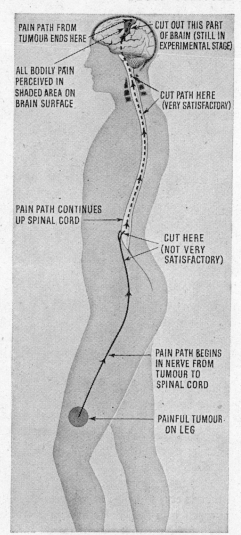

PAIN PATH FROM TUMOUR ENDS HERE

CUT OUT THIS PART OF BRAIN (STILL IN EXPERIMENTAL STAGE)

ALL BODILY PAIN PERCEIVED IN SHADED AREA ON BRAIN SURFACE

CUT PATH HERE (VERY SATISFACTORY)

PAIN PATH CONTINUES UP SPINAL CORD

CUT HERE (NOT VERY SATISFACTORY)

PAIN PATH BEGINS IN NERVE FROM TUMOUR TO SPINAL CORD

PAINFUL TUMOUR ON LEG

CUTTING THE PAIN PATHS

Paths taken by pains have been traced by neurologists and it has been discovered that the fibres which carry sensations of pain eventually pass along the spinal cord. Pain may be stopped by cutting the fibres before they enter the cord, but better results have been obtained by cutting the fibres in the spinal cord itself. The operation is usually carried out under a local anæsthetic.

relieve the condition, but American surgeons have now collected a large series of patients on whom they have operated with results at least twice as good as with any other treatment.

The idea is to cut out parts of the sympathetic system which are concerned with regulating the blood supply to the contents of the abdomen. If this is done, all the blood-vessels to the thirty feet of gut become enlarged and can, therefore, accommodate extra blood. The withdrawal of this extra blood, like the bleeding practised by the barber-surgeons, will relieve pressure elsewhere. The operation is a severe one, and not every patient with high blood-pressure is a suitable candidate, but in the hands of the experts it is bringing relief to many sufferers. Cutting the parasympathetic nerves to the stomach (vagotomy) in order to cure ulcers has now become a fashionable operation in America, but has not yet been widely adopted in Britain.

MENTAL ILLNESS

Until quite recently the proper understanding and, consequently, the treatment of mental disorder was extremely disappointing. It seemed to be taken for granted that there were only two types of disorder from the practical point of view: (1) the psychosis in which the sufferer had to be restrained in the interests of society; (2) the minor mental disturbance, such as the psycho-neurosis (or neurosis), for which nothing could be done anyway. In both types of disorder new hopes for sufferers can be held out, thanks to the fact that the psychologist, the psychiatrist, and the physician have at last begun to co-operate. The divorce of the psychologist, who studies the normal mind, from the psychiatrist, who studies the abnormal mind, is illogical since we cannot expect to understand abnormal human behaviour unless we understand and can define normal behaviour and vice versa. The size of the problem can be judged from the estimate that eight million United States citizens need psychiatric help.

Broadly speaking, all deviations from the normal in human behaviour can be divided into the psychoses and the psycho-neuroses, although the borderline is not so easy to define as was previously thought. The psychotic patient is not in touch with reality. He lives in a world of his own and does not realize it. The psycho-neurotic patient has not undergone such a severe disturbance in his mind. He is usually only too well aware that he is abnormal, but cannot resolve his difficulties unaided. He rarely develops a psychosis, though he may fear that he will "go mad." He may either have symptoms mimicking bodily disease, such as loss of voice, hysteria, or he may simply suffer mental torments, an anxiety state. His state of anxiety is not the same thing as a state of fear. Fear, for example, in battle, is a well-founded emotion, but anxiety is quite unreasonable.

We all spend our lives creating problems for ourselves and then solving them. If we solve them in a manner satisfactory to ourselves and to the demands of society, all is well; if we cannot, there comes a conflict between individual needs and the restraints of society and, out of this, anxiety arises. The difficulty is that

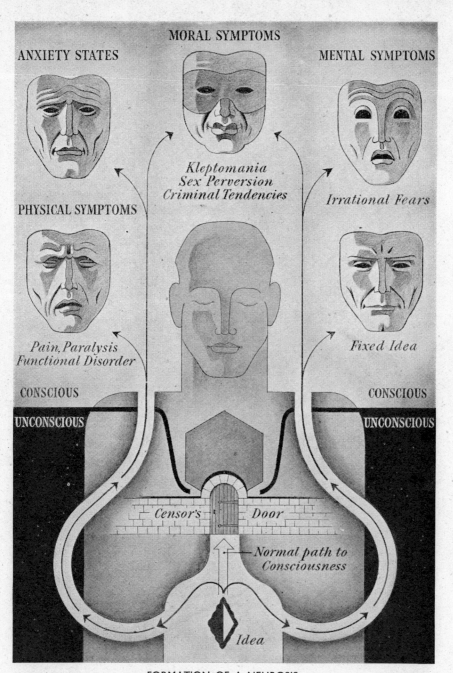

FORMATION OF A NEUROSIS

If a strong idea is repressed in the unconscious it may become a neurosis which can take many forms. It may induce an anxiety state, physical symptoms, irrational fears, fixed ideas, kleptomania, sex perversion, or one of many other conditions.

the psycho-neurotic does not realize what has caused his anxiety. The aim of the doctor who treats him is to turn his anxiety into a fear; that is to say, the patient must be brought to see what has caused his anxiety. If he can then see just what he fears, he may be able to solve his problem in a satisfactory manner.

Why does the neurotic not understand the reason for his anxiety? The answer we owe mainly to the genius of Sigmund Freud, who started to publish his views in 1892. He pointed out that in the human mind there lies not only a mass of material of which the individual is conscious, but also an even larger quantity of ideas which can only be brought to consciousness by special methods such as hypnosis or analysis; this he called the unconscious. He introduced the concept of a censor, the super-ego, which decides what ideas may be introduced into consciousness. If an idea is too unpleasant to be tolerated it is repressed and pushed into the unconscious. Let us take a simple illustration of repression. If you throw a heckler out of an election meeting you "repress" him by getting rid of him from your activities, but a stink-bomb may come sailing into the room later as a reminder that repression has not been permanent. So from the depths of the unconscious under stress of circumstances something may return into the conscious, but it has taken on a different appearance—it is now a neurosis.

FREUDIAN TREATMENT

Freud developed an elaborate theory on this basis, some of which is not accepted by all psycho-therapists. He introduced the idea of the libido or sexual energy, using the word sexual to include all emotions aroused by relations between one individual and another. A badly distributed libido causes a neurosis. He traced the development of an infant through: (1) a stage at which its interests are entirely selfish, the narcissistic stage; (2) a stage of interest in members of the same sex, the homosexual stage; (3) a heterosexual stage of interest in the opposite sex. In his opinion, in mental disorder the individual has failed to pass normally through these stages but has developed a fixation at one or the other intermediate stage. In the Freudian treatment of the psycho-neuroses the patient undergoes an exhaustive analysis, gradually bringing to the surface all sorts of things from his unconscious until eventually he draws up out of the distant past the source of the conflict which has produced his neurosis. When he can inspect and recognize this source there is a better opportunity to solve his problem rationally.

Jung differs from Freud in his explanation of the neuroses. He introduced the idea of a collective unconscious, containing material derived from the individual's ancestors and his race. He also contributed to therapy the word-association tests. Words are read out to the patient and he is asked to give the first word which they bring to his mind, for example, "father"—"man." His delay in answering is timed. Where a word recalls something unpleasant or embarrassing, the patient will hesitate or remain silent. In this way, a valuable clue to the underlying conflict may be obtained by the psychologist.

Adler, once a disciple of Freud, was the great exponent of the inferiority complex. He thought that man was not motivated so much by sex as by the will to power, the desire to dominate. If he cannot achieve his desire he develops an inferiority complex and therein lies the beginning of a neurosis.

It must not be thought that all neuroses require prolonged analysis in treatment. Often a short analysis suffices, aided by the interpretation of the patient's dreams, during which the censor tends to let slip some of the material from the unconscious. Further, treatment by suggestion, aided perhaps in some cases by hypnosis, may produce satisfactory results.

NEW METHODS OF TREATING PSYCHOSES

Within the last twenty years new methods have been tried and there has been an increasing tendency to treat psychotic patients by so-called "shock" therapy; an unsatisfactory term, but one which has become rooted in the language. Sakel treated patients with insulin, the substance given to diabetics, with the idea of increasing their weight, and found by accident that if he gave too much the patient passed into a deep state of unconsciousness called coma, and the symptoms of mental disorder improved. He then deliberately gave large doses to produce coma, knowing that he could always restore the patient to consciousness by giving an injection of sugar solution. The treatment is now widely used with good results in schizophrenia, the common mental disorder in which the mind is split.

Meduna noticed that if schizophrenics had epileptic convulsions they sometimes improved, so he deliberately gave them convulsions by injecting a drug called leptazol, allied to camphor. In 1938, Cerletti and Bini suggested that it might be easier to produce convulsions by giving electric shocks and this method has been widely adopted. An electric current at, say, 100 volts is passed through the patient's head for a tenth of a second. The treatment is repeated at intervals, the total number of shocks given depending on the nature of the illness and the patient's progress. The best results from this method of treatment are obtained in psychoses associated with depression, when the patient may be transformed once more into a bright and cheerful individual.

CURING WORRY

It is known that primitive man drilled holes in the skulls of lunatics to let out the demon contained therein, but it was not until 1935 that modern science returned to a surgical attack on the brain to cure mental disorder. It has long been recognized that part of the front end of the brain, the prefrontal lobe, is not essential to life, although it appears to be related to the emotions.

In 1934 an American scientist studied the effects of removing parts of the frontal lobes of two tame chimpanzees, Becky and Lucy. He set them various problems before and after the operations and observed that whereas they flew into a temper before operation if they could not solve their problems correctly,

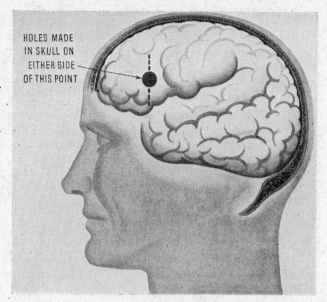

HOLES MADE
IN SKULL ON
EITHER SIDE
OF THIS POINT

Acute distress, anxiety, and misery suffered by patients with some forms of mental illness can be relieved by making a hole in both sides of the skull and by cutting a part of the brain (as shown by the dotted line).

after losing parts of their frontal lobes they became calm and unemotional. If they could not solve their problems, they did not bother but went on doing something else. From being worried, they became gay and irresponsible. When he heard about these experiments, a Portuguese surgeon, Egas Moniz, took his courage in both hands and deliberately destroyed a portion of the frontal lobe on each side in patients whose state of anxiety and worry was so great that they were no longer able to live useful lives. The results were encouraging. American surgeons were not slow to follow, and even their more cautious British colleagues are now practising the operation known as prefrontal leucotomy.

CUTTING THE BRAIN

The technique is not very difficult. A special cutting instrument is introduced into the brain through a small hole in the skull on either side, the situation of the cut being carefully marked out on the skull. The patient who benefits most from the operation is the person with marked symptoms of mental conflict such as intense anxiety, suicidal tendencies and attacks of extreme violence. The patient who is completely and unreasonably obsessed with an idea loses his obsession, the violent patient becomes docile, and the suicidal patient regains the desire to live. Nevertheless, there are drawbacks to the operation. The change in character of the patient is not always very acceptable to his relatives. In the first place, he may manifest a dislike for work. He will probably be intensely pleased with himself and careless about money matters or the welfare of others. He will make acquaintances readily, but be incapable of deep affection. The operation should only be performed as a last resort and in very carefully selected cases.

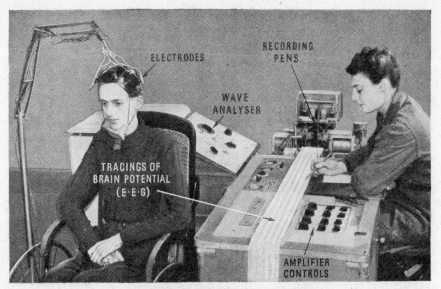

ELECTRIC CURRENTS IN THE BRAIN

The human brain emits a series of minute electrical impulses and the recording of these with a machine called an electro-encephalograph can reveal much of the mental condition of the patient. The waves are picked up by electrodes, transmitted through amplifiers, and finally traced on to a moving surface.

For many years the action of the heart has been closely studied by recording the electrical changes which occur during its action—electro-cardiography—but it is only very recently that the function of the brain has been studied in a similar manner. The study of the electric currents which are produced in the cerebral cortex is called electro-encephalography. The changes in potential recorded, even when electrodes are applied to the surface of the brain, are extremely small, and when the electrodes are merely applied to the scalp they are even smaller (a few millionths of a volt). The electrodes are connected through amplifiers to an ink-writing oscillograph, an instrument whereby a wave is recorded in ink on a moving surface.

In a normal brain the most characteristic wave is called an alpha wave, and has a frequency of about ten cycles a second. This wave is only present when the eyes are shut and disappears when they are opened or with intense mental concentration. Thus it can be used to distinguish true blindness from simulated blindness, because if the patient is really blind the alpha waves will still go on when he opens his eyes. There are also smaller, faster beta waves whose origin is not understood.

The most interesting application of electro-encephalography is in epileptic states, in which abnormal waves are frequently but not always found. Furthermore, the wave pattern is different in different types of epilepsy. Since epilepsy is inherited, it is not surprising to find that a proportion of the relatives of epileptics have an abnormal electro-encephalogram.

A large proportion of problem children and delinquent types also show abnormalities. About 50 per cent of psychopathic personalities have abnormal waves, the psychopath being the type of individual who is completely callous and selfish, and not infrequently ends a career of delinquency by committing a particularly nasty murder for no apparent reason. The electro-encephalogram may be of great value in courts of law, since an abnormal recording affords evidence of altered brain function. On such evidence a man tried in 1942 for a brutal and motiveless murder was found guilty but insane. Electro-encephalography has been used to predict the site of a brain tumour with a fair degree of accuracy.

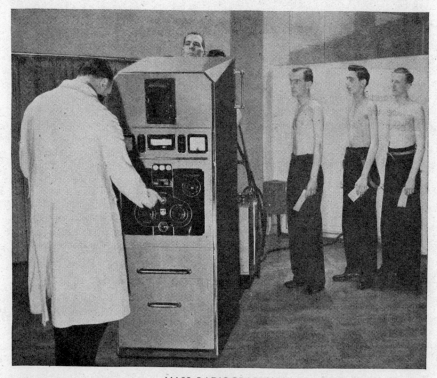

MASS RADIOGRAPHY

Radiography has proved a valuable weapon in the struggle against tuberculosis. X-ray photographs of the lungs of thousands of apparently healthy young people have revealed traces of the disease in a small percentage. This information obtained at an early stage often makes a cure possible, whereas had the onset remained undetected the disease might well have gained an unshakable hold.

Many other diseases can also be detected by the use of X-ray photographs.

X-rays and their application have long ceased to be a curiosity in medicine, and have become wellnigh indispensable in the diagnosis of many conditions. There is often, however, a tendency to overestimate their value. An X-ray photograph of a diseased part may only reveal to the inexperienced a vague shadow. Everything depends on the correct interpretation of the cause of the shadow. For this great experience is necessary, and even the elect are sometimes deceived. The best results are only obtained when a careful assessment of the patient's history and examination by simple means are combined with consideration of the X-ray picture. There is nothing magical about X-rays. They are simply ordinary electro-magnetic waves, which differ from the waves of ordinary light only in having a much shorter wavelength. X-rays are generated by applying a high electrical potential to a vacuum, producing a discharge of electrons, and setting a metal target in their path. The result of bombarding this target is to cause emission of X-rays. Of recent years, better pictures have been obtained by the use of new types of tube, by which more detail can be made out with a shorter exposure. The greater the voltage applied to the tube, the greater the quantity of radiation produced and the shorter its wavelength. The shorter the wavelength, the more penetrating are the rays to the human body, or, as the radiologists say, the harder are the rays.

X-RAY DIAGNOSIS

In this type of diagnosis two main methods are used, radiography and radioscopy. In radiography, a permanent record is made by interposing the part to be X-rayed between the tube and a film coated with a silver emulsion, and contained in a light-proof case, called a cassette. The denser the body tissue, the less it permits passage of the X-rays, and, therefore, the less the latter can affect the film. As a result, structures like bone show up as light areas, and softer tissues such as muscle and fat show as shadows on the negative. Plain radiographs find their commonest employment in the diagnosis of fractures of bones, in which they often afford the only certain evidence that the bone is broken. In order to compare films from different patients, a standard technique of taking films has been carefully worked out with standard positions of the patient for various purposes.

In radioscopy no record is made, but the X-ray tube is placed behind the patient, X-rays are passed through his body, and the result is viewed through a fluorescent screen which is coated with a salt such as calcium tungstate, which fluoresces on exposure to the rays. This method is the first line of attack when disease of the lungs, heart, stomach, or bowels is sought for. If any suspicious shadow is seen, a radiograph can then be taken to make a permanent record.

Of recent years surveys have been made of the chests of many thousands of apparently healthy young people by mass radiography. In these the photographs are taken on a tiny film to save expense, and the miniature film is viewed by means of a projector, which enlarges the image. The resulting record is good enough

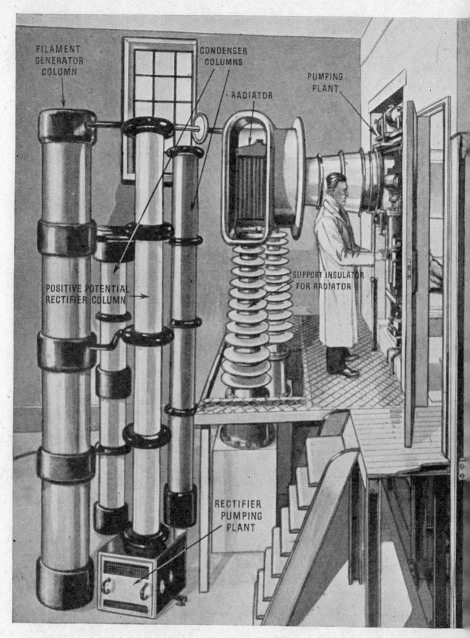

FILAMENT
GENERATOR
COLUMN

CONDENSER
COLUMNS

RADIATOR

PUMPING
PLANT

POSITIVE POTENTIAL
RECTIFIER COLUMN

SUPPORT INSULATOR
FOR RADIATOR

RECTIFIER
PUMPING
PLANT

HEALING POWERS

X-rays are used successfully in the treatment of malignant growths in the body.
Here is a high-voltage therapeutic installation. The X-ray tube extends into three
rooms, these being, from left to right, the anode apparatus room, the treatment
room, and the cathode apparatus room. The controller sits in a separate cubicle.
When the beam is not needed it can be turned so that it points upwards into a

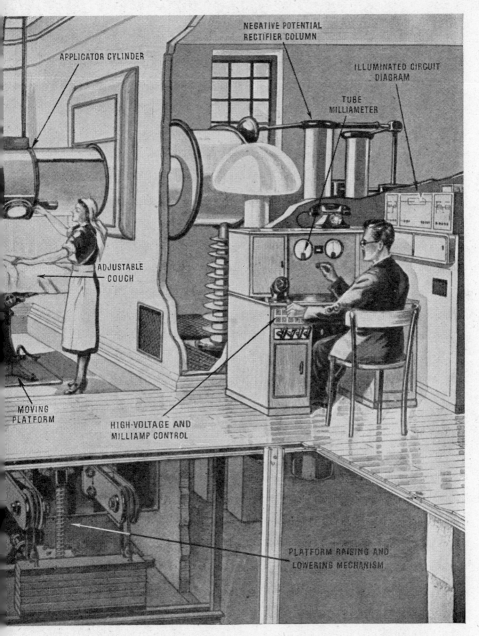

APPLICATOR CYLINDER

NEGATIVE POTENTIAL
RECTIFIER COLUMN

ILLUMINATED CIRCUIT
DIAGRAM

TUBE
MILLIAMETER

ADJUSTABLE
COUCH

MOVING
PLATFORM

HIGH-VOLTAGE AND
MILLIAMP CONTROL

PLATFORM RAISING AND
LOWERING MECHANISM

OF X-RAYS

five-inch block of lead. The object of this is to avoid turning off the high-voltage generators and to assist the accurate timing of the X-ray. In the treatment room, all parts of the X-ray tube are earthed and shielded with the exception of the port through which the rays are directed on to the diseased parts. In the other rooms the tube is also shielded and is bolted to porcelain insulators.

to permit distinction between normal and abnormal chests, and in all abnormal cases a full-size picture can then be taken. That this is the only way of detecting early tuberculosis was confirmed by the finding that over 1 per cent of people who thought themselves healthy had an infection of the lung, and that about 1 in 250 had active disease.

For the examination of organs which do not normally cast a shadow on exposure to X-rays a contrast medium is used. This is a substance which casts an X-ray shadow and so, when used to fill a body cavity, yields a picture of the outlines of that cavity. For example, the stomach is outlined by filling it with suspension of barium sulphate.

Again, the X-rays have a place in the study of childless marriages. In order that the male and female cells, the spermatozoon and the ovum, may come in contact and produce a fertilized ovum from which the child develops, it is obviously necessary that there should be no mechanical bar between their sites of production. Normally, the ovum is produced by the ovary, lying within the abdominal cavity. It reaches the womb, where it will nest if fertilized, by passing into and through a tube, the Fallopian tube, attached to the side of the womb. If this tube is blocked, the ovum cannot pass through. Blockage can be demonstrated by injecting an oil containing iodine into the womb, and then taking X-ray photographs. The oil casts a shadow, and if this shadow is seen not to extend from the womb through the tubes to the abdominal cavity, a blockage can be inferred and operation be undertaken to remedy it.

TREATMENT WITH X-RAYS AND RADIUM

When radium atoms break up they give off three kinds of ray, called alpha-, beta-, and gamma-rays (see Chapter 7).

This occurrence is called radio-activity. Alpha- and beta-rays are of no interest to physicians, but the gamma-rays have a penetrating power similar to that of X-rays. In fact, there is no essential difference between the actions of gamma-rays and X-rays on human tissue. The reason that both are valuable in treatment is that, although the rays attack all human tissues, there are certain tissues which they pick out for a more vigorous onslaught. In particular, they attack malignant tumours such as cancers. Their action is to slow down or stop cell division. Since the cells of a cancer divide at a prodigious rate in an anarchical manner without any reference to what the rest of the body is doing, these cells are particularly vulnerable or radio-sensitive.

The ideal in treatment of a tumour by either X-rays or radium is to stop its cells from dividing, and shrivel up the tumour without injuring the surrounding cells of normal tissue. Since tumours vary in their susceptibility or radio-sensitivity, and since they are situated at varying distances from the body surface, it becomes a complicated mathematical problem to calculate the best dose of radiation for each tumour. Dosage has been carefully worked out for all sorts of tumours by physicists with special training. Where X-rays are used, the wavelengths of the rays chosen will depend on the depth of the tumour. Since soft rays do not penetrate far, and are produced by using a low voltage, a relatively simple apparatus can be used at, say, 50 kilovolts, close to the skin in order to kill skin cancers. This is called contact therapy. If, however, the tumour is deep-seated, harder rays are needed, generated at, say, 180-400 kilovolts, for greater penetration. This is called deep therapy. Very deep tumours may require the 1,000-kilovolt installation producing very hard rays—supervoltage therapy.

HOW RADIUM IS APPLIED

Radium is always used in containers whose walls filter off the useless alpha- and beta-rays and let the gamma-rays pass. Platinum is a suitable filter; the simplest type of radium container is the hollow needle containing two-thirds of a milligram of radium as the sulphate in every centimetre length of that needle, with walls of platinum. A number of these needles can be inserted into a tumour for a time calculated in accordance with the dose of radiation it is desired to apply.

It is more convenient when some tumours are treated to apply radium containers to the skin surface by embedding them in a piece of vulcanite moulded to the body surface, or to insert the containers into a body cavity as in treatment of cancer of the womb. Lastly, the more inaccessible parts of the body may be irradiated by using the so-called radium bomb. This consists of a container holding large quantities (up to 10,000 milligrams) of radium whose walls only transmit the gamma-rays at one point, from which a beam of radiation, resembling the radiation from a supervoltage X-ray plant, passes out. This method is called radium-beam therapy.

As regards the treatment of tumours in general, we can say that it has now been decided that some are better treated with X-rays or radium than by cutting them out, while in the case of others, fierce argument still rages on the relative merits of radiation and surgery. Obviously, a surgeon who has brought the technique of removal of a certain type of tumour to perfection may prefer to rely on the knife, while a radiologist who has devoted his life to radio-therapy may prefer to irradiate the tumour.

Finally, mention must be made of artificially radio-active elements. Since we learnt how to split the atom, an apparatus called a cyclotron has been used to bombard elements such as phosphorus or iodine with free electrical particles and make their atoms unstable. As a result, the phosphorus or iodine becomes radio-active. Phosphorus, for example, gives off beta-rays and changes to sulphur. In contrast to radium it does this very rapidly; half the phosphorus is broken down within a fortnight. The important point about such radio-active substances is that, when they are injected into the blood-stream, their rays do not attack everything indiscriminately. The substances come to rest in certain selected parts of the body, according to the element used, and there irradiate the surrounding tissue. For example, phosphorus comes to rest in the bone marrow; in diseases, such as polycythæmia and leukæmia, where the marrow

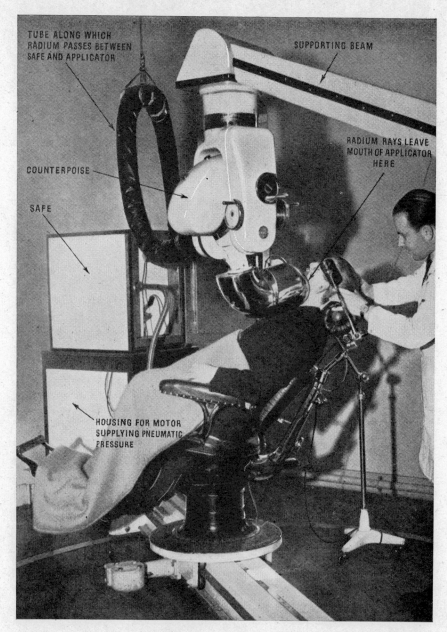

TUBE ALONG WHICH RADIUM PASSES BETWEEN SAFE AND APPLICATOR

SUPPORTING BEAM

COUNTERPOISE

SAFE

RADIUM RAYS LEAVE MOUTH OF APPLICATOR HERE

HOUSING FOR MOTOR SUPPLYING PNEUMATIC PRESSURE

RADIUM AS A HEALING AGENT

In the treatment of malignant diseases one of the methods used involves subjecting the affected parts to emanations from a relatively large quantity of radium. This radio-active element is stored in a safe to absorb the dangerous radiation, and only when the machine is required for use is the radium container propelled (by pneumatic pressure) along a flexible tube and into the applicator.

cells are running wild, the activities of the latter may thus be restrained.

The use of these radio-active elements is, of course, still in its infancy. Ironically enough, our chief supplies of these elements come from the Atomic Bomb Project in the U.S.A., and so with the change from war to peace scientists are adapting the weapons of destruction, not only in the treatment of disease as indicated above, but also in the diagnosis of disease processes by injecting radio-active elements into the unhealthy body and finding out what happens to them and in what way their fate differs from that in the normal healthy body.

GROWING OLD

In the heyday of the Roman empire the average citizen's expectation of life was twenty-four years. Fifty years ago an Englishman was lucky if he reached the age of fifty. Today he is unfortunate if he dies much under sixty-five. As a result of this, the number of older members of the race has increased enormously, particularly in more peaceful lands such as the U.S.A. These older people demand the right to live a comfortable and full life, and therefore the youngest medical speciality, gerontology, the study of old age and ageing processes in general, has recently been born. There is no apparent reason why we should not all live to one hundred, and research is now being directed towards reaching that goal. But what is more important is that we should in our old age continue to lead a useful and interesting life.

The fundamental process of ageing is not understood. It is now realized that we begin to age at birth, that the wear and tear starts when we emerge into this world, or even in our mother's womb. It is also realized that two parts of the body suffer most—the heart and the blood-vessels. The heart muscle tires and no longer propels the blood around efficiently, the arteries grow old and can no longer deliver the blood to the tissues, such as the brain and the kidneys, which need it most. The greater number of those who reach the allotted span die as a result of this. The deaths from cancer form only a small part of all adult deaths.

Medical science has given us a chance to live to old age chiefly by the strides it has made in combating infections of every sort. Infants no longer die like flies of diarrhœa, young adults are no longer swept away by epidemics of plague, cholera, typhoid and smallpox, and elderly people can now take pneumonia in their stride. But we still cannot stop that insidious degeneration of our organs which goes on with increasing pace throughout later years. We can, however, retard it by cultivation of the right attitude to old age. The fact that the health of the mind influences the health of the body is being forced upon doctors more and more. There is, for example, a mental component behind such diseases as high blood-pressure and gastric ulcer. The desire for idleness in old age is also a disease which requires psycho-therapy. Our old people must be taken out of institutions and put in a happy environment where they can employ body and mind in a manner suited to their age. Only in this way can the society of the future achieve its ideal of the greatest good for the greatest number.

Aerofoil: Surface which is designed to produce an aerodynamic lift or thrust normal to its surface when air flows over it, for a low resistance or drag in the direction of flight. The wings of an aircraft are aerofoils, while propeller blades and the rotors of a helicopter also have an aerofoil shape.

Amoeba: Primitive form of life, consisting of a single cell. There are various species of amoeba, the greatest number living in the water and mud of ponds and ditches; some live in salt-water or in soil, and others in the blood or alimentary canal of man. The largest can just be seen with the naked eye, but the majority are microscopic in size. The amoeba feeds by literally flowing around a particle of food, which is then digested within the cell; it reproduces itself equally simply by developing a marked waist which becomes narrower until the amoeba divides into two separate cells.

Anaemia: Medical term for bloodlessness. The term generally refers, however, to deficiencies in the quality of the blood, particularly in the red corpuscles which give it its colour. It is caused by a poor diet, or by illnesses which destroy the quality of the blood or which cause loss of blood. An important form is pernicious anaemia (Addison's anaemia), which was at one time considered incurable, but which has now yielded to medical science.

Anaesthesia: Condition of insensibility to pain, combined with loss of the sense of touch, which can be produced either generally throughout the body, or locally in a restricted area, by certain drugs termed anaesthetics.

Angle of Attack: Angle at which an aerofoil surface, such as the wing of an aircraft or the blade of a propeller, meets an airstream. An increase in the angle of attack creates an increased lift or thrust as the case may be, but too great an angle causes the airflow to break down into eddies and swirls. The aerofoil is then said to be stalled.

B.Th.U.—British Thermal Unit: Primarily a measure of heat, used, for instance, to express the heating value of any fuel. One B.Th.U. is equivalent to 252 calories (one calorie represents the heat required to raise one gramme of water through one degree Centigrade). Since forms of energy are interchangeable (see Energy), the B.Th.U. also represents 788·3 ft.lb., or 1·4147 horse-power-second. To produce one kilowatt-hour (see Kilowatt), 3,411 B.Th.U are required.

Calendar: Machine which incorporates two or more heated and polished steel rollers, used to impart a smooth or a glazed finish to sheets of paper, cloth or plastics passed between them.

Catalyst: Substance which is instrumental in bringing about a chemical reaction, although remaining itself unchanged.

436

Cell: Term applied to the units from which plant and animal life are built up. The botanists of the seventeenth century, who first examined plant tissues under magnifying lenses, were struck by the similarity of their structure to the cells of a honeycomb. Assuming the boundary walls of the cavities to be the most important parts of the structure, they termed each cavity a "cell." Nowadays it is realized that the contents of the cell are the most important, consisting of a jelly-like substance known as protoplasm. Protoplasm is made up of carbon, hydrogen, oxygen, nitrogen and sulphur, with traces of phosphorus and other elements. Since chemical analysis kills the cell, however, it cannot explain the most vital quality of the protoplasm: why it lives.

Cellulose: Substance resembling and allied to starch, which forms cellular plant tissues. Obtained from wood-fibres, grasses, and many other sources, it is the basis of several important industries.

Celt: Weapon or instrument of stone or metal, dating from prehistoric times and resembling a chisel or the blade of an axe, and found in ancient burial places. The term is also applied to the branch of the Aryan family which includes the Irish, Welsh, Manx, Cornish, and Bretons.

Charge: Accumulation of electricity. In nuclear physics the unit of charge is the positive charge on the proton. The charge on the electron is equal but negative. In electrical engineering the charge is measured in coulombs; the charge on the electron or proton is equivalent to $1\cdot6 \times 10^{-19}$ coulomb.

Cycle: Term used to denote a recurring sequence. Thus an alternating current or a wireless wave is said to have a frequency of so many cycles per second, while a vibration or a sound wave has a frequency or pitch similarly expressed in cycles per second.

Deciduous: Term which strictly means "falling off at maturity," but which is usually applied to trees which shed their leaves in the autumn, rather than to the leaves themselves.

Detergent: Substance which lowers the surface tension between water and oil or between any other two compounds or mixtures, allowing them to mix. Thus the cleansing action of soap is due to its detergent properties.

Deuteron: Nucleus of the atom of heavy hydrogen, an isotope of hydrogen termed deuterium. It is thought that the deuteron consists of one proton and one neutron, instead of one proton alone as in the hydrogen atom.

Diesel Engine: Internal-combustion reciprocating engine in which relatively heavy fuel oil is metered and injected into the combustion chambers by a special type of pump. Owing to the high compression of the air in the cylinders of the engine, its temperature is raised sufficiently to ignite the fuel.

Distillate: Product of distillation.

Distillation: Process of vaporizing a liquid and then cooling the vapour in order to condense it back to a liquid. The object may be to purify the liquid, or to separate the more volatile, easily vaporized fractions from the less volatile, a process known as fractional distillation or fractionation.

GLOSSARY

Diurnal: Term applied to any daily event, such as the rising or setting of the sun.

Electric Eye: Another name for the photo-electric cell, especially when used for detecting, counting or checking purposes.

Electrolysis: Decomposition of a chemical compound into its constituents, by passing an electric current through it.

Electro-magnet: Magnet formed by winding a coil of wire around an iron core. When an electric current is passed through the wire, lines of magnetic force develop around the electro-magnet, but collapse, apart from a slight residual magnetism in the core, when the current is cut off. The electro-magnet thus differs in this respect from a permanent magnet.

Element: All matter consists of two types of substances: elements and compounds. The elements are the simplest bodies, forming compounds by chemical combination. Each element is composed of a number of atoms, the smallest units of which it is built, and its properties depend on the number of electrons in the atoms, this number ranging from one in hydrogen to ninety-two in uranium. The nuclei of the atoms may also vary in weight, so that atoms of the same chemical element, having the same number of electrons and, therefore, the same chemical properties, may have different atomic weights. Such atoms are termed isotopes and account for the different forms in which certain elements, such as uranium and lead, are found to exist.

Endemic: Term applied to a disease which is prevalent in certain countries and communities. It should not be confused with epidemic, which describes a disease which attacks a large number of people at the same time.

Energy: Capacity for performing work. Energy exists in a number of different forms: mechanical energy, heat energy, chemical energy, electrical energy, molecular energy, atomic energy, and so on. The various forms of energy can be transformed into heat energy, and vice versa, while the individual forms of energy are themselves interchangeable.

Eurasian Continent: Great land mass that comprises the continents of Europe and Asia.

Extrusion: Act of forcing a substance through an orifice. A simple example is the extrusion of a ribbon of tooth-paste when the tube is squeezed. Various extrusion processes are widely used in industry to produce rods, bars and tubes of simple or intricate sections simply and economically.

Fischer-Tropsch Synthesis: Production of hydrocarbon oils and waxes, resembling naturally-occurring petroleum products, from coal, coke or natural gases. In Great Britain and Europe, coal and coke, or coke-oven gas, are the usual raw materials, whereas in America abundant and cheap natural gases are used. In either case a mixture of hydrogen and carbon monoxide is produced; these gases are then purified before being caused to react in the presence of a catalyst to form hydrocarbon products.

Fluorescent Screen: Sheet of cardboard or other material covered with a film of zinc sulphide, barium platinocyanide, or calcium tungstate, which glows or fluoresces when struck by a beam of electrons or other atomic particles.

438

Examples are the screens used to view X-ray images, including those in the viewing cabinets installed in many shoe shops, the screen of a television receiver, etc.

Fractionating Tower: Tower in which the vapours of volatile liquids, such as petroleum oils, tars, etc., are cooled and condensed. Distillates of differing volatility are drawn off at various levels, the most volatile from the top of the tower, and the least volatile from its lower levels. *See* Distillation.

Fractionation: See Distillation.

Fungicide: Chemical which destroys or inhibits the growth of fungi and moulds. Fungicides may be divided into three types: those containing copper, those containing sulphur, and the more recent mercuric salts, such as mercuric chloride. As fungus diseases are of two kinds, endophytic and ectophytic, meaning respectively those living within the plant tissues and those which live on the outer surfaces of the plants, fungicides must be chosen according to the particular fungus to be treated.

Gammexane: Artificial insecticide which is the most effective at present known in killing or discouraging many types of agricultural pest. Farmers have found it remarkably effective against the enemies of cabbage and similar crops, including flea-beetles, aphides, and caterpillars, while an application of only a few ounces of dilute dust per acre will enable excellent cereal crops to be grown in fields previously useless for this purpose because of wire-worm infestation. Gammexane has also been used effectively in fighting locust plagues in tropical countries. Its full chemical title is the gamma isomer of benzene hexa-chloride, $C_6H_6Cl_6$.

Glucose: Sugar present in blood.

Glycogen: Form in which carbohydrate is stored in the liver. *See also* Pancreas.

Hormones: In medical terms, hormones are excretions of certain glands, of which the thyroid is one. They stimulate the functions of the body, including the control of growth. Synthetic hormones are, therefore, valuable to make up deficiencies and also to treat abnormalities. The synthetic oestrogens, for instance, are used to treat certain types of cancer, particularly of the prostate gland. Silboestrol, useful in the treatment of various diseases, may also be effective in cancer. Hormones also control growth and cell formation in plant life. Synthetic hormones, such as alpha-naphthalene-acetic acid and beta-indolyl-butyric acid, appear to act as "triggers" to change the cell action in most plants. Cuttings and shoots steeped in hormone solution, for instance, in most cases form roots more rapidly. Hormones are also used in spray form to prevent the fall of certain varieties of apple, and also to "set" the blossom of tomatoes, strawberries and some other fruits, so that the embryo fruit develops to full size without the need for normal fertilization of the blossoms. Yet another use of synthetic hormones is as selective weed-killers, their effect being so to upset the cell formation of most plants having two seedleaves that the plant dies. Plants with single seedleaves, such as grass, wheat, corn, and so on, are not affected.

Horse-power: Theoretical unit of power or work. One horse-power is the equivalent of raising 33,000 lb. through one foot in one minute; this is expressed as 33,000 ft.-lb. This unit originally intended to represent the maximum effort exerted by a healthy cart-horse, as determined by James Watt when he wished to find a convenient means of expressing the power developed by his steam-engines, is in fact rather on the high side for a normal cart-horse. When considering the power output of an engine, various qualifying terms are used, that is, brake horse-power, or the power developed at the output shaft; indicated horse-power, which is the sum of the powers developed by the cylinders; maximum or peak horse-power; rated horse-power, or the standard power which the engine is designed to produce; and similar definitions, depending on the use to which the engine is put. In addition, since the various forms of energy are interchangeable (*see* Energy), horse-power can also be expressed in terms of heat, electrical energy, atomic energy, and so on.

Humus: Decayed vegetable matter which forms a large proportion of the top, fertile soil of the earth. The action of soil bacteria is responsible for the humus produced when any form of vegetation decays, such as weeds, grass, the leaves of trees, and even twigs and branches. The bacteria are of two types: aerobic and anaerobic. Aerobic bacteria thrive in well-aerated vegetable matter, causing fermentation and a rise in temperature inside the heap. When the aerobic bacteria have completed their task the anaerobic bacteria take over, causing putrefaction and carrying on the process of decomposition more slowly. If air is excluded, the anaerobic bacteria alone are active, producing a slimy mass of decaying matter instead of a good humus.

Hydrocarbon: Substance consisting only of carbon and hydrogen. The arrangement of the atoms gives a wide range of substances within this definition, from coal to bitumens, petroleum and edible oils.

Hydrogenation: Process by means of which hydrogen is added to certain compounds to change them into other compounds. Examples are the hydrogenation of coal to produce petrol, and the production of edible fats from waxes and oils.

Induced Current: Electric current which is set up or induced in a wire or coil of wire when relative movement takes place between the wire and the lines of force from a permanent magnet or an electro-magnet. The movement may be caused by rotating either the coil or the magnet, or the current may be induced by the collapsing and building up of the magnetic field surrounding a second coil in close proximity to the first. This occurs when the flow of current through the second coil, termed the primary, is interrupted and restored. The coil in which the current is induced is termed the secondary. A typical application of this principle is the coil in a motor-car.

Kilowatt: One thousand watts. A convenient unit for measuring the consumption of electricity. One "unit," for instance, represents one kilowatt used in an hour. A small electric fire, rated at 1 kW, will thus cost one unit per hour to use; a 100-watt lamp, on the other hand, may be used for 10 hours for the same cost.

Lines of Force: Path taken by the magnetic flux of a magnet can be made visible by placing some iron filings on a sheet of paper above the magnet. When the paper is tapped the filings arrange themselves into lines.

Mass: Property of a substance which determines its inertia, weight, or the amount of energy which can be extracted from it. The unit of mass used in nuclear physics, for instance, is one-sixteenth of the mass of the most common oxygen isotope, O^{16}, which is equal to $1\cdot6604\times10^{-24}$ gram.

Metabolism: Continuous process by which living cells and tissues store up and liberate energy in the body. Metabolism includes two processes: the building up of complex substances in the cells, in which energy is stored, a process termed anabolism; and katabolism, or the breaking down of complex compounds into simpler ones, thus releasing energy.

Metamorphism : Term used in geology to describe the process by which stratified rocks have been changed from their original structure by heat, pressure, and chemical action. An example is the conversion by this means of limestone to marble. Such rocks are termed metamorphic.

Molecule: Smallest quantity of an element or compound which can exist separately, consisting of a number of similar or differing atoms combined in such a manner that they behave as a unit.

Orbit: Astronomical term for the path described by a body during its periodical circuit in space.

Pancreas: Organ of the body close to the stomach and liver. It pours into the bloodstream a hormone which helps to convert the starchy elements of food into glucose, which is in turn stored in the liver in the form of glycogen or liver sugar.

Pellagra: Disease which causes disturbances of the stomach and intestines, a rash followed by skin eruptions and, finally, death. It is caused by vitamin deficiency due to poor diet, and is endemic in the southern states of North America, particularly among the negroes, and also in southern Europe.

Planet: Heavenly body which moves on an orbit around the sun.

Polymerization: Linking together of molecules or atoms of a substance to form larger and larger molecules, which are then called polymers. Under certain conditions, as during the manufacture of plastics, the molecules can be built up to relatively huge polymers.

Prototype: Strictly, an original from which others are copied. In engineering, the term is applied to the first aircraft, automobile, weapon or other product which has successfully passed all experimental and development trials, and which is ready for production in quantity.

Protozoa: Simplest animals known, consisting of one cell only. All other animals belong to the metazoa forms, which consist of many cells.

Reciprocating Engine: Type of engine in which power is obtained from the reciprocation, or movement to and fro, of a piston in a cylinder. The piston is coupled by a connecting-rod to a crankshaft which converts the reciprocating movement to a rotary one.

Refractory: Refractory materials, which are capable of withstanding very high temperatures, above about 1,500 deg. C., are used for lining furnaces, crucibles, ladles and other surfaces in contact with molten metal or subject to great heat. In some processes they are used in the form of pebbles. Classed as acid, basic or neutral, they are chosen in accordance with their effect on the metal or other substance being heated. Acid refractories include sand, some fireclays and ganister. Basic lining materials, consisting of acid and basic substances in suitable proportions, include special fireclays, carborundum, graphite and chrome bricks.

R.p.m: Revolutions per minute; a means of stating the rotational speed of any engine, motor or machine part.

Satellite: Small body which moves in an orbit around a larger one.

Schizophrenia: A mental disease often referred to as a "split mind" or a "split personality." The patient withdraws from the real world into an imaginary one. His reactions, such as laughter or grief, refer only to events in his imaginary world; he may sit silently for long periods, staring into space.

Shock Wave: A phenomenon which occurs when any part of an aircraft, a rocket or a shell, is moved through the air at a speed greater than the speed of sound (760 m.p.h. at sea-level). When the speed of sound is reached, the air has insufficient time to divide and flow smoothly around the object. Instead, it is compressed, and a shock wave is formed, similar to the waves caused by the passage of a ship through water. It is possible to watch these waves developing around a model in a high-speed wind-tunnel, since the compression of the air is sufficient to form a marked shadow if a bright light is placed behind the model, so that its silhouette is thrown on to a screen. As the air speed nears the speed of sound the waves resemble a few short hairs moving to and fro on the wings or fuselage of the model; at higher speeds the shadows are hard and well defined.

Slake: To mix with water.

Solstice: Point in the ecliptic, or the path of the earth around the sun, at which the sun is farthest from the equator. In the northern hemisphere, the sun is to the north of the equator at the summer solstice, and to the south of it at the winter solstice.

Spectroscopic Analysis: Method of analysing the light from any glowing source, such as the sun, a star, or a metal or gas heated in the laboratory, in order to determine the constituents of the glowing material. The light is passed through a prism which breaks it up into its various colours, forming a spectrum. The bands and lines of colour reveal the presence of elements in the material being analysed and also, in the case of astronomical work, indicate whether a star is approaching or receding from the earth, according to displacement of certain lines from their normal positions.

Spinneret: Organ from which certain insects, such as spiders, caterpillars and silkworms, exude a viscous liquid which hardens on contact with the air into a fine filament, forming the spider's web or the silk of a cocoon. In industry, the term is applied to the nozzles or orifices through which plastic is extruded.

Stream-line: Term applied to lines which show the direction of flow of a fluid at any given moment. A body shaped to afford the least resistance to the flow of fluid past it, creating the minimum of eddies, is said to be stream-lined. The term may thus apply to objects which move through water, or past which water or any other liquid flows. During recent years the term has been used most generally in connexion with the flow of air past aircraft, motor-cars, ships and locomotives.

Synthesis: Combination of separate elements or compounds to produce a fresh substance or one resembling a natural product. The term synthetic, applied to substances and chemicals artificially produced in this manner, should not be regarded as necessarily implying an inferior product; in many cases the result is better than the natural product.

Theodolite: Instrument used for measuring horizontal and vertical angles, and for ascertaining distances and heights. It consists of a telescope, pivoted vertically and horizontally, through which the object is viewed. The angle of the telescope, as it is swung round or tilted upwards, is read off on scales on the base of the instrument.

Therapeutic: Curative; in medicine the term therapeutics refers to the art or science of treating diseases.

Therapy: Curing of disease. The knowledge of the chemist allied to that of the physician has produced the science of chemo-therapy.

Thyroid Gland: Large, ductless gland, situated at the front of the neck in man and mammals and on the floor of the mouth in fishes and amphibians. It plays an important part in controlling the metabolism and growth of the body. In man, too little secretion from the gland causes a condition known as myxoedema; the patient is tired, lazy, and suffers from loss of memory and falling hair. Less serious thyroid deficiency is quite common when a man or woman passes his or her fortieth year, the most usual symptom being the deposition of unwanted fat on the body—the familiar "middle-aged spread." Thyroid deficiency can be corrected by administering thyroid extract. Too active a thyroid gland, or an excess of thyroid extract, causes rapid heart action, nervousness, restlessness and over-excitability. An enlarged gland is also the cause of the swelling of the neck termed goitre.

Transmutation: Transmutation of metals was the goal of the alchemists of the Middle Ages, who believed, in common with older Grecian philosophers, that all matter was composed of one fundamental material, or "protyle." It was, therefore, logical to assume that "base" metals, such as lead, could be changed or "transmuted" into gold. Recent atomic research has proved that there was some truth in the alchemists' unitary theory of matter, and it has also proved possible to change a thin film of mercury into gold by bombarding it with atomic particles. This type of transmutation is carried out in a cyclotron or Van de Graaff machine.

Vertebrate: Form of life in which the body is supported by a backbone and a bony framework, in contrast to invertebrates, such as earthworms and insects in which the tissues of the body wall are strengthened to give support.

INDEX

(Figures in italics refer to illustrations)